W9-BAO-552

The Boatkeeper's Project Book

The Boatkeeper's Project Book

BY TOM BOTTOMLEY

Line Illustrations by Richard Meyer

Ideas and instructions for modifications, improvements, and equipment installations

MOTOR BOATING & SAILING BOOKS
224 WEST 57th STREET, NEW YORK, N.Y. 10019

959 Eighth Avenue, New York, N.Y. 10019

Library of Congress Catalog card number 72-89235

ISBN 0-910990-08-5

Composition, printing, and binding by
The Haddon Craftsmen, Inc., Scranton, Pa.

CONTENTS

PREFACE

While Noah is said to have built the *Ark* to the specifications of the Supreme Naval Architect, the chances are he couldn't resist adding a few personal touches. And if the *Ark* was sold to a new owner after the flood, it's likely that the new owner—or his wife—decided a few new lockers or a change in berth arrangement would make the craft a bit more convenient.

It has been that way ever since. No boat owner can resist the urge to modify what the designer, builder, or previous owner hath wrought. For many, this is one of the pleasures and rewards of boat ownership.* Such modification may be limited to addition of a single shelf; or it may involve extensive changes in the boat's structure.

Since the project possibilities are infinite, and the space available here is limited, we have tried to provide a range of project *types*. Some simply illustrate one owner's solution to a particular problem; others give dimensions and step-by-step procedures for project completion. On the one hand we are presenting an *idea*; you provide materials and dimensions suitable to your own boat. On the other hand, we are providing *instructions*, for a process or project suitable to almost any boat.

T.R.B.

* One such owner is writer-photographer Gordon Manning, who has been supplying project articles to *Motor Boating & Sailing* magazine for more than 20 years, and whose work provides the basis for much of the material in this book.

1. HULLS

STABILIZING SYSTEMS

Flopper-Stoppers

If your boat has a tendency to roll uncomfortably when at anchor or otherwise moored in any sort of a sea, one way to reduce the roll is to rig "flopper-stoppers," as illustrated in *Fig. 101*.

While the arrangement shown is very simple, it is subject to considerable strain, and the spars and rigging set up to support it must have ample strength. It's best to work out actual sizes with a naval architect.

In this system, an iron ring, about 2′ in diameter, has a screen of hardware cloth welded to it. A sheet of rubber is affixed to the top, and cut into four pie-shaped sections. The units are made up in pairs, as shown in *Fig. 102*, and one is suspended from a bridle at each side of the boat.

When the boat starts to roll, the rubber flaps open on the stabilizer that is starting down, allowing it to drop easily. On the other side of the boat, the flaps close on the rising stabilizer, and the resistance created helps to reduce the roll.

Cables used to suspend the stabilizers must be held

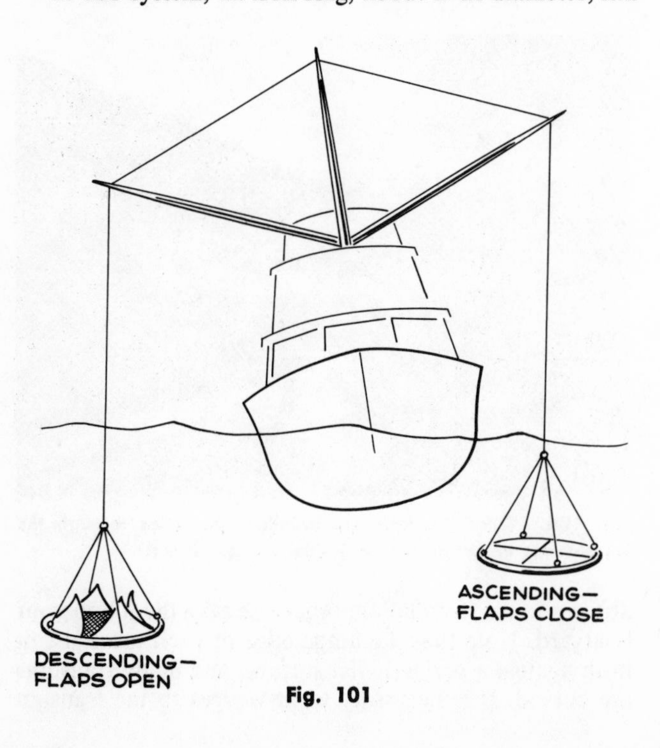

Fig. 101

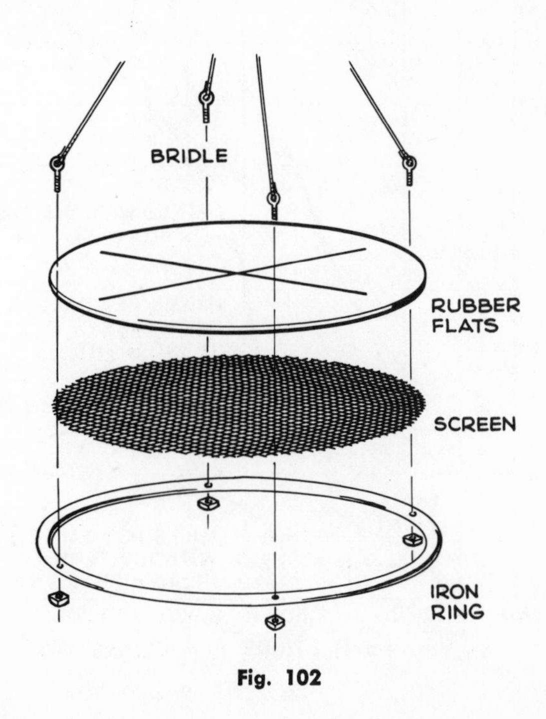

Fig. 102

well out from the hull to prevent chafing the sides, and all components must be guyed to prevent movement in any direction, and to transmit the stabilizer action to the hull.

More sophisticated flopper-stoppers can be used to reduce rolling of *displacement hull* boats when they are under way. However, these *must* be designed by a naval architect to suit the particular boat.

Trim Tabs

Most of today's power boats are based on semi-planing hulls that provide a fairly good turn of speed with moderate power. They operate most efficiently when they are planing with the line of the keel almost parallel to the surface of the water, but poor design, or even poor distribution of passenger and equipment weight, may cause the stern to squat and the bow to ride high. This attitude requires more power in order to maintain a given speed, or for given power, the speed is reduced.

Trim tabs of the proper type and size, and properly installed, usually provide a marked improvement in performance, as shown in the graph (*Fig. 103*) prepared by Col. George Byrnes. It is based on the addition of tabs to his 37′ double cabin flying bridge cruiser.

Fixed tabs are available that are suitable for installation on small runabouts, but the adjustable tabs, offered by several manufacturers, are most popular and best for larger craft. These can be set to match trim to load conditions, and some are entirely automatic in their operation.

If you are moderately handy with tools, you should be

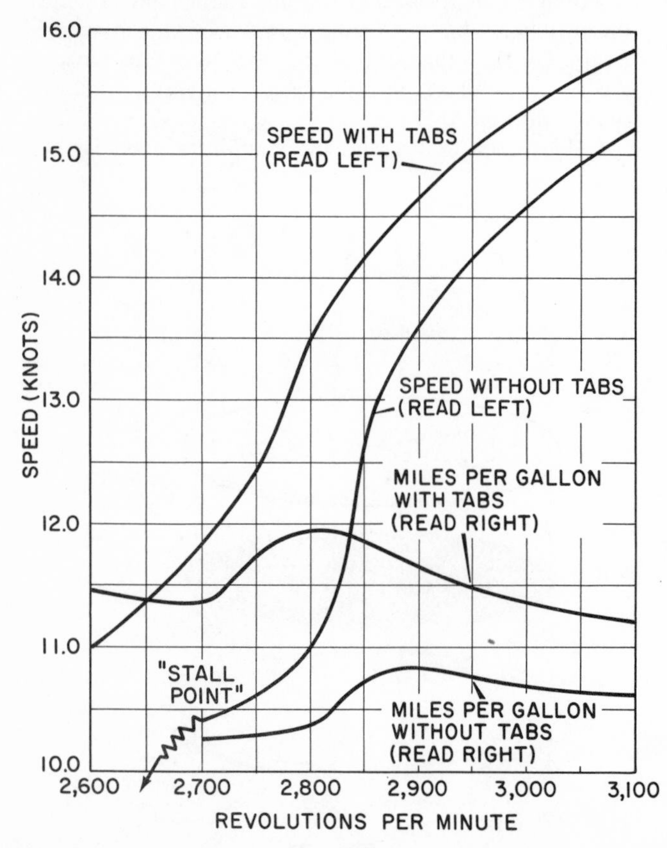

Fig. 103

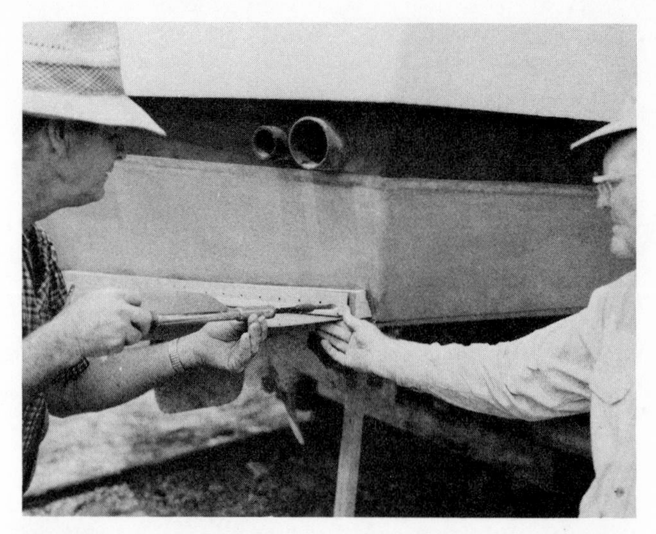

Fig. 104. If the transom is curved, wooden mounts with a curved forward edge and a straight trailing edge must be installed first.

Fig. 105. With wood mounts in place, the hinged joint of the trim tabs can be securely fastened to the mounts.

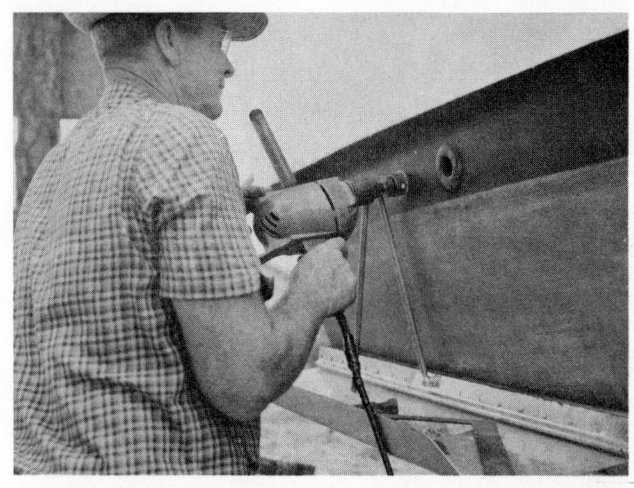

Fig. 106. Once the tabs are installed, the holes through the transom for the motor mount (inside) can be drilled.

able to do the installation, otherwise take the job to your boatyard. Note that the hinge edge of each tab must fit flush against a perfectly flat surface, and many transoms are curved. It is necessary to fit wedges to the transom

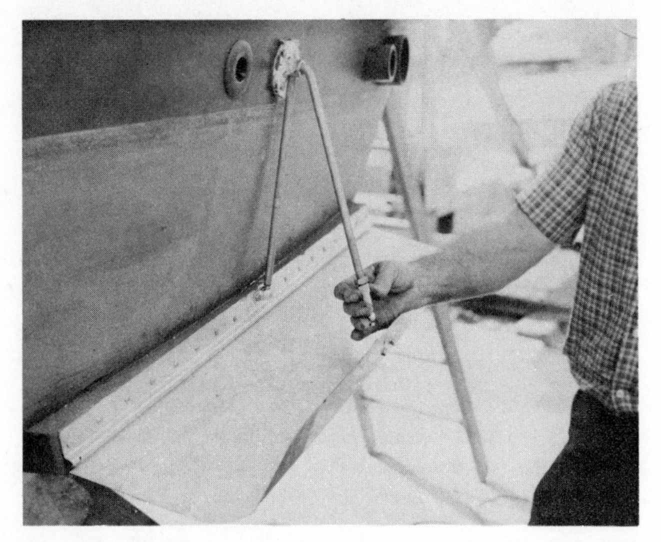

Fig. 107. Installation complete. This particular stainless steel trim tab is controlled by a wishbone type arm.

—strips with a curved forward face—before the tabs themselves can be mounted. The Gordon Manning photographs, *Figs. 104-107,* show the major steps in a typical job.

Because tabs are available in so many sizes, types, and styles, step-by-step installation instructions cannot be given here. Be sure to order the tabs designed for your particular boat; the manufacturer will provide explicit directions for their installation.

Keel Plates Reduce Roll

Keel plates provide one method that can be used to reduce roll of a displacement hull boat when it is underway. They are plates that run along each side of the keel, perpendicular to the keel (see *Fig. 108*), and they act in the same manner as bilge keels, but are less expensive and easier to install.

As is the case with any addition or alteration to a hull structure, the advice of a naval architect is necessary when it comes to designing the keel plates for any particular installation. The notes here are based on a keel plate job done on Jack West's 90-foot cruiser, *Monsoon II.*

For this installation, naval architect Arthur DeFever recommended "L" shaped plates approximately ⅓ the length of the keel. In section, the plates measure 6″ wide by 4″ high, and they are ½″ thick. Steel "angle iron" plates were available with these dimensions, in 20′ lengths. Three of these were purchased, one was cut in half and each half welded to a 20′ length to provide the two 30′ keel plates needed.

Next the port keel plate was drilled, on 16″ centers, for through bolts, and it was placed in position on its side of the keel. Because the horizontal plane of the plates was to be 4″ above the bottom of the keel, blocks were cut to that height and placed on the marine railway keel blocks to hold the plates at this level.

Before positioning the port keel plate, it was given two coats of rust-preventive paint, and the keel itself was given two coats of anti-fouling paint. When the port plate was clamped in position, the starboard plate was set into position temporarily. Using the port plate as a template, bolt holes were drilled through the wood keel, and the drill marks, on the starboard plate, were used as guides for drilling the holes through it.

With the starboard plate painted and clamped in position, round-head galvanized bolts were used to fasten the two plates permanently in place. Extra bolt length on the nut side was burned off with a torch, which welded the nuts to the bolts.

In addition to effectively reducing roll, Jack West notes that engine fuel economy improved because propellers were maintaining their smooth water efficiency for a greater part of the time.

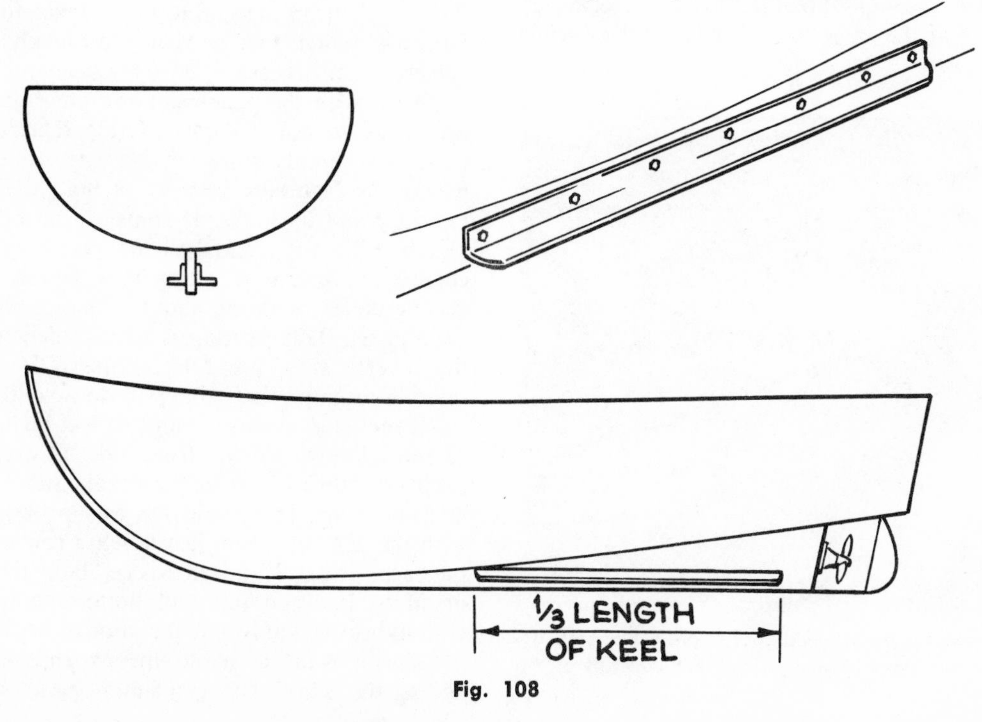

Fig. 108

COCKPIT IMPROVEMENTS

Fig. 109

Scupper Strainers

This simple way to keep cockpit scuppers clean is the idea of Natalie and Al Levy. Just go to your local hardware store and purchase stainless steel cup strainers (*Fig. 109*) that are slightly smaller in diameter than the scuppers. The strainers will nest neatly in the scupper openings, flush with the cockpit sole, and they can be removed easily for cleaning.

Cockpit Pegboard Panels

Gordon Manning has made several old boats look like new—in some cases better than new—and one of his tricks is to cover bare, unsightly cockpit sides with common pegboard. Here's how he describes the job:

"Easiest and best material is ⅛″ tempered hardboard, the kind with the perforations every couple of inches. This lets the hull "breathe," while covering up the crude parts at the same time. Stretch a good vinyl

Fig. 110. Before: engine box and cockpit present a drab appearance on this old Lyman Islander. Note exposed ribs of this lapstrake hull.

Fig. 111. After: Painted pegboard conceals ribs, helps to brighten the refurbished hull. Pegboard could be fabric covered, as outlined in text.

fabric over the board, sticking it on with adhesive.

"First step is to measure the spaces to be covered on the sides (the ceilings) of your cockpit. If there are not too many knees and braces that require cut-outs, make the panels just as large as convenient. If there are several cut-outs, small panels will be easiest to handle. The number of panels you join side by side is of no importance since the seams are almost invisible.

"Because this ⅛″ hardboard handles so easily, you can work directly from it, by-passing the need for patterns. Just hold the board against the hull in its proper position, mark it for knees or other necessary cut-outs. Try the panel in position after finishing each cut. See that the panel fits right before temporarily securing it in place (use a couple of screws). Ordinarily, you can screw right into the frames or longitudinals.

"These panels make ideal cover-ups for motor controls, cables, fuel lines, and wires which usually litter cockpit sides. If necessary, you can 'block' the panels far enough from the hull to make space for these items, Since the panels can be removed quickly, reaching the cables, when necessary, is easily accomplished.

"Now, with the panels cut and fitted in position, you are ready to cover them. Marine fabrics are sold by most boat supply stores. I chose 'perforated headliner #7001' by Nautolex because of both the ventilation it provides and its looks. It comes in an off-white which blends with any color scheme you may have in the cockpit. Covering the panels is merely a matter of cutting pieces of fabric about 2″ larger all around than your panel. This overlap is then cemented in place on the reverse side. I use Herculite CCV adhesive, and there are many others that will do a satisfactory job.

"If the panel is more than two feet high, spot in some of the adhesive on the front side as well, in order to keep the fabric close to the hardboard. Use a squeeze dispenser, like those sold for catsup or mustard, filled with the cement. Then just touch a row of spots, along the face, about 3″ apart. Make about three such rows of spots, between top and bottom, horizontally, and your fabric will stay put for good.

"If you want to avoid the expense and bother of adding the fabric, you can simply paint the face of the hardboard in a color that matches or blends with others on your boat. The illustrations (*Figs. 110* and *111*) provide a good before-and-after look at an installation of this type.

"Finally, mount the panels permanently. Use chrome-plated brass screws with cup washers, so you can remove them easily without damage to the fabric or hardboard."

Cockpit Stowage

No boat seems to have enough stowage space for all the gear that's brought aboard. Here are some ideas, developed by fiberglass expert Charles Bell, that can help solve your stowage problems.

First is a self-closing bin, of any convenient size, that will fit under seats, bridge decks, side decks, or any other similar spot on your boat. The self-closing feature is made possible by supporting the bin by hinges on the front bottom edge only, so the weight of the bin and its contents pulls the bin shut and keeps it shut. To open, simply pull the bin from the top.

The bin shown in *Fig. 112* can be molded of fiberglass, and attached to a front piece of mahogany plywood. You can make the mold for the fiberglass from

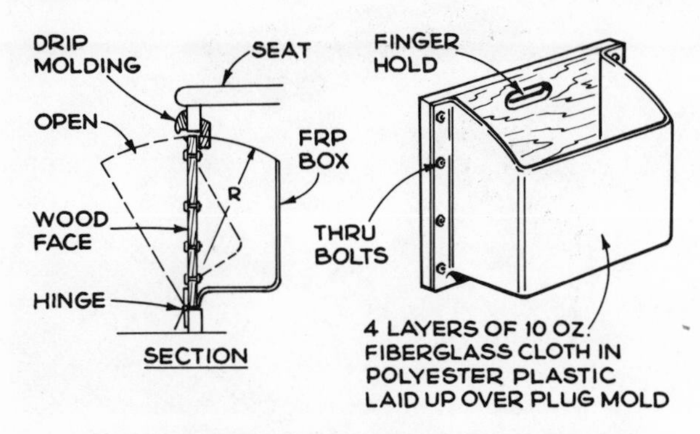

AUTOMATIC SELF CLOSING STOWAGE BINS
SIZED TO FIT INTO UNUSED SPACE ON YOUR BOAT

Fig. 112

smooth cardboard joined at the corners with masking tape. Give the cardboard three coats of thin shellac, and then three coats of hard wax as a parting agent. Lay four layers of fiberglass cloth—anything from 6 to 10 ounce will do—over the mold, bedding them in polyester resin. When you remove the cured unit from the mold, the inside surface will be a smooth, faithful reproduction of the cardboard mold. You can use wood, hardboard, or a plastic laminate such as Formica for the mold, if you prefer.

Storage boxes under the helmsman's and passenger's seats of small cruisers are next. Bell credits Charles Brooks of Sacramento, Calif., for this idea, which provides one box that serves as an ice chest, and another that serves as a dish locker. Note in *Fig. 113* that these provide the proper height for the seats. Naturally, the boxes must be strong, and bolted to the floor. The seats can be mounted on swivels that can be locked in any position.

The boxes shown have aft doors that provide ac-

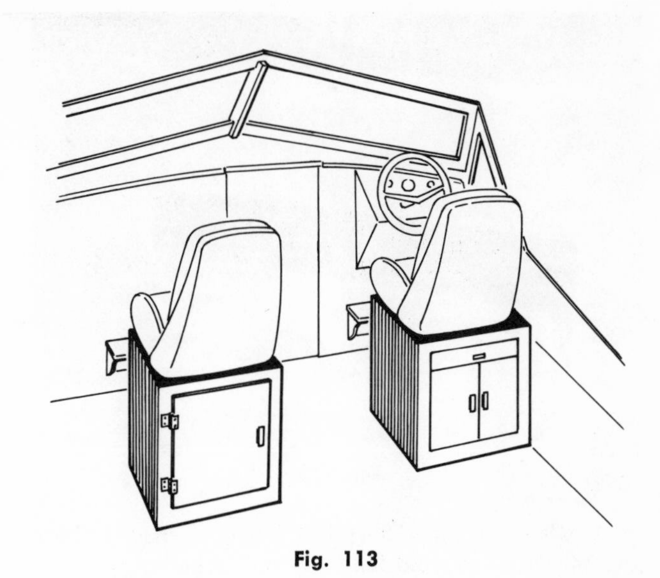

Fig. 113

cess without disturbing the seats, but they can be made with lids in the tops that open when the seats are tilted.

Each box is framed with 1½″ mahogany rabbeted out for ¼″ mahogany-faced plywood, as shown in *Fig. 114*, top view. Plywood panels are fastened in place with glue and screws.

The inside of the ice chest is lined with 1½″ thick Styrofoam, fitted tightly between the 1½″ framing

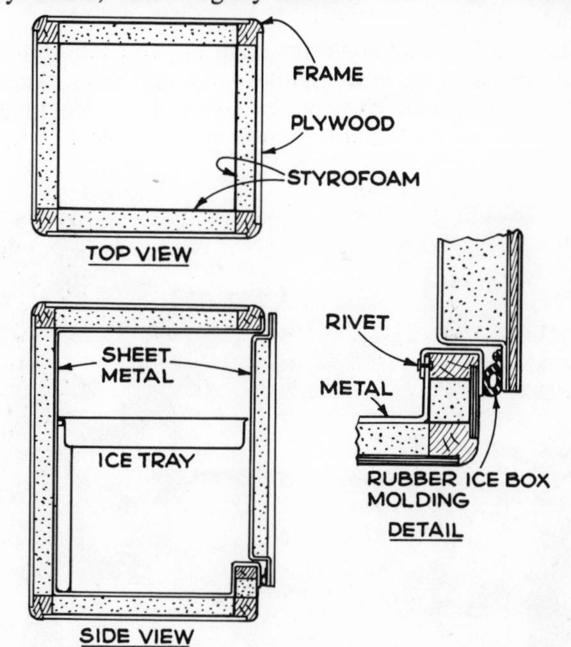

Fig. 114

members, including the bottom, and the top lid (or door as the case may be). A sheet metal lining can be ordered from a sheet metal shop (check your Yellow Pages); the detail drawing in *Fig. 114* shows how it should be fitted. Note the rubber insulation molding that must be used around the flange of the door.

Cut-Out Cockpit Locker

Here's a variation on the stowage bin above. In this case you use space inside an enclosed cockpit bulk-

Fig. 115

head; where an inner fiberglass facing is spaced about four inches or so from the outer hull skin.

As Gordon Manning's photograph (*Fig. 115*) shows, a panel has been cut from the inner skin, with a saber saw. This panel then was edged with wood to match nearby trim, and a length of piano hinge was installed along its lower edge to hinge it back into place on the bulkhead. An inner storage bin could be made up to mount behind the panel, or plywood bottom, end, and back panels could be added to form a "drawer." In many cases, as is shown, the existing floor behind the panel is sufficient.

This same panel could be made up with the bottom trim strip and an inner bottom strip that both extend below the bottom edge of the panel itself. No hinge would be installed, and the entire panel would be lifted out to provide access to the storage area. A top catch would hold it in position when set back in place.

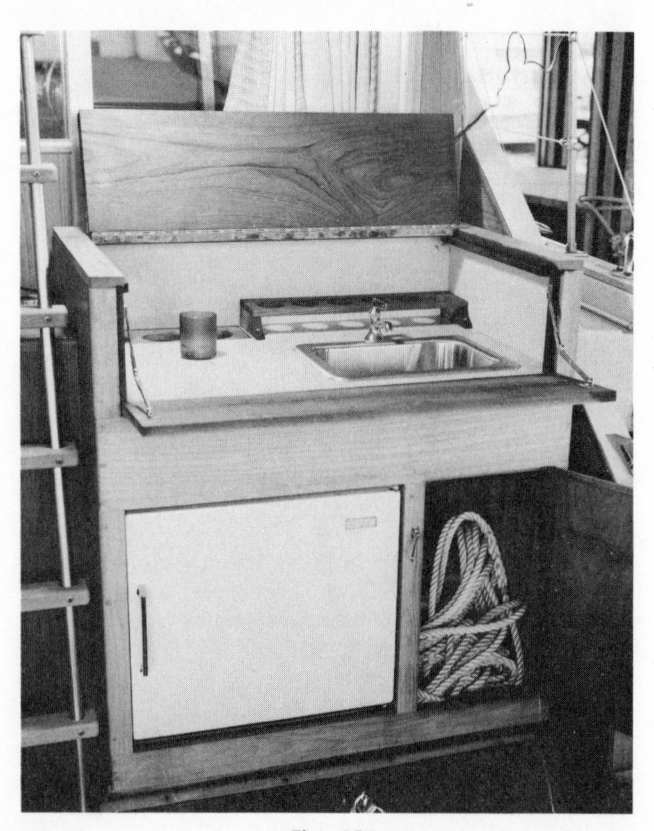

Fig. 116

Cockpit Bar Unit

One way to save space on a small cruiser with a fairly large cockpit is to use a corner of the cockpit for some installation that normally would be found inside the cabin. Gordon Manning photographed this teak bar unit (*Fig. 116*) that was set into a corner alongside the ladder to the flying bridge.

The bar takes up only 20″ x 42″ of deck space, and its double-hinged top folds back to expose a Formica work table, sink, and glass and bottle racks. A front panel hinges down to add extra work space.

On the left side of the lower section, a small refrigerator is built-in, leaving room on the right for a handy rope locker.

This particular unit has water piped to the sink, and the refrigerator is set up for 110 volt AC operation.

Fig. 117

Corner Bait Boxes

The stock bait box or fish well often takes up too much room in the cockpit of a small boat. One solution is to replace it with two small boxes, one in each corner where it is out of the way.

The box shown in Gordon Manning's photograph, *Fig. 117*, is made up of plywood, fiberglassed on the outside to match the cockpit liners. Inside, the box is fiberglassed to make it watertight. This box is fitted with a plug and scupper arrangement that permits it to be drained overboard. The matching box, mounted at the port side, has a circulating pump and a drain tube to control water level.

Of course the boxes are secured in place, and vinyl-covered cushions placed over the hinged teak tops convert them into handy cockpit corner seats.

Aluminum Frame Deck Locker

Here's an idea for a deck box that can be adapted to interior cabinet work, and is based on the do-it-

Fig. 118. Finished box provides trim, attractive stowage unit.

Fig. 120. Aluminum corners assure a perfectly squared box.

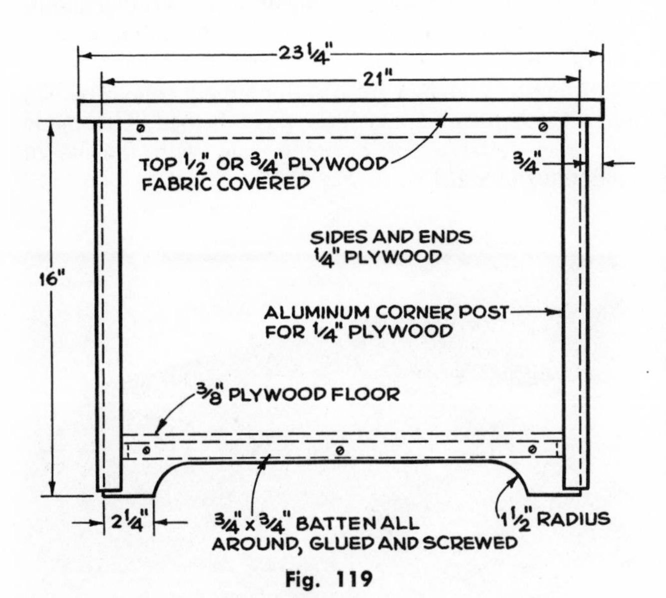

Fig. 119

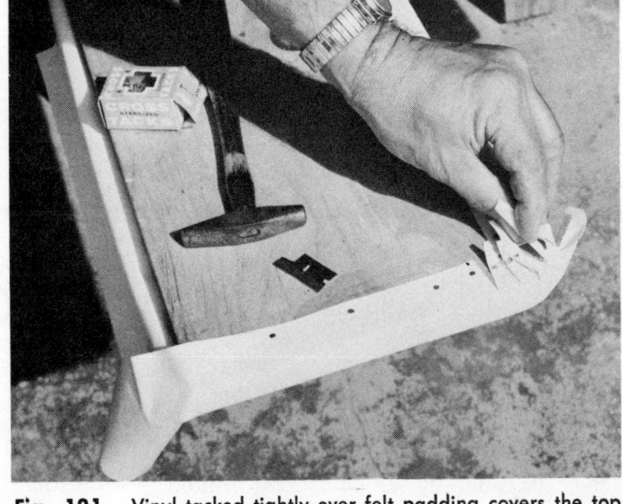

Fig. 121. Vinyl tacked tightly over felt padding covers the top.

yourself aluminum corner posts that are available at hardware stores and lumber yards. These corner posts can be cut to suitable lengths, and they are designed to hold panels of ¼″ plywood.

This particular box, *Fig. 118*, was designed, built, and photographed by Gordon Manning. Here's how he went about its construction:

The four sides of the box were laid out on a sheet of ¼″ marine plywood. In this case it was mahogany finish plywood, and pieces were laid out with all the grain running horizontal as the finished job was to be varnished. The side pieces are 16″ high by 21″; the end pieces are 16″ high x 15″. The box was designed to fit a particular space, so the finished size of the chest was about ¾″ larger than the cut length of the wood, due to "make up" in the corner posts.

Note the cut-out sections in the bottom of the panels. These not only improve appearance of the finished box, they keep the bottom up off the deck itself, allowing no water to be trapped underneath.

The four corner pieces were cut from the Reynolds aluminum corner post material. They were cut 1/16″ less than the height of the box to prevent the metal from touching the deck (see *Fig. 119*).

The four sides were assembled temporarily to the corner posts to check fit, and lines were scribed on each panel where they tucked into the corner post slots. The box was disassembled, and three ⅛″ holes were drilled through the *inside* lips of each corner post. These are for the ⅜″ length metal screws used to hold the final assembly together, along with glue.

Varnish was applied to each panel up to the scribed lines at each end. Leaving the ends bare provides a better grip for the glue to be used there. The inside as well as the outside of each panel can be varnished or painted, if so desired.

In this case the varnished panels were again assembled to the corner posts, with two-part epoxy glue. This was done on a flat surface in order to make sure the finished box would be square. Note in *Fig. 120* how shock cord was used to hold the assembly while the epoxy cured. Screws were installed through the corner posts from the inside after the glue had hardened.

Next the ⅜″ plywood bottom panel was cut to fit

Fig. 122. Battens help stiffen top edges of side panels.

snugly within the four sides. It was glued and screwed to ¾″ x ¾″ battens as shown in *Fig. 119,* after it had been painted inside and out.

To stiffen the top of the box and provide a place to hang the hinges, more ¾″ x ¾″ battens were glued and screwed around all the sides, flush with the top of the box. These can be seen in *Fig. 121.*

The hinged top is a piece of ½″ plywood that overhangs the sides by about ¾″ all around. The corners were rounded to a ¾″ radius. It was covered with a layer of felt followed by a vinyl supported fabric. Note in *Fig. 122* how the vinyl was worked around the corners.

While a pair of butt hinges were used on this box, a piano hinge could be used. A pair of metal or rope handles also could be attached to each end of the box, if desired. The bill of materials for this box is given below.

Bill Of Materials

Sides	2 pcs. ¼″ plywood 16″ x 21″, fir or mahogany faced
Ends	2 pcs. ¼″ plywood 16″ x 15″
Top	1 pc. ½″ fir plywood, 23¼″ x 17¼″
Bottom	1 pc. ⅜″ fir plywood, 15″ x 21″
Battens	12 ft. ¾″ x ¾″ soft wood strips
Corner Posts	64″ #101 Aluminum corner post (Reynolds) for ¼″ plywood (⅜″ & ½″ also available)
Screws for Posts	24 ⅜″ #6 Aluminum pan head self-tapping
Screws for Battens	24 1″ #8 Flat head brass wood or (chromed)
Hinges	1 pr. 2″ x 1½″ Butt hinges, with screws or 20″ 1¼″ Piano hinge, with screws
Vinyl Top	1 pc. 24″ x 30″ Nautolex or equivalent
Tacks	Box ⅜″ copper, galv. or aluminum

An Inboard-Outboard Table

Boating writer Jack Seville describes seeing this handy little table first on the Allied Marine boats built in Florida by Captain Jack Manson.

A rather narrow taffrail was backed up with a strip of 2″ x 4″ mahogany. A pair of holes were drilled horizontally through the taffrail and the back-up strip, and vertically through the strip.

A panel of Formica-covered plywood, about 3′ x 4′ had a matching pair of holes drilled on one edge. With brass bolts and wing nuts, the plywood panel could be hung out of the way, flat against the weather cloth, (*Fig. 123*) or secured horizontally and inboard as a handy table (*Fig. 124*). In this particular installation, according to Seville, a fresh water supply was available, and a kitchen sink spray hose was attached. This made the table suitable for cleaning fish, with the board mounted outboard as in *Fig. 125.*

Fig. 123

Fig. 124

It would be easy to adapt a similar three-way table to fit the gunwale of most small boats. Even without the convenience of a fresh water spray, it would soon earn its keep.

A mahogany lip about ½″ thick, extending approximately ½″ above the working surface along the edge behind the holes would keep tools or other materials from sliding overboard, when the board is mounted inboard. When the board is mounted outboard for cleaning fish, the lip would keep entrails from sliding forward into the cockpit.

Fig. 125

SHELTERS & AWNINGS

Cockpit Curtains

Good, snug-fitting curtains are useful in providing protection under an overhanging cabin top when the rain is pouring down, or when a boat is left at its mooring. While it is possible to make up curtains that snap into place with any number of types of patented fasteners, the problems of stretch and shrinkage, as well as corrosion of fasteners, often make it difficult to get the curtains in place, or back off once they are in place.

The curtain shown in *Fig. 126* can be made of heavy canvas or Dacron, with grommet holes in its upper and lower edges. Lacing through these holes is looped over grommet hooks installed on the cockpit coaming below the lower edge of the curtain, and under the edge of the cabin top. The lacing is drawn up tight to secure the curtain, and belayed to cleats at each end.

In some cases it is advisable to add a stanchion at the after end of the overhang, to which the curtain also can be laced.

Note that if the bottom of the curtain hangs inside the coaming, an outer flap should be provided that hangs over the outside of the coaming to keep rain from running right into the cockpit. An alternative is to have the bottom of the curtain lash to the outside of the coaming.

When not in use, the curtains can be rolled up under the top, and secured with narrow straps with grommets that slip over the hooks installed there.

A refinement to this curtain would be to add clear plastic windows of the type used in convertible tops on cars. You would have the protection of the curtains, but without obscuring your vision out to the side.

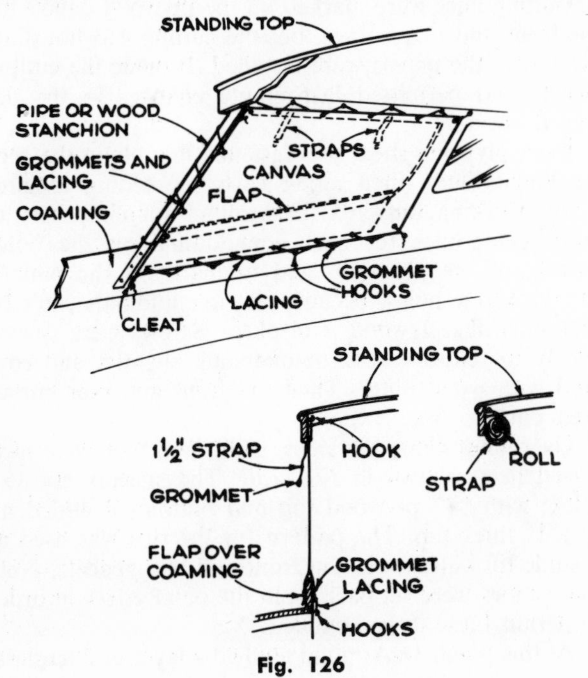

Fig. 126

Day Cruiser Enclosure

The average day cruiser has all the comforts of home, but with galley and dinette often exposed to the elements when the weather is really bad. All that's needed is some means of closing off the after end of the cabin, and you'll have an all-weather cruiser.

Gordon Manning's photo (*Fig. 127*) shows the results of one boatman's work. Using the back of the

Fig. 127

dinette on one side of the boat, and the aft end of the galley unit on the other side of the boat as a base, teak framing was installed to take sliding glass windows. Between the two sides, a door was fitted with its bottom panel of plywood painted to match the rest of the cockpit area.

It would be fairly simple to add screens across the sliding window area, so that insects will stay out when the windows are open for ventilation.

If your dinette and galley do not lend themselves to this particular treatment, the panels below the sliding windows could be cut from marine plywood and faced with Formica to provide a strong, decorative, and weather-proof enclosure.

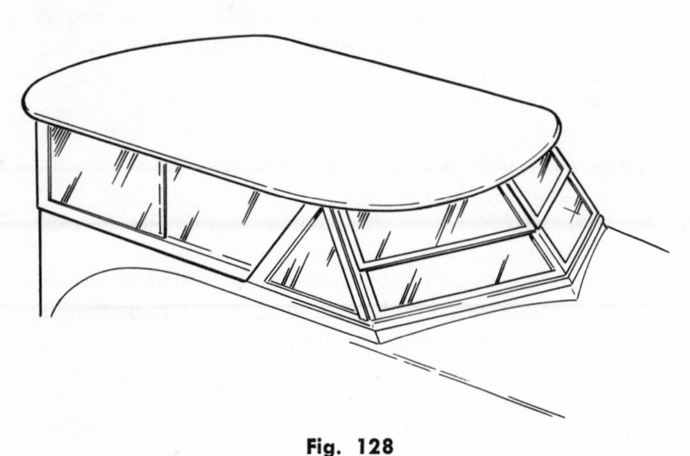

Fig. 128

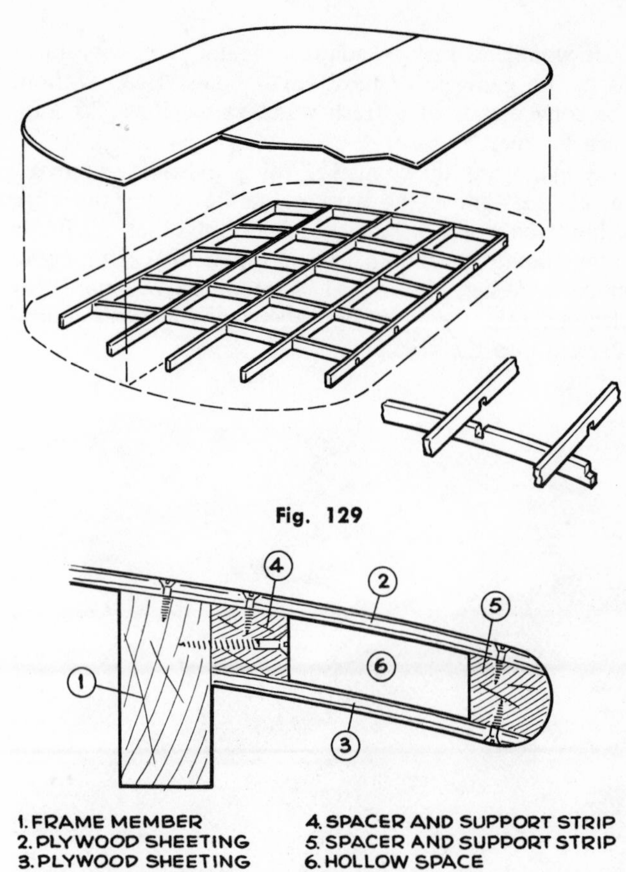

Fig. 129

Fig. 130

Ragtop to Hardtop

If you have an express cruiser, and want to convert a navy top to a permanent hard top, it can be done. Of course each boat will require individual design work, but in most cases construction can follow procedures used by V. J. DeArmond, Jr., for his hard top project (*Fig. 128*).

The top unit itself is of marine plywood encasing a solid wood framework. The top was mounted on the windshield at the front; filler panels and sliding windows made up the two sides, and the rear was left open.

Because ¼″ plywood panels were used, in order to get the needed curvature, a layer of fiberglass was applied to add strength to the top. However, ⅜″ plywood could be used and the fiberglassing omitted. Side framing panels were of a light-grained mahogany-faced marine plywood, and they were stained to match other brightwork on DeArmond's boat.

Full-size cardboard patterns for ribs were made up first, and transferred to inexpensive pine stock for the working pattern. The actual ribs were cut from 1½″ mahogany, and the seven 1½″ x 2″ longitudinal frame members were ripped from a single length of mahogany 2″ x 8″ (1½″ x 7½″ finished) stock. The four ribs were clamped together for trimming and sanding to uniform shape, then the tops of the ribs, and the bottoms of the longitudinals, were notched at the points of intersection (see *Fig. 129* for details).

Distance between the outer right and left longitudinals is the same as the distance across the windshield frame. This provides support for the top at the windshield end, and accommodates the window framework on the two sides.

After assembling the frame with a screw at every intersection, tops of longitudinals were bevelled to match curvature of the ribs, and all intersections were sanded smooth so the plywood panels would lie flush. The framework then was braced, top side up, in a level, well-supported position. This was to prevent it from warping during application of the plywood.

Cutting lines were marked on the plywood panels for the front and rear curves, but the cutting was not done until after the panels were installed. It made the cutting easier, and permitted last-minute changes in the designed curves.

Each plywood sheet was fastened first along the center longitudinal, then along each succeeding longitudinal, working outward. DeArmond found it best to mark centerlines for each longitudinal on the outer surface of the plywood, and to mark off the pattern for the screw holes, because the longitudinals can't be seen once the plywood is in place. Screws were spaced evenly to reduce stress, countersunk slightly, and covered with wood putty. Then the front and rear curves were cut.

Overhangs along the sides, front, and rear were next boxed in as shown in *Fig. 130*. The spacers are ½″ thick; with ¼″ plywood top and bottom; it added up to a 1″ thick top. The pattern for the ribs was used as a guide for cutting out the front and rear spacers. Note that screws were set back from the outer edges in order to permit these to be rounded.

At this point, DeArmond applied a layer of fiberglass,

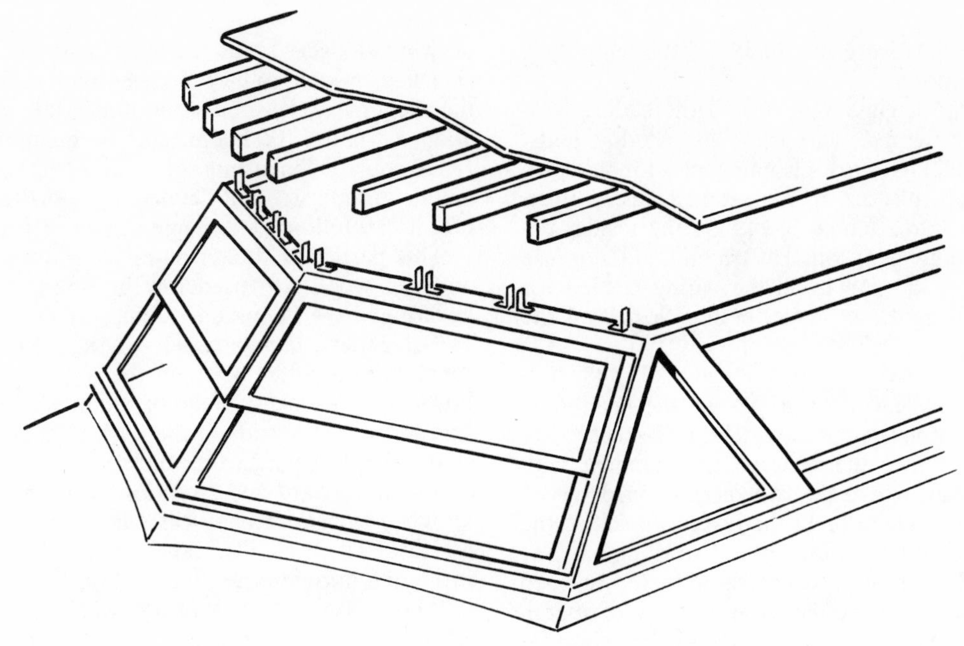

Fig. 131

although this could be skipped if 3/8″ plywood is used. When the resin had cured, it was sanded smooth, and the entire top unit was painted.

Now the top was ready for installation on the boat. A complicating factor in DeArmond's case is that it had to be done with the boat in the water. Temporary braces of a length to provide the desired height were cut to support the rear end of the top, and the entire unit was placed aboard the boat. Then the front end was centered and levelled across the windshield, at the required height above the windshield. Temporary braces were fastened here to hold the top securely, yet allow a little side play while the rear was being aligned. When the centerline of the top at the rear was aligned with the centerline of the boat, and the entire top was levelled, the temporary braces were secured to prevent further movement.

The gap above the windshield at the front was then faced with mahogany panels on the outside, after metal angle braces had been installed to permanently hold the front end in position (see *Fig. 131*). Facing panels also were installed on the inside, after the headlining was in place.

At this stage, you could add chrome-plated tubing as rear supports, and you would have your hardtop. DeArmond, however, installed side panels and sliding windows to provide additional protection from the elements. Existing cockpit coaming made an excellent base for the panels.

It was necessary to make up full-size paper patterns for side window framing which could be checked and adjusted for an exact fit. Again, a working pattern was made up of cheap pine, and the final framing pieces were cut from mahogany 1½″ x 2″ stock. See *Fig. 132*. It was important that the top and bottom pieces be exactly parallel so that sliding glass windows will neither jam nor fall out. With the framework secured, the mahogany

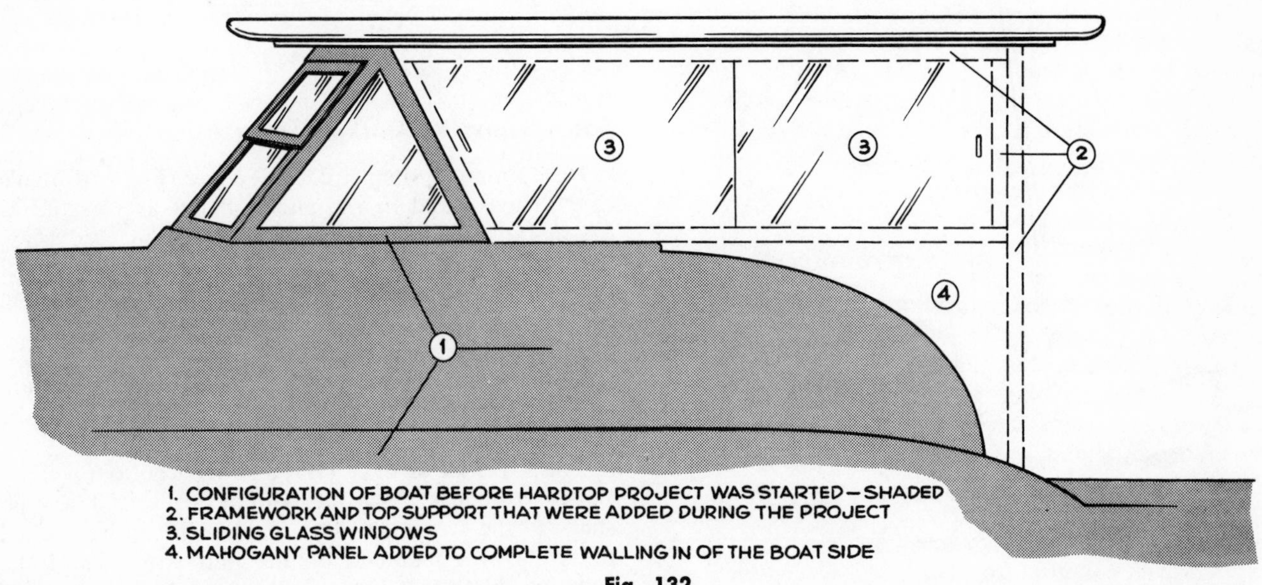

Fig. 132

plywood filler panels were installed, and the temporary rear supports removed.

DeArmond had a glass shop install the sliding windows, along with the necessary track and window pulls. Safety glass or Plexiglas are recommended for this use.

If outside grab rails are to be installed, fasten them through the top into backing blocks on the inside, before the headlining goes on. DeArmond did not use grab rails, but he did run in all the wiring needed for dome lights, spot light, and hailer before closing off the inside of the top.

For headlining, he used two lengths of 54″ perforated plastic vinyl-faced cloth. To get the headlining to hold to the contour of the cross ribs, it was necessary to sew a 1″ tuck into the material in alignment with each rib (the seam where the two pieces joined served as one such tuck). These tucks then were stapled to the ribs, starting with the forward rib and working aft, one rib at a time. The staples do not show in the finished job. An alternative would be to use strips of metal, plastic, or mahogany to hold the fabric in place at each rib.

Inner facing at the windshield, and trim strips along sides and rear completed the job.

Cockpit Shelter for an Open Sailboat

There's nothing that extends the usefulness and possibilities for weekend cruising of a small open-cockpit sailboat more than an easily-stowed cockpit cover.

A good cover transforms such a boat into a cruiser, in which you can find shelter from sudden rain squalls, privacy in which to change into a bathing suit, relief from hot summer sunshine, and snug sleeping quarters at the night's anchorage.

Obviously, no one-piece cockpit cover can provide all of these features, but by dividing the cover into easily-rigged sections (*Fig. 133*), you can employ different combinations to suit the barometric readings and temperature.

The best shelter is one which combines the features of wind dodger, spray curtains, and an awning with side flaps which roll up for ventilation. In order that the shelter may be used when under sail, a clearance of about 6″ under the boom must be maintained.

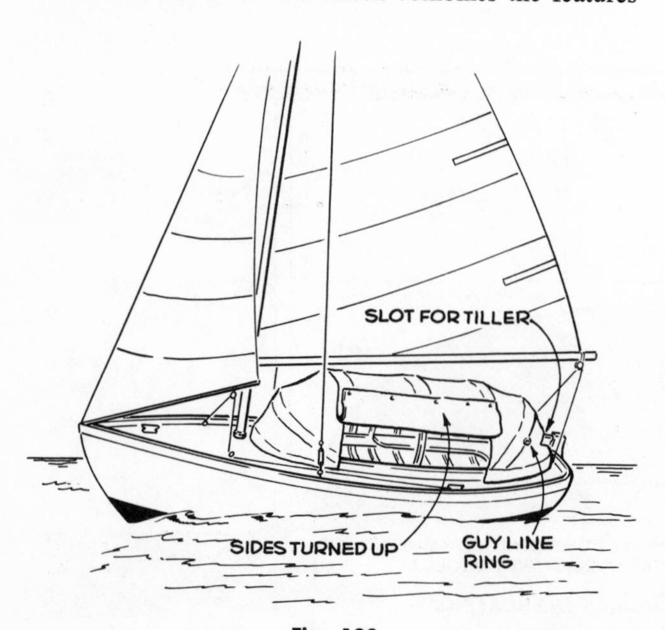

Fig. 133

Of course dimensions of your boat and its cockpit will determine size and details of the shelter, but in general it can follow the scheme shown in *Fig. 133*.

This particular design dates back quite a few years, and ash wood was used for the bows, canvas for the covering. Now aluminum tubing, or even flat strips of ⅛″ thickness, can be used for the bows, and dacron sailcloth is a better bet than the old canvas duck. The bows fit into sockets made of aluminum or brass strips screwed to the outside of the cockpit coaming, and bow shape should be such that they can be stowed easily.

To the forward and aftermost bows, a smaller bow is attached to form a baby carriage-type spray hood, fore and aft. These smaller bows should be able to swing inside the upright bows, for stowage.

About 10 to 12 yards of 36″ width sailcloth, or 13 to 15 yards of 24″ width material, should be ample for the average small boat's cockpit. Sewing can be done on the standard home sewing machine, fitted with a heavy needle. A palm and sail needle with some beeswaxed sail twine is handy for the heavier work. All edges can be reinforced with ⅜″ dacron line.

Use dot fasteners, grommets and lashings, buttons, or zippers for fastenings. Install grommets at the fore and aft corners of the spray hoods to take rough-weather guy lines which attach to the mast, or to pad eyes on the deck. A reinforcing length of dacron should be sewn over the bow pockets, and all points of chafe or wear should be reinforced with leather or an extra layer of cloth.

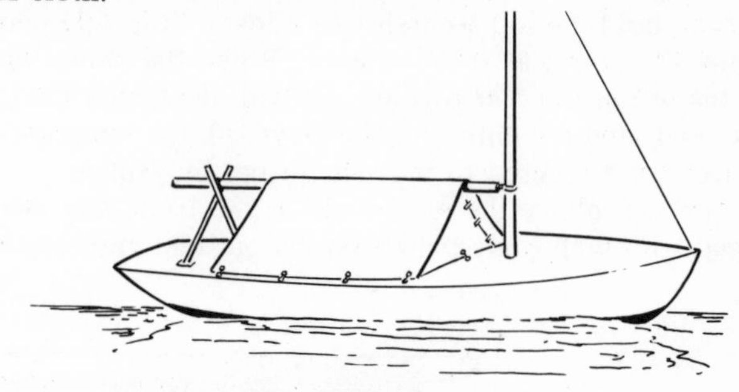

Fig. 134

Boom-Supported Cockpit Cover

Here's a much simpler cockpit cover (*Fig. 134*) that's easy to make and to rig, although not as versatile as the multiple-use unit above. This can't be used while the boat is under sail, as the boom provides the central support. You'll need a sturdy boom crutch, or topping lift, to support the after end of the boom.

If your boat's cockpit is of the Type (A), *Fig. 135*, some curvature will have to be worked into the bottom side of the cover. For the ends, the sailcloth should be cut to fit snug with any camber in the deck.

For a cockpit of Type (B), a straight bottom will do. Install grommets along the bottom edges, and sew jib snaps to the grommets. The snaps then can be hooked to screw eyes mounted on the outboard side of the coaming. Note that brass rings are sewn to squares of

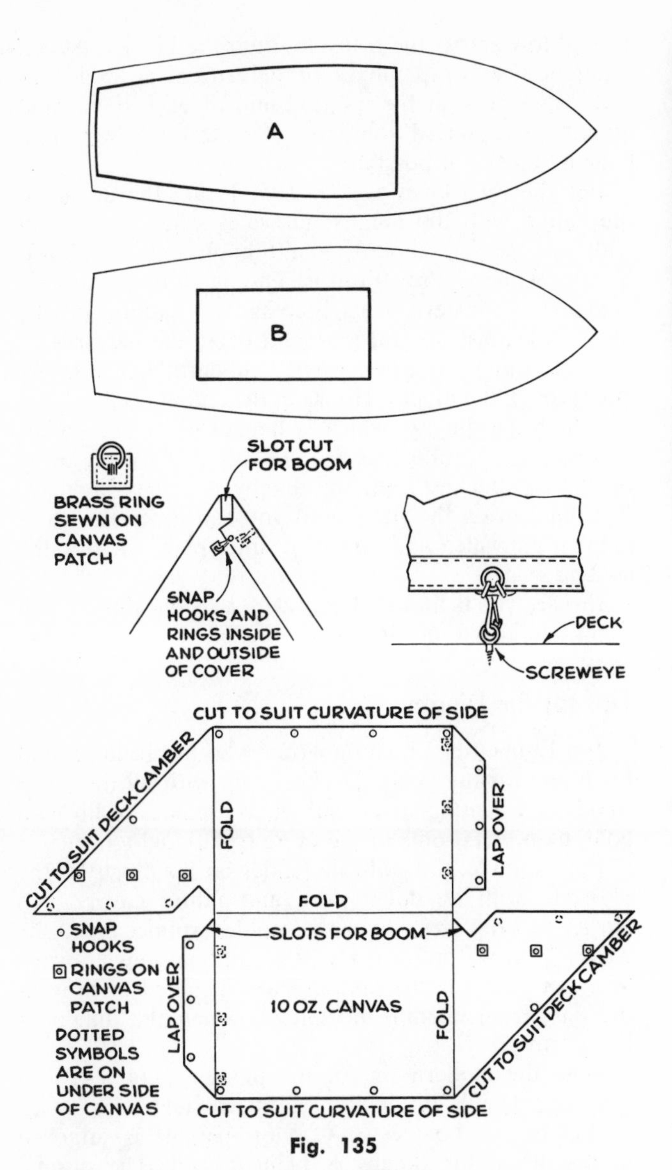

Fig. 135

sailcloth, which in turn are securely stitched to the front flap. Jib snaps on a flap at the forward edge of the matching side panel can be hooked to these rings to seal off the forward end of the shelter.

Fig. 136

Formica Weather Cloths

Here's a simple and effective way to make up long-lasting weather cloths that need a minimum of maintenance to maintain their "new" appearance for many years. Double-faced Formica is used, with oversize holes drilled for every screw fastening, and nylon washers used under the screw heads. Gordon Manning's photo (*Fig. 136*) shows a panel screwed to stanchions at the after end of a flying bridge. A less expensive way to achieve the same result is to use Masonite panels, and paint them to match the color scheme of your boat.

DINGHY MANAGEMENT

Securing the Dinghy On Board

Here are two simple rigs for securing the dinghy on a cabin top, assuming that you have some means of getting it up there in the first place.

If the dinghy is to be carried upright, cradle members must be made up that fit both the contour of the cabin top and the bottom of the dinghy. Hardwood stock

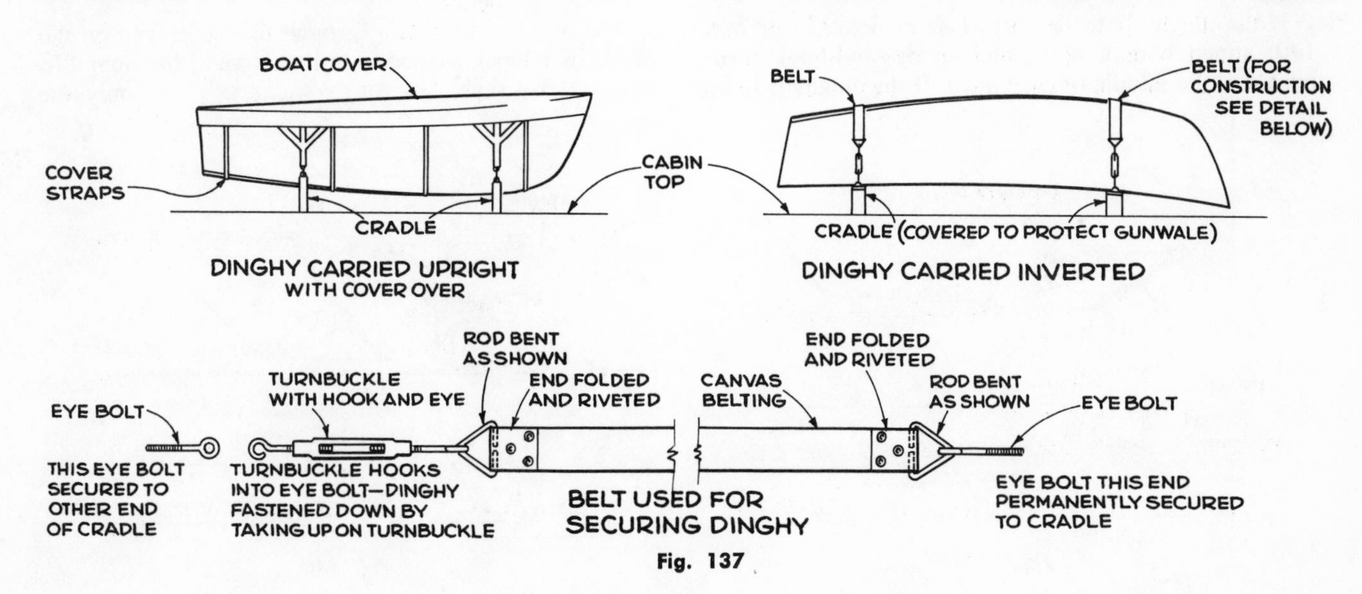

Fig. 137

should be at least 1″ wide (¾″ dressed), and the upper edge should be padded to protect the dinghy bottom. Be sure to bed the cradle members in a compound that will prevent water from getting underneath.

By carrying the dinghy upside down, you eliminate the above problem, and simplify the cradle construction. The cradle members still must be curved to fit the cabin top, but the upper edges can be left straight, and padded just where the gunwales make contact.

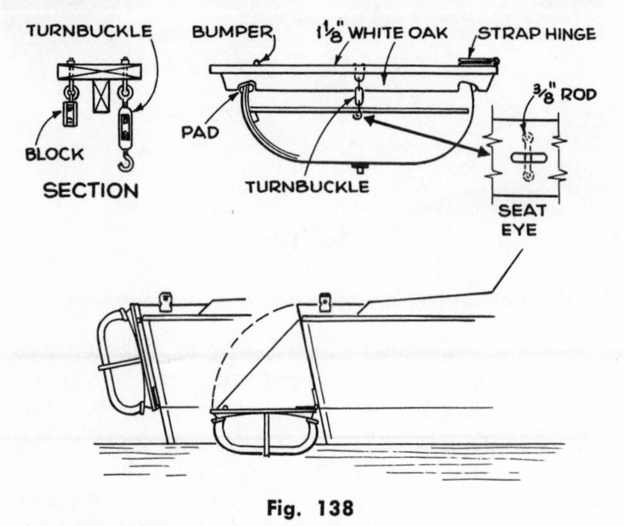

Fig. 138

Stowing the Dinghy at the Stern

For those cruisers with no cabin top to spare, the best place for the dinghy is across the transom. Make up a pair of the davits as shown in *Fig. 138*, and you can sling it low, just above the waterline, let it all hang out (*Fig. 139*), or bring it right across the top of the cockpit (*Fig. 140*). This latter is recommended only if you have a wide transom deck that will accommodate the dinghy.

Each davit arm is made up of two pieces of white oak, glued and bolted together in a "T" section. Use 1″ x 4″ stock for the horizontal members; 1″ x 2″ stock for the vertical members. Length should suit the beam of the dinghy. Notch each end of the vertical members as shown in the detail drawing, to fit the dinghy's gunwales.

If the dinghy is to be carried as in *Fig. 139* or *Fig. 140*, attach both a block and an eye-and-hook turnbuckle at the middle of each davit. If the dinghy is to be carried low across the transom, omit the blocks. Attach stainless steel strap hinges or galvanized strap hinges with brass pins, at the inboard end of each davit, and mount them aboard your boat. Use through bolts into backing blocks, if possible.

For the rig shown at *Fig. 138*, locate the davits so they align with the dinghy gunwales when it is afloat with one person aboard; you'll hook onto the turnbuckles while you're still in it. The halyards for this rig lead up to your stern cleats. Step aboard, haul the dinghy up flush against the transom, and belay the halyards.

If the dinghy is to be carried inboard, halyards are run through the blocks. Hooks at the end of each halyard attach to the dinghy, which is hauled up to the davits, and then the turnbuckles are hooked in place. Take up on the turnbuckles until the dinghy is snugly in place, then haul in on the stays until you can grasp the outer dinghy gunwale, and lower it into place across the cockpit.

In use, you'll find that any water in the dinghy will drain overboard, not into your cockpit.

Tips for the Dinghy

Jim Emmett is a boating writer who has been around for a good many years. He keeps up with all the latest trends and boating styles, but when it comes to his own boat, he prefers some of the more traditional touches.

For example, the gunwale fender on his dinghy is the old-style with a rubber core and fabric cover. "It's harder to keep clean than the molded rubber type," he writes, "but we prefer it for its traditional appearance." Wooden pads for the oarlocks are installed to prevent the oars from chafing the fenders when the dinghy is being rowed.

Note the modern rig for the painter (*Fig. 141*): a four-foot length of flexible stainless steel wire is attached to the bow eye. A nylon painter is attached to this when the dinghy is being towed. The normal painter, attached directly to the boat, is almost continuously wet under these conditions, and the wetness helps bring about early failure. Also, Jim feels that the stainless steel wire is less likely to get entangled with his boat's propeller.

The bow eye itself is a through fitting, backed on the inside by a block shaped to fit the curve of the stem. "In towing," he says, "in rough water, it's not only the

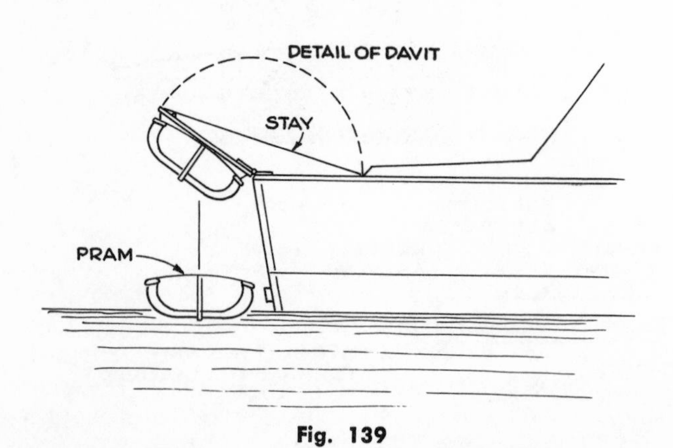

Fig. 139

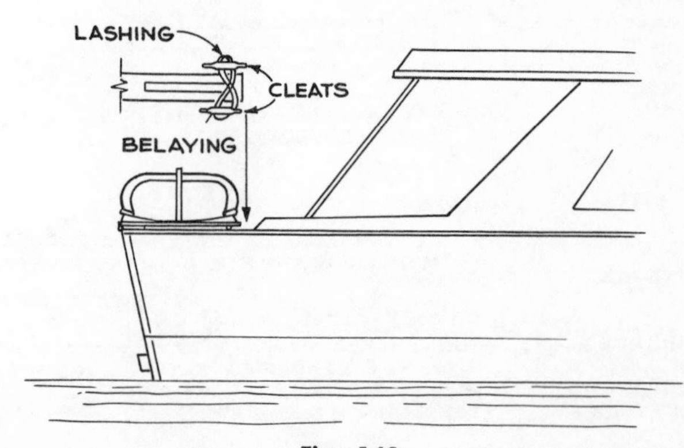

Fig. 140

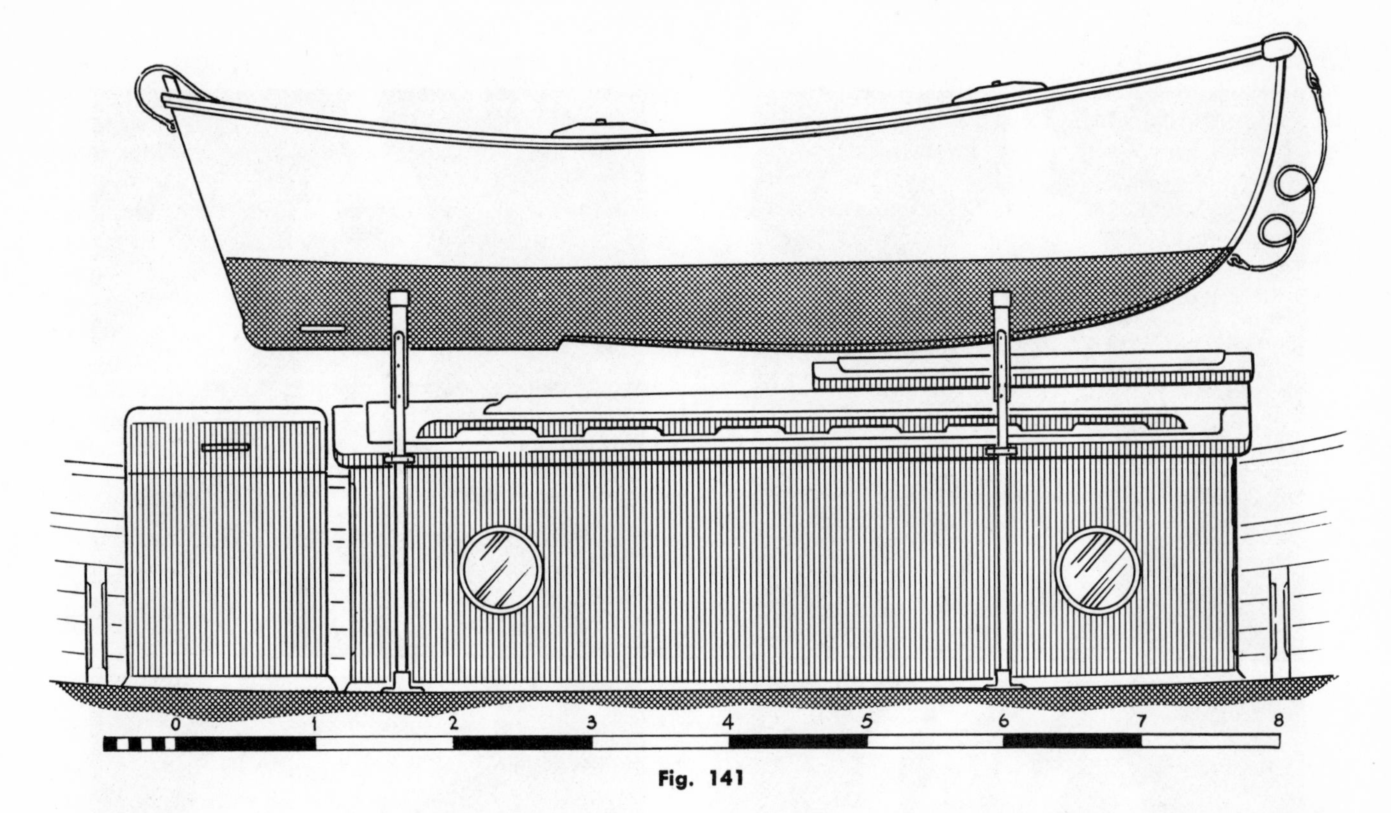

Fig. 141

tender's behavior that's on one's mind but how the stem is standing the yanking strain."

FENDERS & LADDERS

Rugged Boat Fenders

To protect topsides against rough lock walls, creosoted pilings in a high tidal area, or any barnacle-encrusted bulkhead, you'll want something tougher than standard rubber or plastic boat fenders.

In the New York State Canal System, where boatmen contend with numerous locks, they have developed a simple fender consisting of a 2 x 4 board hanging vertically over the rubrail from a stanchion or cleat (see *Fig. 142*), chamfered on the ends to prevent snagging. Up to six are used on either side when locking; boards hang from about 5″ above the rubrail to within 10″ of the waterline.

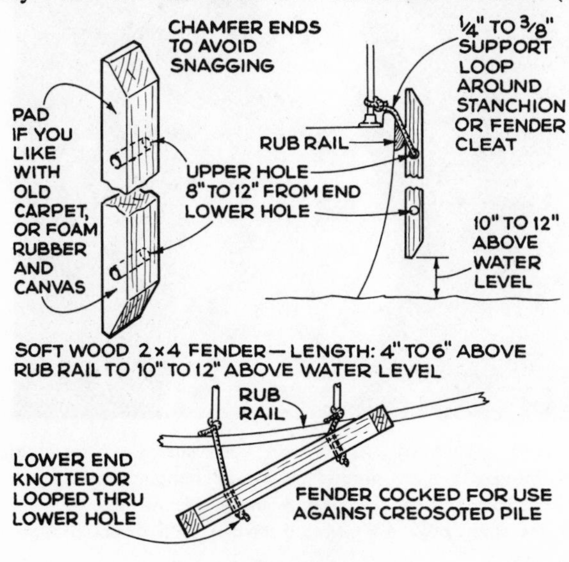

Fig. 142

They will protect topsides without adjustment in the vertical position. If you have no rubrail, line the inside of the fender with old carpet, or strips of foam rubber sewn into canvas.

A lanyard through the lower hole permits you to draw up that end, forming a conventional fender board. In this case always hang soft rubber, canvas, or plastic fenders between the board and topsides. Fender material should be soft pine or cedar, lengths of 3′ to 5′ are ample. Use a ¾″ bit to bore holes for the lanyards.

Fig. 143

Re-Cycled Rope Fenders

Rope fenders are not a new idea; they have been around for many years. It's a good use for old lines that have outlived the service for which they were intended originally, and the fenders themselves are quite handsome. Jack Dillon's photographs show how to make the fender shown in *Fig. 143*.

Fig. 144. Start with about 15′ of old ⅝″ rope. Form a bight at the center and secure it with a seizing. Eye splice a length of ¼″ or ⅜″ line snugly to this bight as a pennant. Unlay both ends of the ⅝″ line to form six strands.

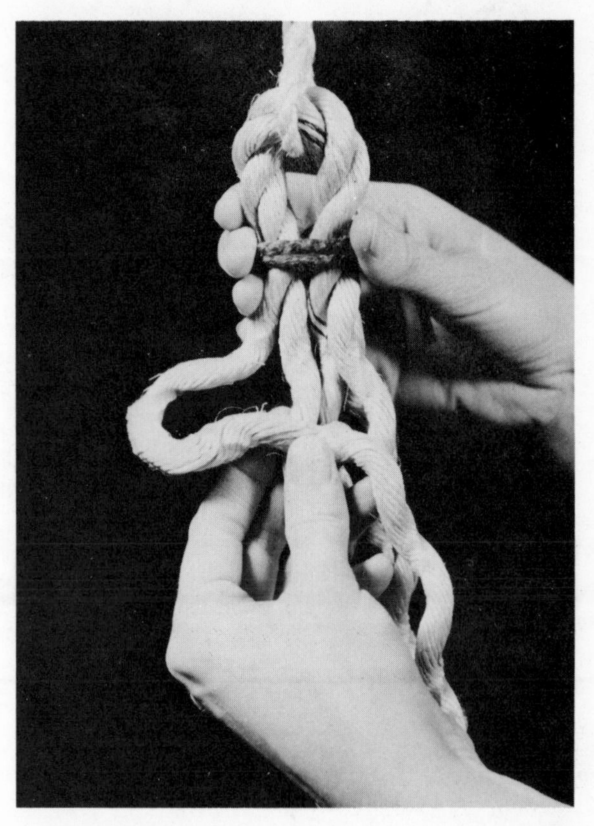

Fig. 145. Take a strand in the left hand and form a bight. Hold the rest of the strands in your right hand.

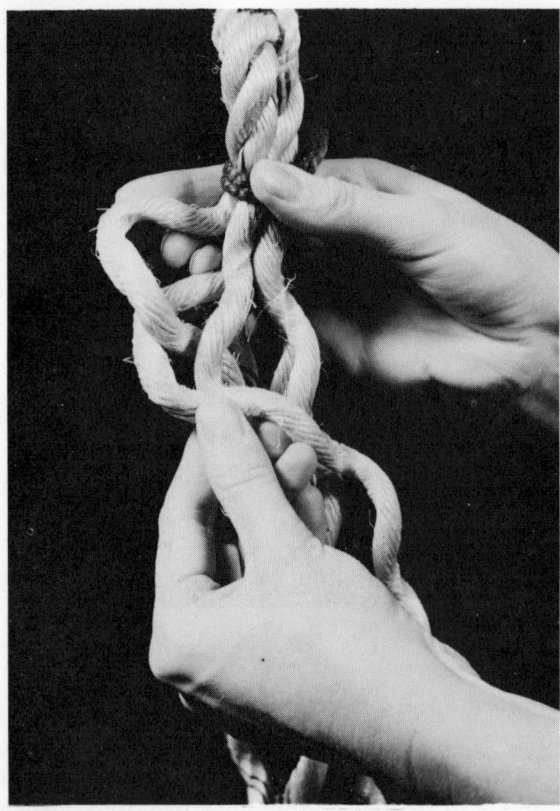

Fig. 146. Pick up the strand immediately to the right of the bight. Pass it under, then over the strand hanging down from the bight, forming a second bight around this strand.

Fig. 147. Continue around with each strand to the right in turn, forming a bight around the strand hanging down from the previous bight. After forming a bight around the fifth strand with the sixth, poke the strand from the sixth down through the first bight.

Fig. 148. Pull all the strands with even tension until the bights are up snug against the seizing. Repeat the entire process to form a second row of bights under the first.

Fig. 149. Take a rounded section of Styrofoam, or a length of old radiator hose, about 2" in diameter, and insert it into the center of the strands. This forms the core of the fender.

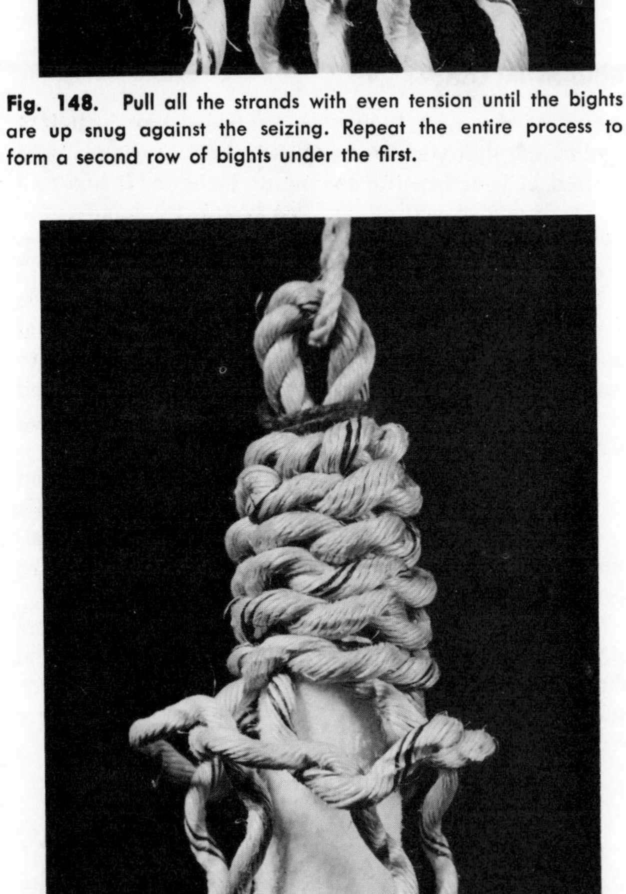

Fig. 150. Continue forming additional rows of bights around the core, in the same manner as the first two rows, until the core is covered. Be sure to cut the core to the desired length.

Fig. 151. To finish off at the end of the core, use a fid to tuck the end of any strand through a bight in the second row from the bottom, and two to the right of the strand being used. Do not pull this strand up tight.

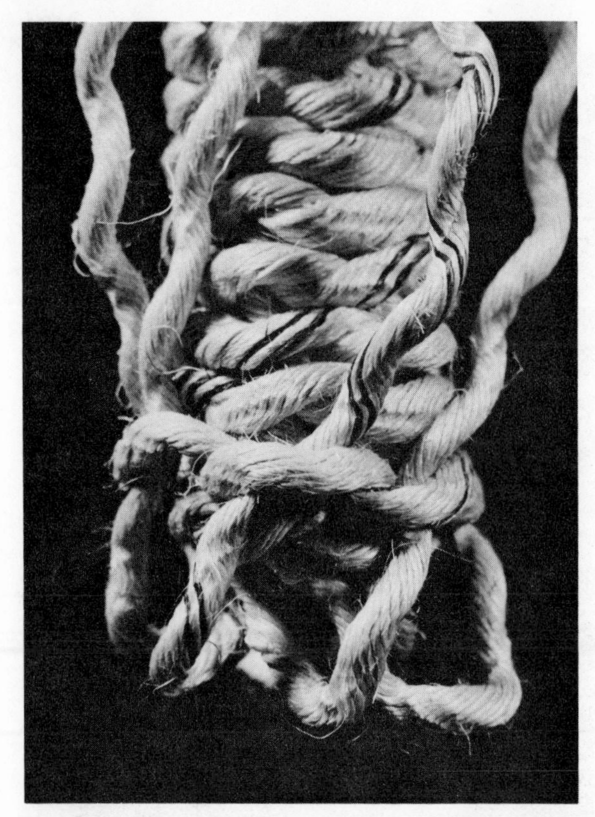

Fig. 152. Tuck the remaining strands through the corresponding bights in the second row from the bottom, then pull all the strands up tight. You'll note that this pulls the bottom row of bights in under the core.

Fig. 153. Continue tucking the strands up through the bights above, one row at a time; about five rows of tucks will make a good job. Cut off the excess line, and roll the fender under your foot to smooth it out.

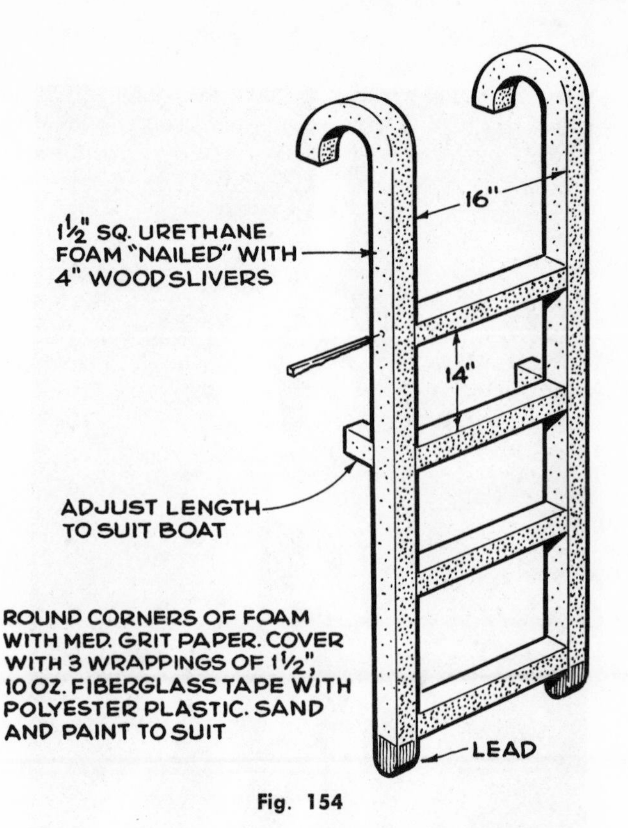

Fig. 154

Rigid Swim Ladder

One of the most useful items aboard any boat is a rigid ladder that you can hang over the side when you're moored in your favorite swimming location. It takes all the strain out of getting back on board. It's handy, too, for persons who have fallen overboard, and are encumbered by clothes and other gear.

Naval architect Charles Bell, one of the earliest specialists in fiberglass construction, offers this rigid ladder made of urethane foam and fiberglass. Be sure to use *urethane* foam, not *Styrofoam*. Polyester resin used in the fiberglassing process would completely destroy Styrofoam.

The urethane foam comes in boards that can be cut to the desired shape (see *Fig. 154*) with a sharp knife or a saw. Length of the ladder will depend on your boat, but rung width and distance between rungs should be as illustrated.

The rungs are "nailed" to the side pieces with slivers of wood split off from any straight-grained stock, and sharpened at one end. They should be about 4″ long, and about the thickness of a pencil. Leave them square

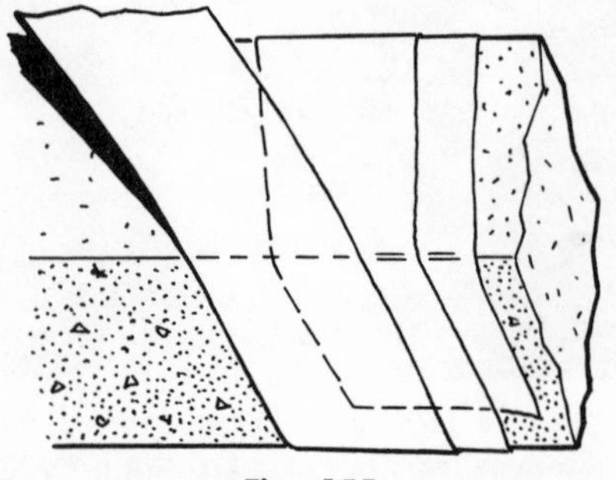

Fig. 155

and do not smooth them off. The rougher they are, the better they will hold.

After the ladder is assembled, round off all corners with sandpaper. Round off the feet so that rubber tips can be slipped on later. Then wind on 10-oz. fiberglass tape, as shown in *Fig. 155*. Coat the urethane foam with resin, working just a little ahead of the tape as you wind it on.

It's a good idea to encase a couple of lead weights at the base of each leg to overcome the ladder's tendency to float—to pop right up out of the water. Normally the hooks at the top of side pieces, and the spacers that hold the ladder away from the side of the hull, will combine to prevent this floating action.

Fig. 156

Side Flying Bridge Ladder

This is a project we recommend only where side deck space is ample, because you don't want anyone hanging out over the side of the boat, particularly when it is under way. But when the flying bridge ladder can safely be set on one side of the cabin, it leaves clear access to the cockpit area, and really increases its liveability. The photo, *Fig. 156*, is by Gordon Manning.

Build Your Own Rope Ladder

An alternative to the rigid ladder is the traditional rope ladder. The rope ladder has its advantages, of course: it can be stowed almost anywhere, it can be hung overboard almost anywhere, the shape of the boat doesn't matter, and it's easy and inexpensive to make.

First determine the number of steps (rungs) you'll need. Plan on 10″ to 11″ between each step, and figure on at least two steps hanging beneath the surface of the water. The top step should come within 8″ to 10″ of the gunwale.

Step length is 15″, and width should be 4″ to 4½″. Use ⅝″ or ¾″ dressed mahogany stock. Note in *Fig. 157* the ½″ cutback: this is required only if the contour of your hull is such that the ladder might rock from side to side if it made contact with the center of the step only.

You can cut a ⅛″ wide slot or two, about ⅛″ deep

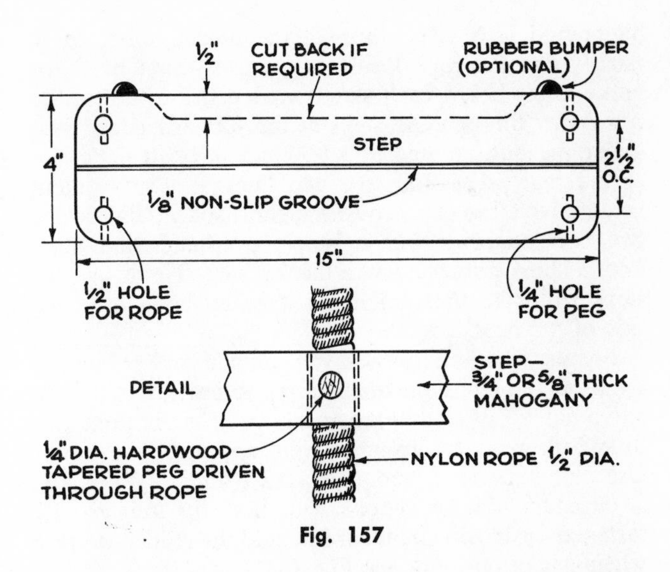

Fig. 157

along each step to provide a non-skid surface, or apply strips of one of the waterproof non-skid tapes that are available.

Round off the corners, sand, and give each step three coats of a good spar varnish. When the finish has dried, lay out the positions for the four rope holes, and bore them out with a ½″ drill bit for ½″ rope. Drill ¼″ holes through from the front and rear edges of the steps, as shown in *Fig. 157*. These holes pass through the rope holes, extending about ¾″ past the far side of the rope holes.

Make up ¼″ diameter pins from hardwood dowel stock. These pins pass through the rope itself, so the front end of each pin must be pointed to part the fibers of the rope. When coated with a waterproof glue and

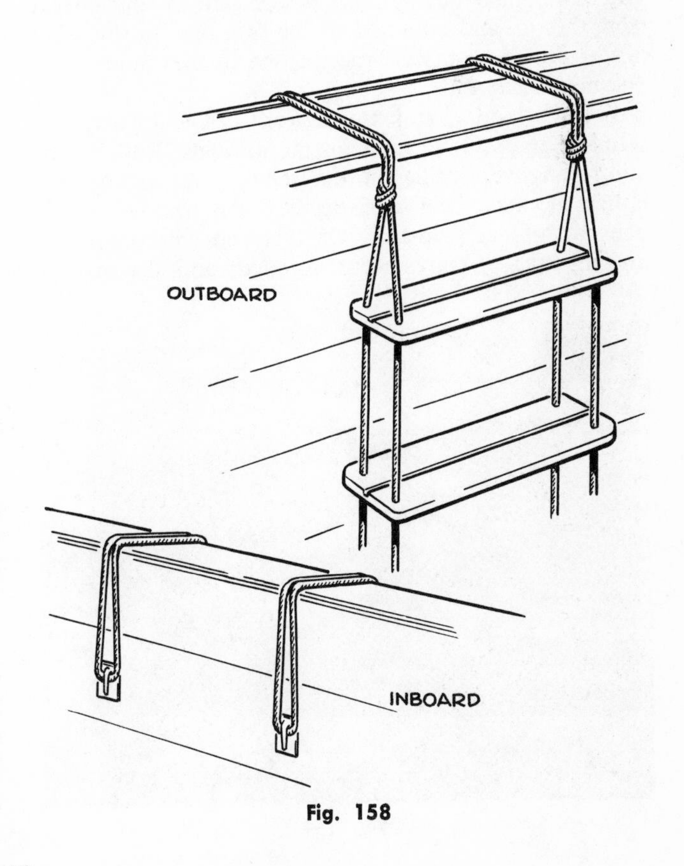

Fig. 158

hammered into place through the dowel holes, these pins wedge the rope firmly in place, without need for bulky knots below each step. One length of line can be run down through the steps at the forward edge, then under the bottom step and back up through the holes at the rear edge. Join the two lines at a convenient height above the top step with a short splice, and tie the two lines together with a simple overhand "anti-slip" knot a short distance above the top step. Tie this so the steps will take the desired angle when hung over the side of the boat.

For the finishing touches, you can add rubber bumper knobs to the rear edge of each step to protect your hull, and a flat bar of lead to the underside of the bottom step to keep lower steps from bobbing up out of the water. Use plumbers' lead, about 3″ x 12″, three layers thick.

Ordinary ski tow hooks with non-slip tongues are fastened upside down inboard to hold the ladder in place when it is in position. See *Fig. 158*.

Swim Platform Boarding Ladder

Here are two projects for the price of one: a teak transom-mounted swimming platform, plus a double-duty boarding ladder.

The swim platform is made up of teak strips, with the long, full-length ones alternating with short spacers. The resulting openings allow water to drain through, eliminating excess strain on the platform in any wave action. The platform is made upside down against a simple jig on which the curve of the transom is reproduced. Each strip, or row of long strips, is glued and clamped to the preceding row or strip. Transverse strips then are glued and screwed into place across the rows. When the glue has set, the whole unit is unclamped from the jig, and mounted on the transom. In this case it was bolted to three "knees"; one in the middle and one near each end.

For the ladder, teak treads were drilled to take the stainless steel tubing used for the uprights. Both treads and tubing were drilled so the treads could be through-bolted in place, and a 90-degree bend was formed in one end of each upright. On this end, chrome-plated awning hinge fixtures were installed, and the awning

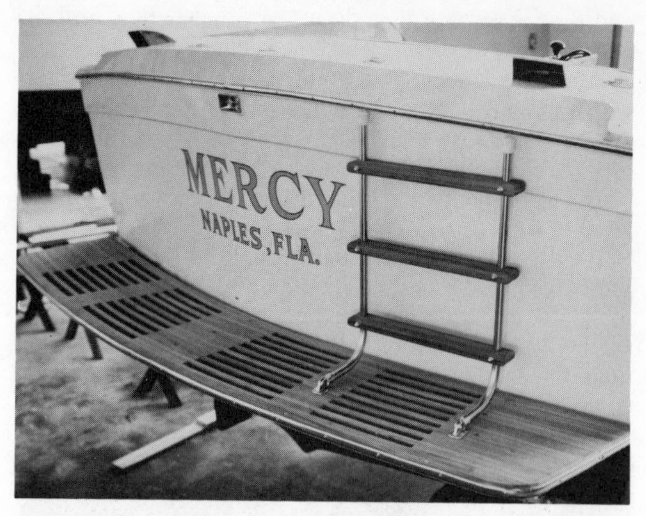

Fig. 160

hinge brackets were bolted to the swim platform.

Fig. 159 shows the ladder in the lower position, where it simplifies the task for a swimmer coming up onto the platform. When on the platform, the swimmer flips the ladder to the raised position, *Fig. 160*, to board the boat. Both photos are by Gordon Manning.

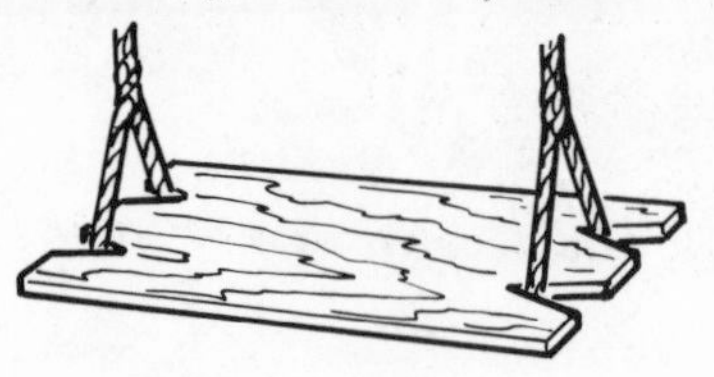

Fig. 161

The Simplest Boarding Ladder

Here's an item (*Fig. 161*) we found in Britain's *Practical Boat Owner*: a board notched with four vees, two at each end, used as a boarding ladder. To prevent splitting, the vee cuts terminate at holes drilled through the board. The vees are said to effectively self-jam the eye splices used to hold the ladder at the side of the boat.

Naturally, it's for use on something with not too much freeboard.

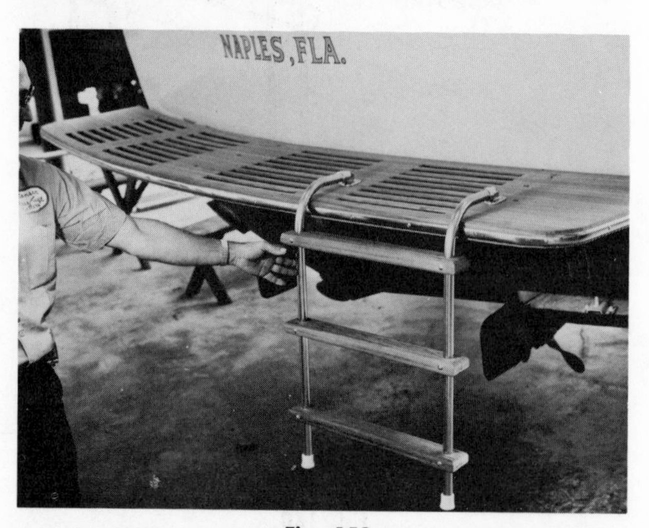

Fig. 159

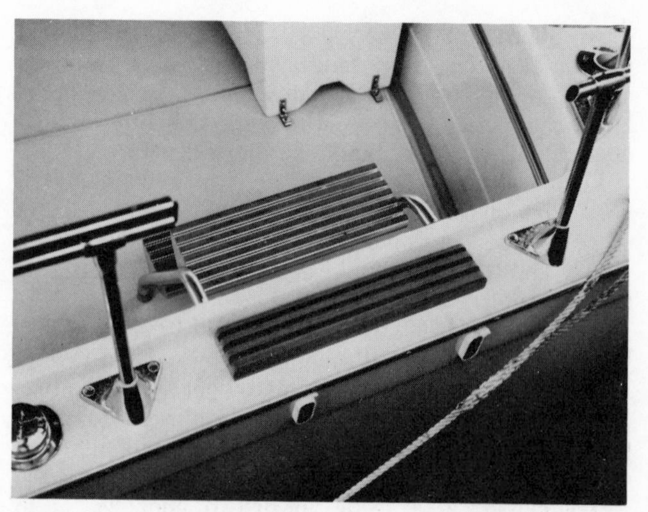

Fig. 162

Slotted Step Pads

Gordon Manning's photograph, *Fig. 162*, illustrates one way to replace worn step pads on cockpit side decks, or to add ones where none was provided by the manufacturer.

These pads are made up of 1″ teak blocks, about 15″ long and 3½″ wide. Slots ¼″ wide and ⅜″ deep are cut into the top surface to provide a gripping area. Six pan head screws, down in the slots, hold the pad to the deck.

HATCH COVERS

Simple Sliding Hatch Cover

Here's a sliding hatch cover arrangement that does not depend on fancy lips, grooves, or hardware. It simply laps over the sides of the hatch coaming, and is held down by cables that run fore-and-aft through the transverse coaming member. The idea was developed by Keith Stanley of England, and presented in *Practical Boat Owner* there.

You can see in *Fig. 163* how the hatch cover end pieces are slotted to act as guides. The fore-and-aft hatch coaming members are covered with nylon strips to provide a long-lasting bearing surface.

Plastic-covered stainless steel wire, such as that used for outboard motor steering cable, was knotted at one end, then run through a hole at one side of the forward end piece, then through a matching hole in the trans-

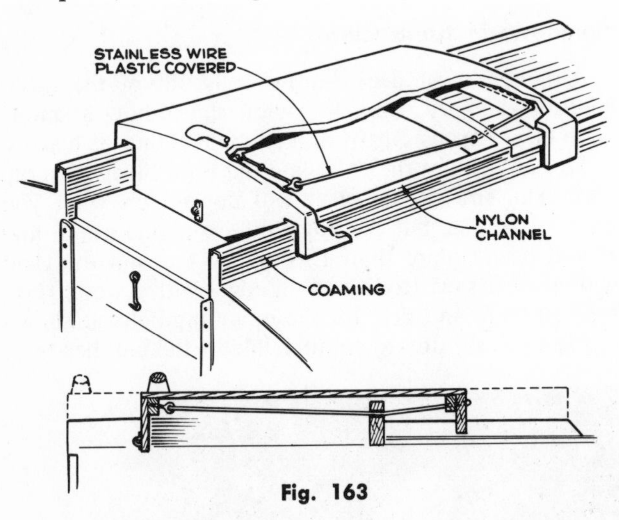

Fig. 163

verse coaming member, then through an eye bolt screwed into the after end piece. A second length of cable was run in the same manner through the other side of the hatch. The two lengths of cable were joined with a tiller rope clamp.

A variation would be to use a lower forward coaming member across the hatch, with nylon tiller rope guides mounted on top of it. Also, you could make the hatch cover slightly longer than necessary, as Mr. Stanley suggests, so the wire could be attached to eye bolts inside the forward cross member and no knots would be left protruding on the outside.

Fig. 164

Foldaway Hatch Cover

Here's a suggestion from Gordon Groene for a folding cover that can be installed over a forward hatch to provide standing headroom, ventilation, and protection against insects.

The top unit is a hinged wood panel supported by aluminum legs. The legs fit over small pins which are let into the deck at the corners of the hatch. At their upper ends, the legs can be attached to the wood panels with hinges or brackets.

In the unit shown (*Figs. 164, 165*), the fabric cover was made up of Weblon, but anything of this type, such as Dacron, is suitable. The screening is fiberglass, and the zippers are brass. If you don't have a heavy-duty sewing machine, assembling the pieces is best done by your local awning shop.

If the windward flap is opened, and the other three are kept closed, the hatch cover will act as a wind scoop.

Fig. 165

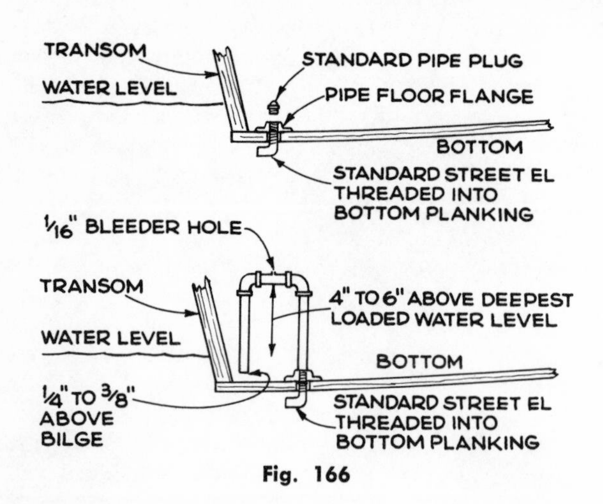

Fig. 166

Home-Made Self Bailers

One way to avoid the expense of installing a commercial self-bailer is to rig your own, using standard pipe and pipe fittings. For a simple bailer, bore a hole through the bottom at the point of the bilge that's lowest when the boat is underway. Over the hole mount a standard pipe floor flange in bedding compound on the inner side of the bilge planking. A standard pipe plug screwed in finger tight will prevent a reverse flow of water into the hull when the boat is not under way (*Fig. 166*).

Through the bottom hole, thread a standard pipe street ell with the open end pointing aft. Suction created by the boat when it's moving at speeds above 5 mph will draw out bilge water. If the bottom planking is not too thick, this ell can be screwed directly into the inside pipe flange. With this rig, it's important to remember to replace the pipe plug when the boat is stopped.

You can make a more sophisticated bailer by eliminating the inside pipe plug and substituting a vertical pipe nipple that will rise 4″ to 6″ above the static water line (*Fig. 166, bottom*). Then, return this gooseneck via two pipe elbows and nipples, so the open end is about ¼″ above the lowest part of the bilge when the boat is under way.

To prevent reverse siphon action while the boat is docked or anchored, drill a 1/16″ bleeder hole in the upper side of the horizontal nipple at the highest point in the gooseneck. This will permit water to drain to the outside water level.

When selecting the length for the vertical nipple above the pipe flange, be sure to consider your boat's waterline when a full load is aboard, because the nipple should reach 4″ to 6″ above the waterline at maximum draft.

Because of the bleeder hole and the extra height of this rig, you'll need a speed of at least 10 mph to create the siphoning action. The action is completely automatic, however, and you can locate the rig in any convenient spot as long as the intake reaches into the lowest part of the bilge.

Select piping in accordance with your location, and the size of your boat. Galvanized pipe is suitable for fresh water; copper pipe should be used in salt water. Use ½″ pipe for boats in the 16′ to 20′ range, and ¾″ or larger for cruisers.

Fig. 167

Home-Made Jamb Cleat

Although most deck hardware is out of the do-it-yourself category, John F. Dillon shows how a simple jamb cleat can be cut from a suitable chunk of teak.

Fig. 167 shows the cleat laid out on a block of scrap teak. The size of the cleat will depend on what you need, of course, but the angle of rise is important, and should be no more than 15 degrees. Cut out the cleat with a saber saw. Round off all edges with a wood rasp, sand smooth, and drill for the mounting bolts as shown in *Fig. 168*. Be sure to countersink for the bolt heads.

Fig. 168

Fig. 169

Fig. 169 shows the finished cleat mounted in place on the deck. Note that it is set at an angle of 10 degrees to the lead of the line. Be sure to coat the bottom of the cleat liberally with bedding compound before bolting it in place. For maximum strength, the bolts should run through a backing block if the cleat is bolted directly to the deck.

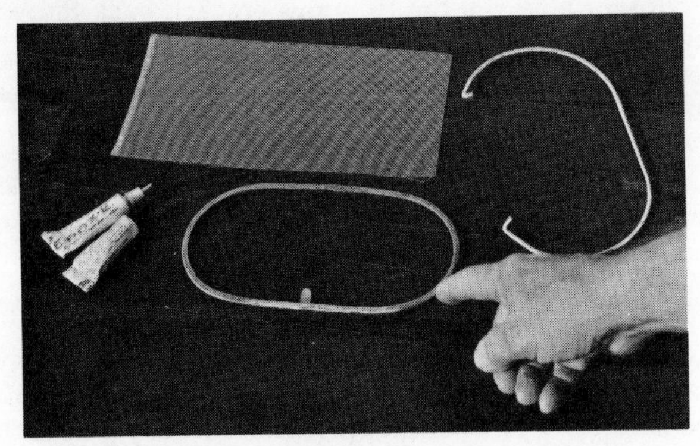

Fig. 170. Screen repair ingredients: The wire on the right is the retaining ring for the screen.

Add New Screens

This project is another of Gordon Manning's productions, and it's designed to make life aboard a little more bearable on those hot evenings when you want to keep the ports open. Too often there's nothing there to keep the bugs out!

Here's an easy way to make up screens for original installation, or to replace old ones. Start by making up frames, if yours is a new installation. The old frames can be used if it's a screen replacement job. For new frames, use the ⅛″ x ½″ aluminum stock of the type that's sold in most hardware stores. It can be bent easily to the needed shape, even round or oval. Lap the ends about ¾″ and fasten with a small bolt, or a pop rivet, after drilling the necessary holes.

If you are replacing old screens, remove all the old screen wire from the frame, and grind, cut, or file away any rough edges that remain. You want to make the metal frame perfectly flat and smooth where the new screen is going to touch it.

Buy enough screen wire to cover all the ports you're working on. Stainless steel is best for strength and permanence, and fiberglass, aluminum, or bronze screening can be used with good results. *See Fig. 170.*

Rough-cut the screening to the approximate sizes needed for each unit. Make sure that the screen is oversize for each frame. Now mix up a batch of epoxy glue, enough to go all the way around all the frames. The kind that comes in two tubes, and results in a thick paste, is quite easily handled with a putty knife.

With the frame laid on a wide, flat board, coat the top surface carefully with a ring of epoxy. On this lay a piece of screen wire, pre-cut, and press it into the cement so that the epoxy works up through the screening all the way around. Be sure to stretch the screen so there are no sags in it.

Lay a piece of waxed paper on top of the whole assembly, and place a weight, such as a heavy board, over it to hold the screen in place while the epoxy cures overnight. When the epoxy has hardened, remove the weight and waxed paper. With sharp tin snips or scissors trim the excess material back to the frame edge. A file or sandpaper block will aid in giving a smooth edge here. If the portlights themselves are painted, give the frames a couple of coats of matching paint to achieve a professional appearance.

In working on new screens, try and make your frame a size and shape that will fit tightly inside the opening of the port. Then all you need is a simple stop on the outside, and the screen will stay in place.

Speedometer Pickup Plate

Lois Kennedy spotted this arrangement (*Fig. 171*) on a Cal-20 sitting in its cradle in a marina. The plate with the speedometer pickup unit is clamped in place from inside over the outboard motor well opening.

Fig. 171

When the motor is to be used, the plate is unclamped and lifted clear of the opening, and the motor is dropped into place. When under sail, the motor is removed from the well, and the plate with speedometer pickup is clamped back in place.

Automatic Windshield Washer

Salt spray, or any other form of dirty or contaminated water on the windshield is an annoyance at best, a real hazard at the worst. And salt, once crystallized, won't come off with normal wiper operation.

Here's an easy way, developed by Gordon Manning,

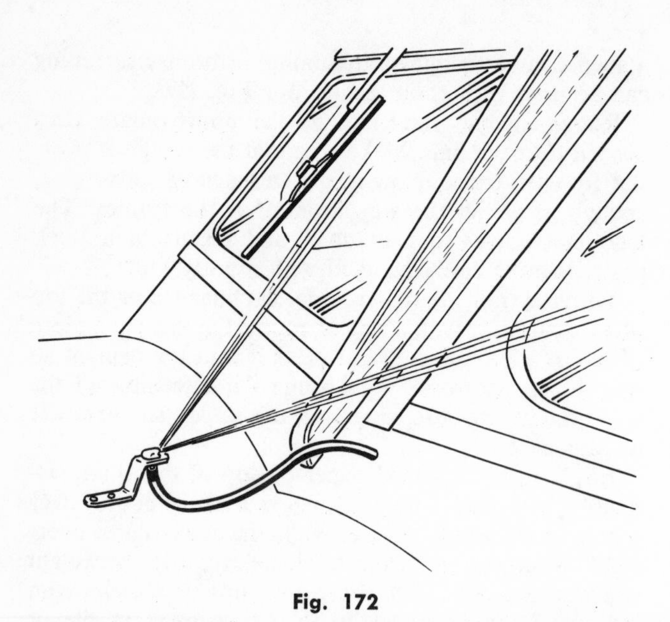

Fig. 172

to install fresh water windshield washers, for use with your boat's pressure fresh-water system. All you have to do is pipe a little of that water up to the front of the windshield. The principle is the same as that for your car's windshield washer, only here pressure, not vacuum, is used.

To make the washers, you'll need only a few inexpensive items, some of which can be of the used variety:

Control valve—A ¼″ or ⅜″ gas cock is fine, if it has an easy-to-use handle.

Windshield Washer Hose—⅛″ i.d. hose, in a length sufficient to run from the valve to the windshield.

Tee for Copper Pipe—Same size as boat's water system.

Copper Pipe—¼″ pipe, in a length to run from the tee to the control valve at the helmsman's station.

Brass Fittings—to reduce copper pipe to tee size, and for attachments.

Connector Fitting—to join rubber hose to valve.

Nozzle—2-jet auto washer type. (see *Fig. 188*).

If you prefer two separate nozzles, one for each windshield, get two single washer nozzles and a tee for connecting the washer hose between them. Single nozzles

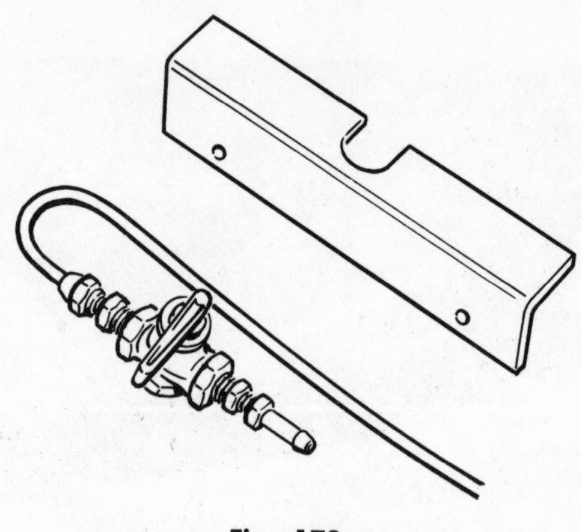

Fig. 173

often are used on top of windshields, aimed down instead of up.

Make up a small metal bracket or wooden block on which to mount the nozzle on the deck. Stainless steel or brass may be used, and a piece about 4″ x ¾″ x 1/16″ thick will bend into the necessary shape easily. *Fig. 188* shows how the bends can be put in, and where holes should be drilled. When you drill through the deck, make the holes a little oversize so you'll have some play for adjusting direction of the two sprays of water.

Washer hose will run from this bracket, back through the windshield frame if this is convenient, or via the deck back to the control position. If run along the deck, anchor it with plastic clips spaced about every 18″.

The control valve itself must be mounted so that it is convenient to operate, right by the helmsman. You can improve appearances by making a little mahogany half-box (*Fig. 189*) cover for the valve, with just the handle sticking out. All it really needs is a top, front, and one end to adequately cover the valve.

Run copper tubing from the inlet side of the valve back to the water pressure line at the nearest point. The tee is inserted in the water pressure line, along with the fittings necessary to bring it down to the ¼″ copper tubing size. Notice that metal tubing is used for strength and leak prevention on the pressure side of the washer control valve. The rubber tubing is perfectly adequate between this valve and the nozzle.

Note: The amount of water needed and used to clean windshields is almost infinitesimal; you'll never miss it.

2. CABIN INTERIORS

BERTHS

Meditations on Berth Control

Several years ago Pete Smyth, now editor of *Motor Boating & Sailing,* wrote an article (with the above title) on some things to consider about boat berths when buying, remodelling, or even designing a boat.

If you have a bunk problem on your boat, and plan to make alterations, perhaps one of the berth or convertible dinette arrangements on the following pages will suit your needs. But first, Pete's comments are worth reading:

"For use under way, a berth should be, perhaps above all else, safe. And it should *feel* safe. You should be able to slip into it and relax, knowing that you won't be rolled or pitched out. This requires 'bunkboards,' either of canvas or wood, high enough (about 10″) and strong enough to withstand a man's whole weight thrown against them.

"Ideally, a bunk for sleeping at sea should be narrow . . . Experts agree on a length of 6′3″ and a width of 2′ for a single bunk. This width, an average measurement, assumes the berth will be installed in the usual way against the side of the boat. Since most boat sides curve out, this really provides about 2′6″ of sleeping space width.

"Factors which should influence the width of a berth are use (whether at sea or in port) and temperature. A bunk that is to be used at sea should be 21″ wide, and not much more. This holds true, also, if the boating is done in a fairly cold climate, such as that of Maine, or Puget Sound. When a bunk is to be used primarily in port, its width should be increased as much as room within the boat permits, even to the regular twin bed width of 38″. Hot climates call for wider berths, too . . . a reasonably comfortable single berth for hot weather is 30″ wide.

"Height over berths is a consideration, or should be. 'Full' sitting headroom is generally set at 42″. Unless the bunk is also to be used as a seat, this is unnecessary: 36″ is ample; in some special cases, 30″ is satisfactory. Less is too confining, and augments the risk of smashed foreheads. These heights should be maintained for at least

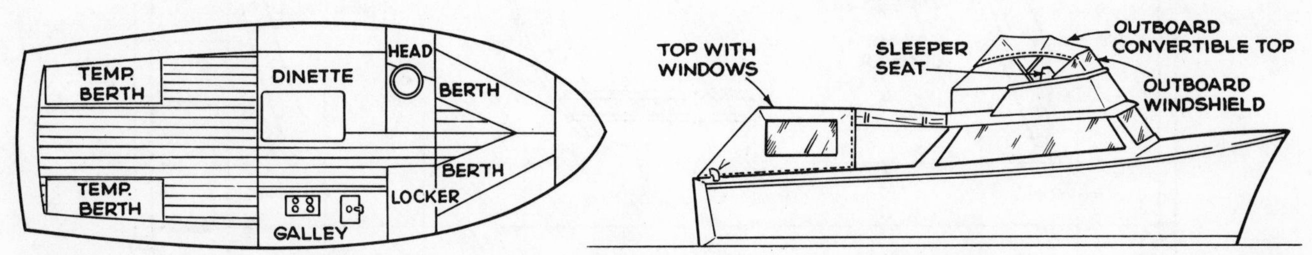

Fig. 201. By keeping berths minimal on at least some models, builders can provide more open cockpit where, when it is necessary, guests can sleep in temporary berths. Right: Sun-lounger type seats on flying bridge, temporary berths in cockpit, and shelters rigged over both areas, provide adequate additional overnight accommodations with ease.

30″ to 36″ from the head of the bunk. Beyond that, in the leg area, it can be as low as 18″ if necessary for quarter berths, or overlapping vee-berths forward.

"A first step to happier snoozing afloat is to leave half the berths at home . . . most boats have more berths than they have use for.

"With fewer berths aboard, more space and attention can be devoted to them. They can be placed for privacy, for convenience, for ventilation. They can be made more comfortable. They need not double as tops of seats or stowage spaces; if they are to be used exclusively for sleeping, certain changes can be made to advantage—most important of which is to discard the unyielding plywood bottom of virtually all built-in berths today.

"What do you do if you have a minimum-berth boat, and you want to invite guests for the weekend?

"Temporary berths, such as folding army cots are one answer, and there are some special boating cots available in single and double sizes, and as uppers-and-lowers. Each folds into a tidy package that's easily stowed aboard, or left ashore when not required. An air mattress and sleeping bag make any of these comfortable.

"Cruisers with aft curtains can provide ample protection for cockpit sleepers. The canvas could be modified to provide more light and ventilation. A more radical modification is to replace the aft curtain with a tent-type shelter on removable supports." See *Fig. 201.*

Pipe Berths for Comfort

A conventional pipe berth is one that's raised by night for use, and lowered by day to form a back rest for the lower berth—which in turn doubles as a seat by day. However, almost any upper berth which swings into position for use may be termed a pipe berth, whether pipe enters the construction or not.

Naturally, the space available will determine maxi-

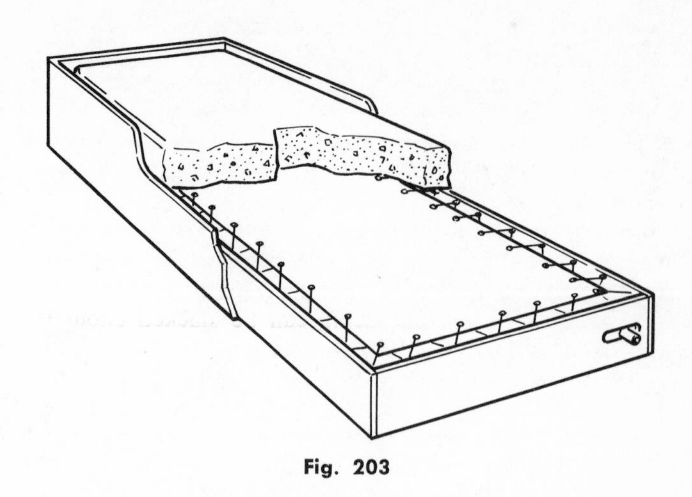

Fig. 203

mum dimensions, but note the recommendations in Pete Smyth's commentary, above.

The pipe frame is made from ¾″ galvanized pipe and fittings. Your pipe shop or plumber will cut the threads and arrange for the last joint by using a right-hand coupling, tapping a left-hand thread in one elbow, or using a long thread which is backed out as the opposing thread is made up. The long thread is secured with a pin or set screw.

If you can revamp the mattress supporting mesh from a rustproof spring cot to fit your frame, it is a safe venture. You will then get spring action, and an abundance of ventilation on the under side of the mattress.

Or, you can use ¼″ cotton or dacron line for the supporting framework, as shown in *Fig. 202.* Longitudinal lines are spaced about 3″ apart, with one spring to each line at alternate ends. The cross lines may be spaced farther apart, and springs are not used on them.

When all lines are taut, with tension on the springs, tie the lines together at each crossing with light line. A little sag is said to be good for sleeping, and unless

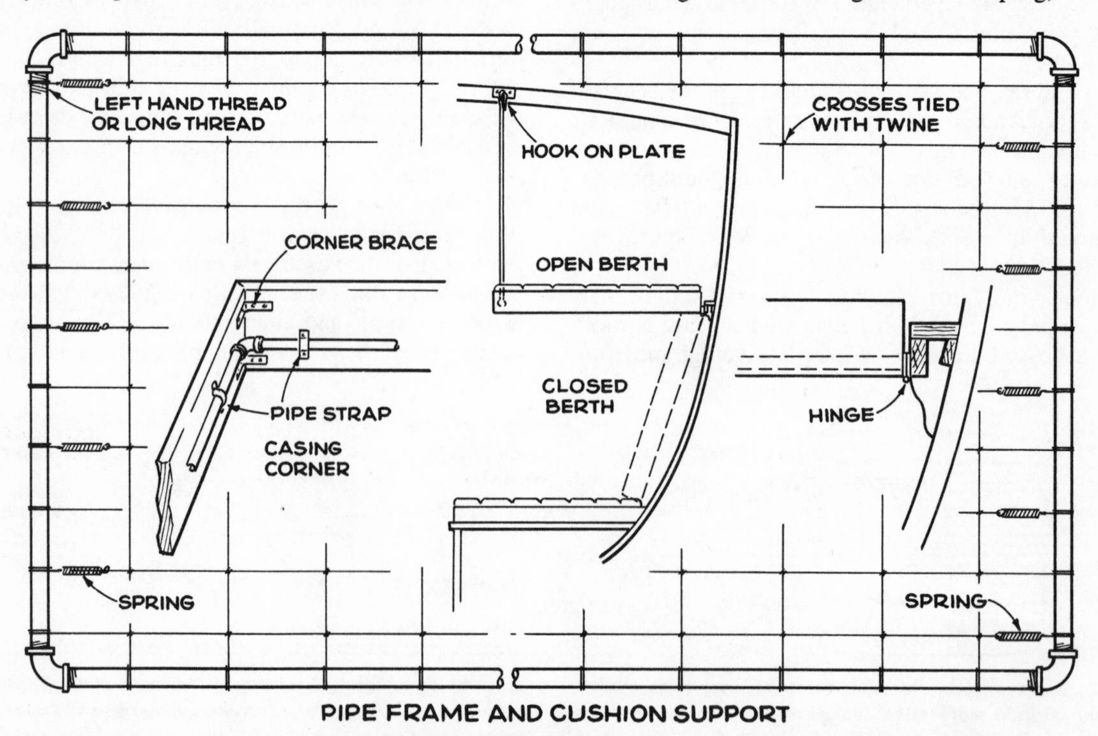

PIPE FRAME AND CUSHION SUPPORT

Fig. 202

your knots slip, the sag will spring back as soon as the weight is removed.

A third alternative is to use a sailcloth edged with grommets, all laced to the frame as shown in *Fig. 203*. Canvas is suitable, but in time will take a permanent sag in the middle, no matter how tightly the lacing is set up. Dacron is less susceptible to this permanent sag.

An advantage to this arrangement is that the lashing can be hauled up tight in warm weather, or when in port, to make the bunk firm, springy, and cool. When the weather is cool, the lacing can be slacked enough to provide a snug, comfortable bunk.

In any case, for additional strength as well as a better appearance, it is desirable that the pipe frame be boxed with a ¾″ casing that extends from the lower side of the pipe fittings to an inch or more from the upper side of the cushion or mattress. Make the back piece of 1¼″ stock, as it will have to take the fastenings for hinges.

Front corners may be mitered and glued and nailed, while the back piece is cut to fit between the two ends. All corners are reinforced from the inside by non-rusting angle braces.

Make the casing a close fit around the pipe frame, and use stock ¾″ pipe strap to hold the pipe to the casing. Space straps about 1′ apart, and install blocks under alternate straps for additional support.

The side of most boats is not straight, so it probably will be necessary to construct a shelf from which the berth is hinged. The inner edge of the shelf is curved to fit flush against the hull, to which it must be securely fastened. A ¾″ strip, about 2″ wide, is run as a truss under the front edge of the shelf, and the hinges are attached to this.

The berth is supported in the open position by strong hooks on plates which are fastened to the sides of deck carlins. These hooks attach to eyes in the ends of rope or wire cable spliced around the pipe frame. An alternative here, on a sailboat, is to provide a lash-up that can be adjusted to keep the berth on on even keel when the boat itself is heeled on a long tack.

Finally, you'll have to rig buttons, snaps, or lacing to hold the mattress in place when it's in the lowered position.

Pipe Berth Alternates

Start with the pipe frame, as for the berths described above, but instead of springs or a lashed-on fabric panel, cover the entire frame with canvas or dacron as shown in *Fig. 204*. The lengths of pipe are slipped through sleeves in the material, then threaded into the corner fittings.

Since the object here is to be decorative as well as functional, you can use striped awning material, or fabric that matches the color scheme of your cabin. Another possibility is use of webbing of the type found on lawn chairs.

Fig. 205 shows how this berth can be set up to form the back for a full-width seat berth. Upper berth corners are tee-fittings, and the outer ends of the tees ride in slots cut in blocks; the blocks, in turn, are secured to bulkheads at each end of the berth.

These blocks should be long enough to take a slot

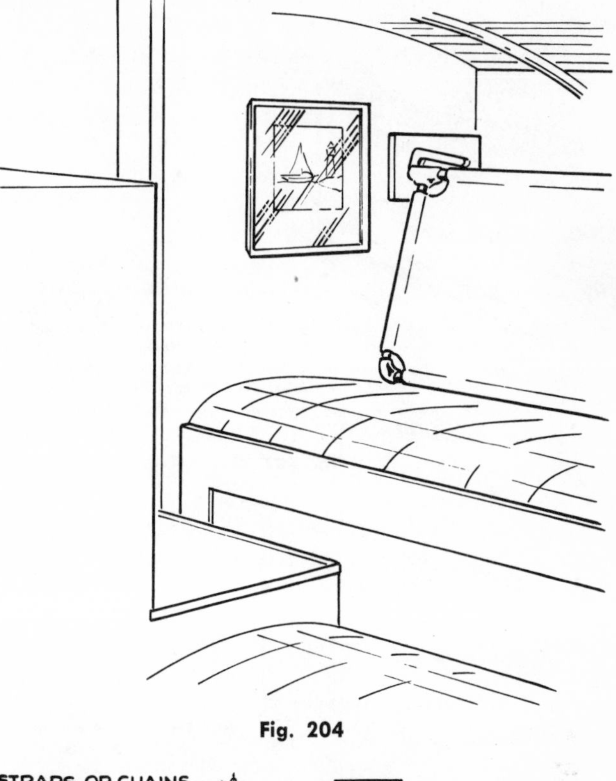

Fig. 204

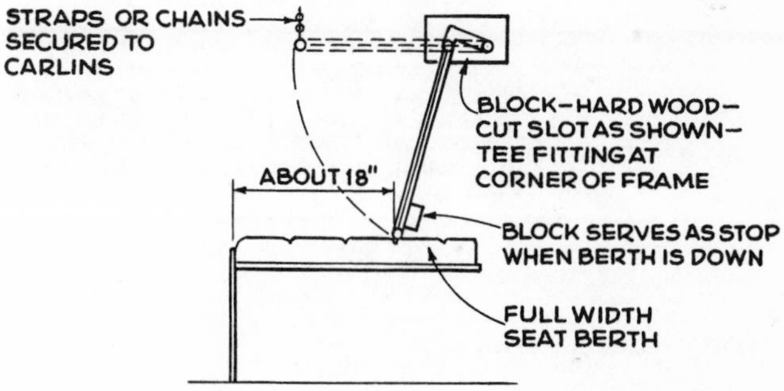

STRAPS OR CHAINS SECURED TO CARLINS
BLOCK—HARD WOOD—CUT SLOT AS SHOWN—TEE FITTING AT CORNER OF FRAME
ABOUT 18″
BLOCK SERVES AS STOP WHEN BERTH IS DOWN
FULL WIDTH SEAT BERTH

Fig. 205

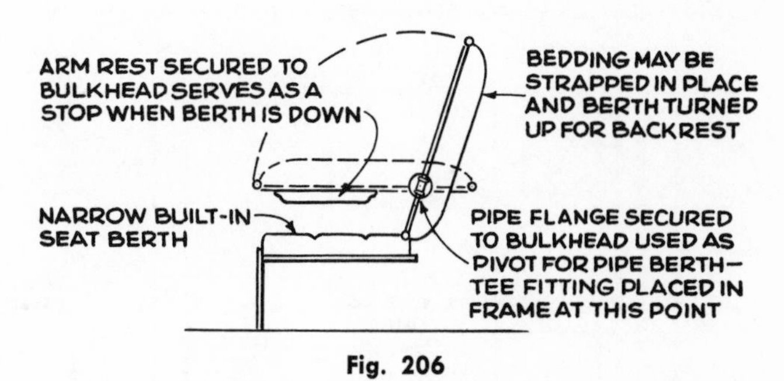

Fig. 206

that permits the berth to rest at a comfortable angle in the vertical position, and to move back from the aisle in the horizontal position.

The same type of pipe berth can be used to provide a more comfortable bunk above a narrow, built-in settee berth. See *Fig. 206*. Here, pipe tees are installed on the frame ends, and they fit into flanges secured to the bulkhead at each end of the berth.

An arm rest of some fairly heavy material, and neatly shaped as indicated in *Fig. 206*, provides sufficient support for the berth in its lowered position. The arm rests also are fastened to bulkheads at each end of the settee.

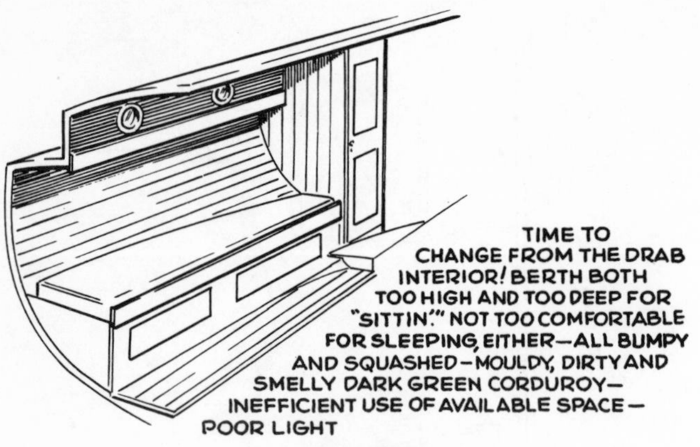

Fig. 207

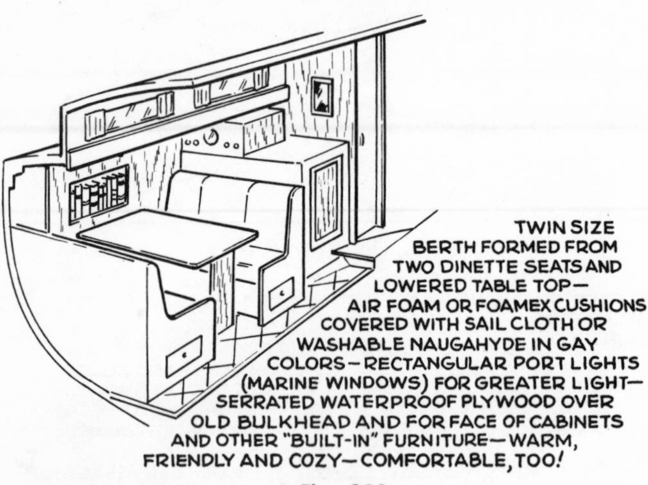

Fig. 208

Modernized Interiors

Many older boats came equipped with a rather drab interior—certainly in comparison to the bright and open layouts now available. However, old interiors can be improved, and you can get better use out of available space in the process.

Fig. 207 shows such an old-style interior, with planked ceiling and bulkheads, plus small, round windows that admit minimum light. *Fig. 208* shows the same interior brought up-to-date: note the rectangular portlights, plywood-panelled after bulkhead and cabinet facing—and the convertible dinette that replaces the narrow, uncomfortable settee berth.

Naturally such a conversion takes a lot of careful planning. Take measurements off the boat, and work up scale drawings. Headroom and aisle width must be considered, as well as leg room under the table.

Construction of convertible dinettes is detailed in the following projects.

Convertible Dinette No. 1

Here's a very simple convertible dinette that can be fitted to boats of very moderate size (*Fig. 209*). It's all made of ¾″ marine plywood. As a finishing touch, you can cover the table top, the outer seat ends, and even the seats with decorative laminated plastic, as detailed later in this section.

Table size shown is 30″ x 48″, which is fairly standard. A 54″ length will make for a more comfortable berth, if there's room in the cabin. Hooks at the inner table end fit into eyes mounted on the cabin side, and the outer end rests on a leg that can be secured both top and bottom.

The backs of seats are hinged at the bottom, and open out from the top, to provide stowage space for linens and blankets. A bar running the length of the seat back can be used as a rod on which sheets and blankets are hung. Seat bottoms also are hinged, and pillows and other bulky items can be stored in the compartments thus formed. Note that vent holes should be drilled to provide air circulation in these enclosures.

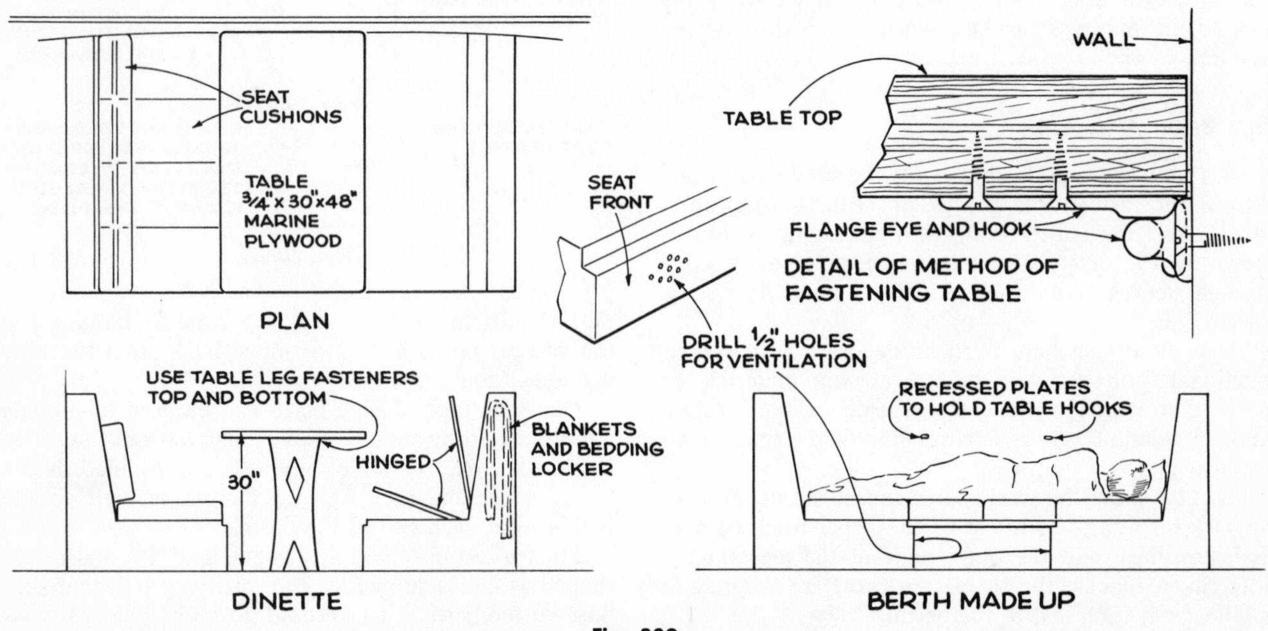

Fig. 209

Four cushions should be provided for the seats. The bottom cushions should cover the entire width of the seat, and the lower edge of the back cushions rest on the seat cushions. The upper edges of these cushions can be fastened to the plywood seat backs with snap fasteners, small hooks, or strips of Velcra.

When lowered, the table top rests in notches that run the full length of the seats. This fit should be fairly snug so the table panel can't drop out. With the seat back cushions placed over the table panel, you have a full-length berth.

Because most boat sides have some curvature, it may be necessary to raise the floor slightly between the seats in order to provide foot room for the entire length of the seats. In this case, height of the seats must be raised an equivalent amount.

Convertible Dinette No. 2

The conventional convertible dinette is made so the table top must be lowered to form the berth. The arrangement shown in *Fig. 210* reverses this procedure, and the following advantages are claimed for it:

There's no special hardware needed, it's easier to build, more rigid in use, and easy to convert from table to berth and vice versa.

Seat backs and bottoms can be angled for comfort,

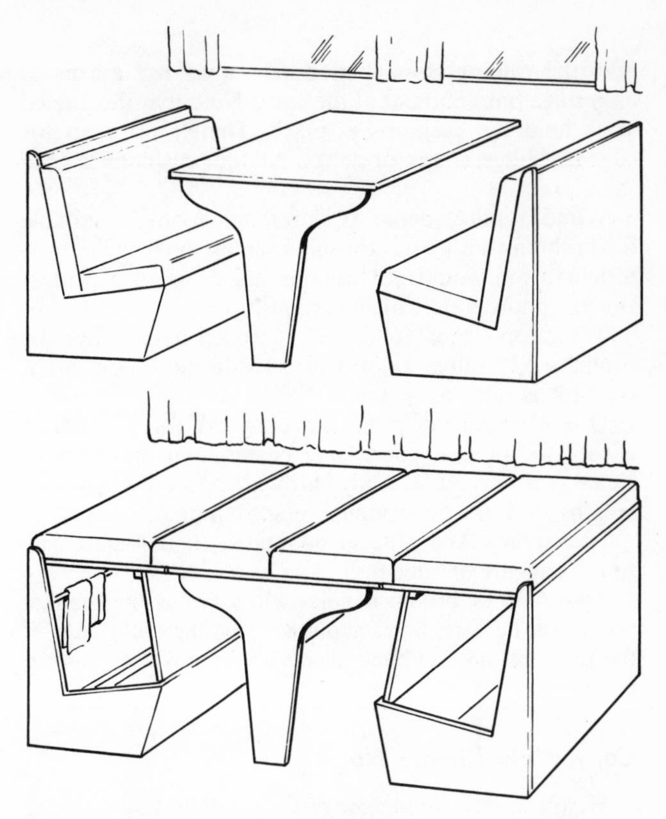

Fig. 210

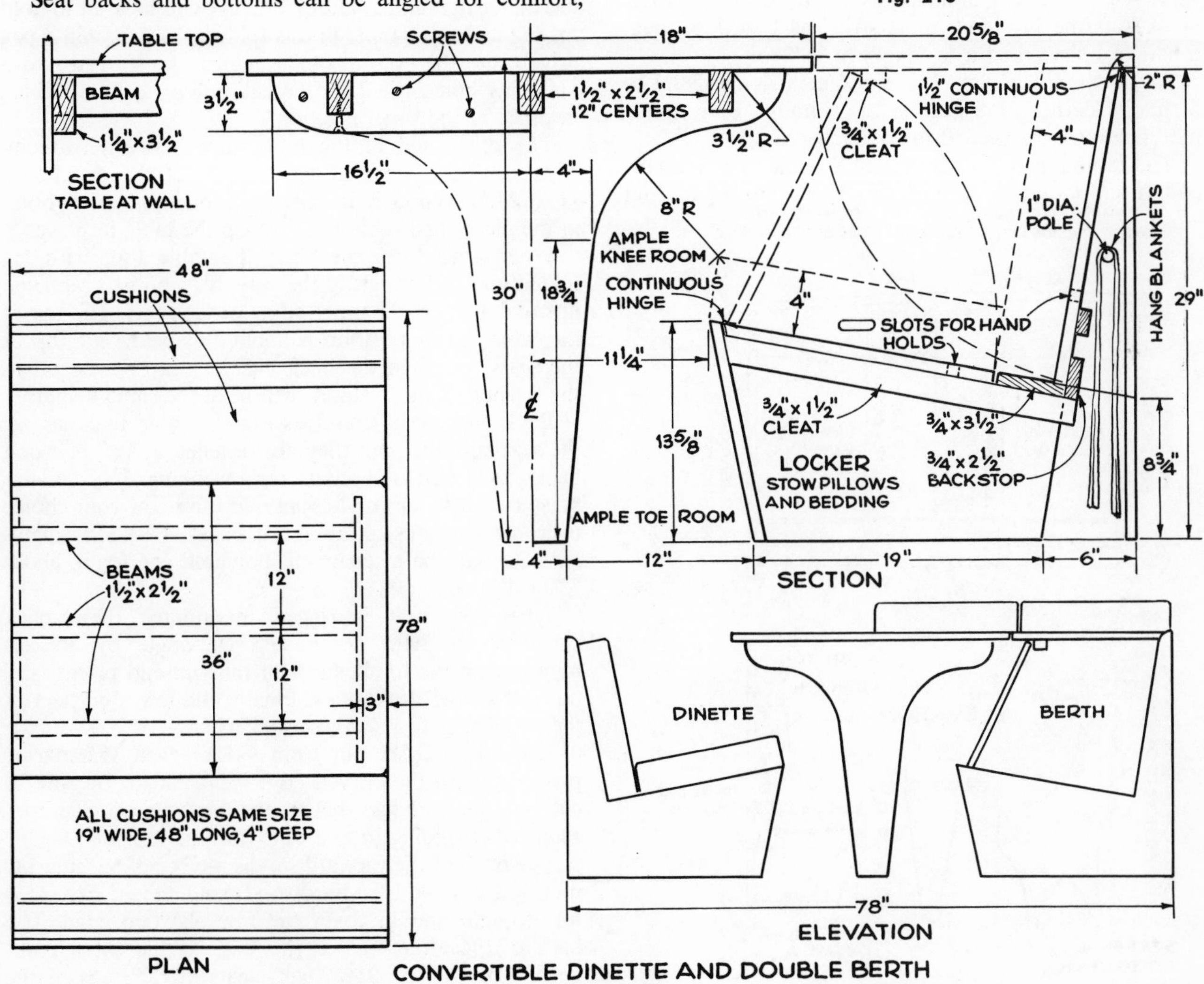

CONVERTIBLE DINETTE AND DOUBLE BERTH

Fig. 211

and the wine-glass-shaped outer table leg makes it easy to get into and out of the seats. Note that the angled seats hold the cushions in place. There's no need for edge moldings, snaps, or hooks. All four cushions are the same size.

While a fairly dense polyurethane foam is suitable for cushions—it's used for this by most boat builders—a deluxe job would be cushions made up by a professional upholsterer, with inner springs.

Table top size is 36″ x 48″, although if you have the room, a 54″ table length will provide more comfort if the unit is used as a double berth.

Use ¾″ marine grade fir plywood for everything except the table header, table beams, and the 1″ x 2″ cleats (see *Fig. 211*). Only hardware needed is four 48″ lengths of 1½″ continuous (piano) hinge.

Use screws and glue at all joints, to eliminate any future sagging or squeaks.

Two mop or broom handles will serve as the blanket rods. Cut the hand holes about 8″ from the outer edge of the seat bottom and back panels so these will be easy to reach.

Convertible Dinette No. 3

Here's a very simple convertible dinette that requires very little in the way of materials and hardware: a sheet of ⅝″ marine plywood, some strips of 1″ x 1½″ oak, a pair of hinges, and a 6″ length of ¼″ rod.

As illustrated in *Fig. 212*, the dinette is designed to fit in the corner of a deckhouse, although only minor modifications are needed for other locations.

The table top is 2′ 6″ x at least 4′ wide. The inboard end is supported by a single leg that's hinged to fold

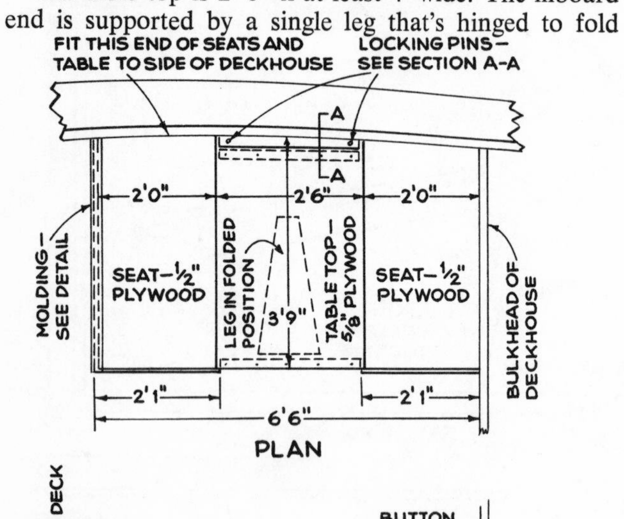

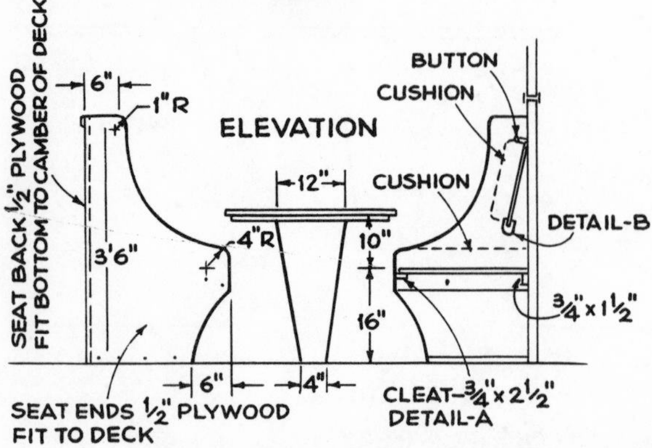

Fig. 212

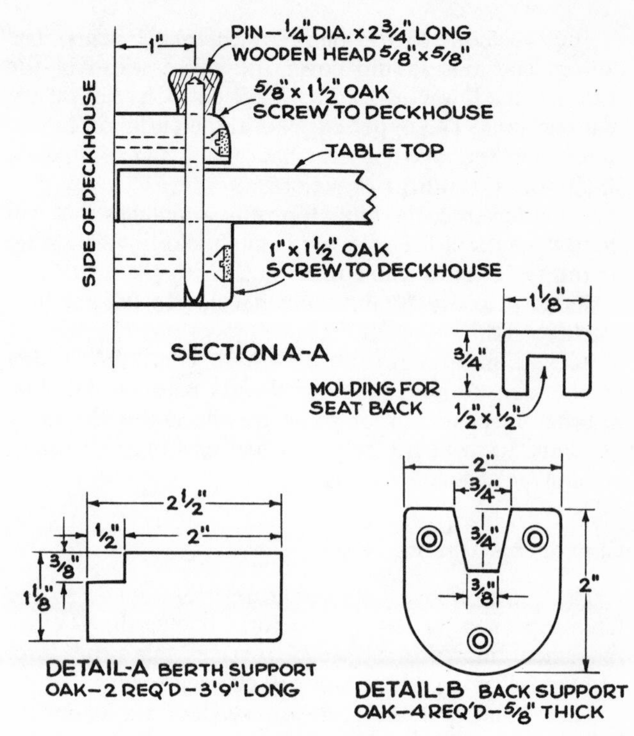

Fig. 213

flat under the table. A hook and eye can be used to hold the leg under the table in this folded position, and a peg driven into the bottom of the leg can be slipped into a matching hole drilled on the cabin floor to hold the leg in place in the open position.

The other end of the table slips between two oak cleats that are screwed to the side of the deckhouse (*Fig. 213*). Wooden dowels slip through matching holes in the cleats and table top to keep the table in place.

When rigged for sleeping, the table top, with leg folded and locked out of the way, rests on two rabbeted lips that support the inner edges of the seats. The top of the table in this position is about ¼″ below the top of the seats, so when the back cushions are placed on it, the tops of all the cushions will be at the same height.

Back cushions themselves are the same thickness as the seat cushions, but they are fastened to ¼″ plywood backs by straps of upholsterer's webbing. Use the upholstery fabric, or vinyl-supported fabric, of your choice over the cushions, straps, and backs. Cushions themselves should be a fairly stiff polyurethane foam, about 3″ or 4″ thick.

When the unit is rigged for dining, these back cushions are held at the proper angle by sockets mounted on the inside faces of the seat end pieces, and the side of the deckhouse. Pins at the lower corners of the seat backs fit into these sockets.

Seat ends can be cut from ⅝″ or even ½″ marine plywood, with the curved edge well-sanded. Be sure to cut out the cutbacks below the seat, to provide foot room when sliding in and out from the table.

The back of the forward seat is a piece of ½″ marine plywood, capped by a hardwood molding (see *Fig. 213*) for strength and to cover the raw plywood edge. The back of the after seat, in this case, is the cabin bulkhead. The ¾″ by 2½″ oak cleats at the ends of the seats should be well fastened to the seat end pieces and to the side of the deckhouse. Each cleat should be notched for the berth support as shown in *Detail A, Fig. 213*, and also for the riser that runs along under the back edge of each seat bottom panel. Use ½″ plywood for these seat panels.

Two suggestions are in order. First, cut the table panel slightly wide. When the seats are finished and in position, trim the top down so that it's an exact fit between the seats.

Second: Get a supply of flexible wood tape, in widths to match the finish and the thicknesses of your plywood panels. With pressure-sensitive adhesive and this tape, you can cover all exposed raw edges of the plywood pieces. It makes for a very neat and professional appearance.

Just Add Blankets

This convertible dinette is much simpler to build and to operate than it may appear in the illustration, *Fig. 214*, and it provides a strong, rigid table in its raised position. Presented in England's *Practical Boat Owner*, it was designed by J. Shaw.

The hull-side table end support folds like an accordion on two substantial hinge panels. The upper one is rigidly fixed to the table top, the lower one is hinged to it and to the cabin side. Note in the detail drawing (*Fig. 215*) that the hinges are bolted to the panels for extra strength. With ⅜″ marine plywood used for the hinge panels, the arrangement should remain rigidly upright when the table is in the raised position, unless the table top is pulled away from the cabin side. However, you can add a couple of locking pins for extra security, if desired.

The front leg should be fairly substantial, too, and hinged to the cabin floor. It is shown with a "break-back" hinged support, but a length of chain would do. As Mr. Shaw notes, whatever is used, there should be no "give" when the table is assembled in the upright position.

To set the position of the cleats under the table top that hold the leg in position, pull the leg fully upright, with tension on the support or chain, and push the table top firmly back against the cabin side. Have someone mark location of the leg's crosspiece on the underside of the table top, and use this line as your guide for gluing and screwing the cleats in place.

In the lowered position, the table top rests on cleats mounted along the front of each dinette seat, and so positioned that the top panel is exactly flush with the seats.

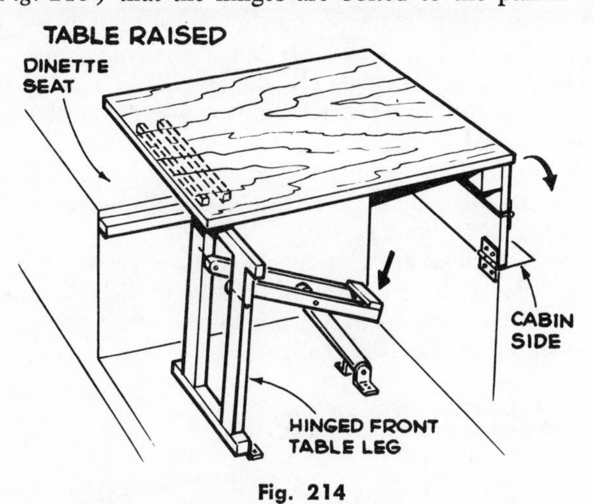

Fig. 214

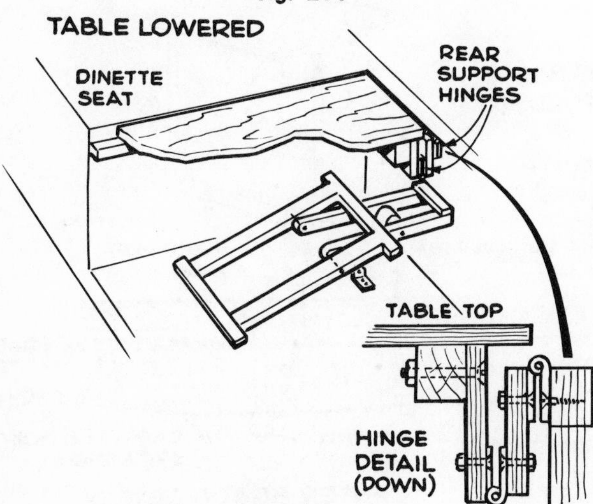

Fig. 215

TABLES

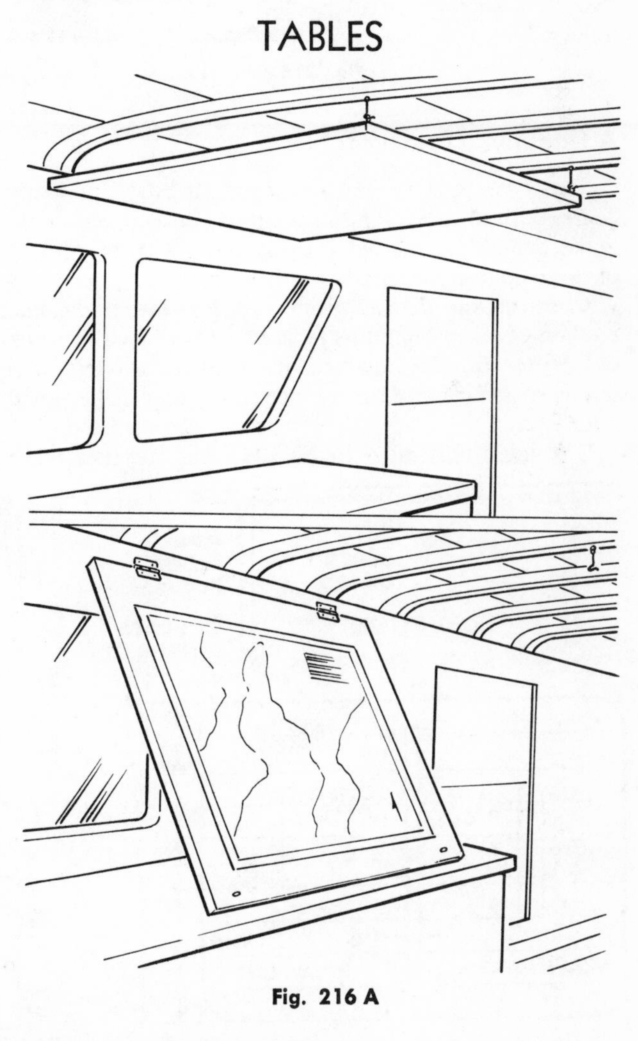

Fig. 216 A

Cabin-Top Chart Table

John Russell of Coral Gables, Fla., came up with this ingenious solution to the age-old problem of how to have a chart table that's large enough, and yet doesn't constitute a road block in the cabin.

As is shown in *Figs. 216A-216B*, the table is merely a large piece of marine plywood hinged at its upper edge. It is lowered for use, and raised to fit snugly against the overhead when not needed. Hooks in the overhead attach to eyes in the table in the raised position.

Fig. 216 B

A Traditional Folding Table

This type of table has been used on boats for many years, both in cabins and in cockpits. In fact, you could make one table, and set it up in the cabin, or cockpit of your boat as required.

Construction details given are for the traditional method of assembling this table; they are taken from an old *Motor Boating* maintenance manual. Modern materials make some short cuts possible, as will be noted later.

The table illustrated in *Fig. 217* has a center piece that mounts on two pipe legs, and to which folding side pieces (leaves) are attached with hinges. Use of 1⅛″ stock is recommended for the center piece, to furnish a secure anchor for legs and leaves. The leaves may be of lighter stock and preferably in single sections to eliminate jointing. If a small circular saw is available, run in several longitudinal cuts extending halfway through the material. This will prevent practically all tendency to warp, and do away with the necessity for cleats.

The floor sockets are made up of regular deck plates having 1″ diameter pipe threads. A short length of 1″ pipe is added to provide a bearing for the table legs. The lower end of this pipe must be capped, or there must be a structural member directly beneath it, to support the ends of the legs.

Legs themselves are of ¾″ brass tube, which will just slide inside the 1″ pipe in the floor sockets. It may be necessary to ream the sockets slightly, but the fit should be snug. When not in use, the floor sockets may be covered with the threaded discs furnished with the deck plates.

The "floor flanges" used at the upper ends of the legs are threaded, and have six holes for the mounting screws. Turn the legs in tightly with a stillson wrench.

Use of skylight hinges for attaching the leaves is not essential, but they are particularly adapted to this use, and they are heavier than ordinary "T" or strap hinges.

The brace pads should be made thick enough to put considerable pressure on the brace, when it is swung open. The use of a carriage bolt is recommended because it permits turning the brace without fear of the bolt itself turning. The addition of two brass plates—one fastened to the center piece and one to the brace—will permit easy turning of the brace even though the carriage bolt is tight. The brass plates also give a solid bearing, and eliminate wear.

Brass fittings are recommended throughout. The fit of the legs in their sockets will not be spoiled by an accumulation of rust, and the cost of the other parts over galvanized fittings is very slight.

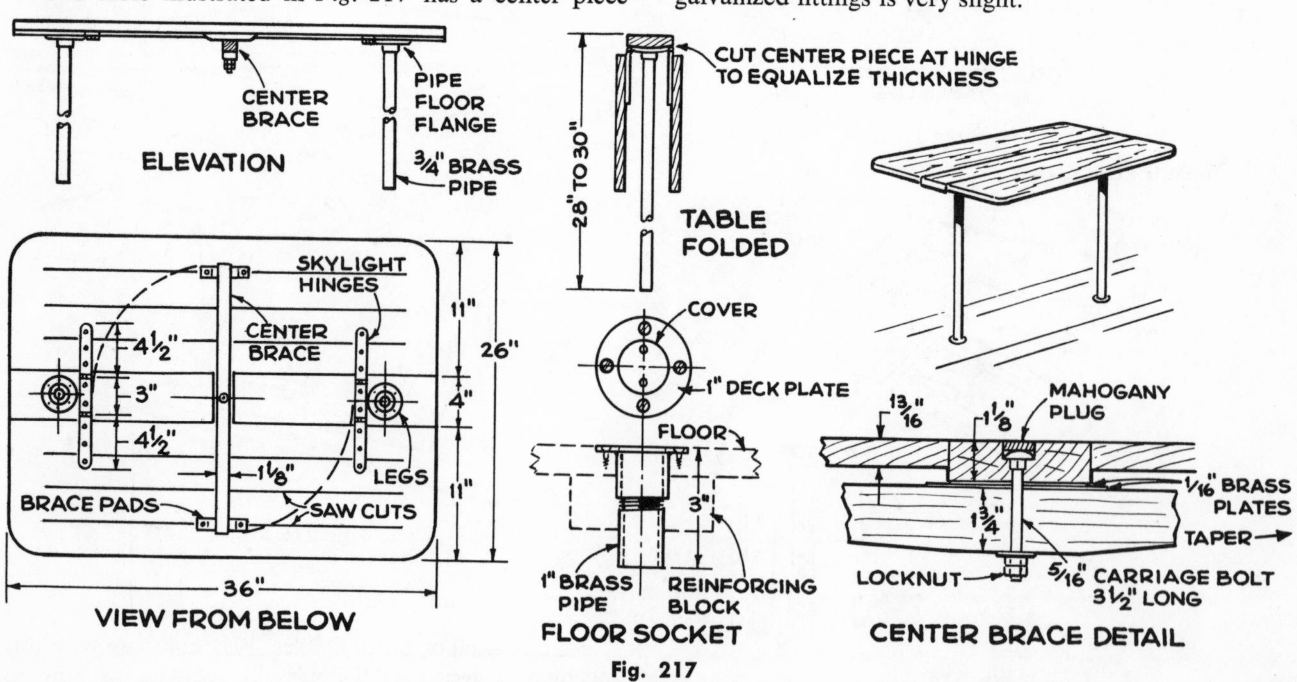

Fig. 217

A rubbed linseed oil finish—using three coats—will give a surface resistant to marring by spilled liquids or washing. To further reduce the possibility of warpage, apply the same finish to the underside as that used on the top—the same number of coats of the same material.

Now, of course, you can substitute marine plywood for the solid hardwood, for both the center piece and leaves. Use ½″ plywood for all three, and there's no need to bevel the center piece in order to come out with an even top surface when leaves are up. Substitute stainless steel pipe, or even chrome-plated brass pipe, for the legs, and one of the synthetic finishes in place of the linseed oil.

Chart Case Table

This chart case is designed to keep charts flat and easily accessible in a vertical file; the entire case flips up to form a work table for the navigator. Because charts would buckle and slide down in the case if not supported, they are suspended from pins through their upper edges.

Fig. 218 shows details of the case and its construction. Note that the "border" around the drawing illustrates types of corner joints that may be used on the case frame pieces. Use the joint that best matches your woodworking ability.

Size of the charts to be used is an important consideration. The largest are 26″ x 48″, and it is recommended that these be folded in half. The best way to make the fold is to cut the chart in half carefully, with a razor, and run a wide strip of adhesive tape along the cut, on the back of the chart, to act as a reinforced hinge. The case frame then should be made 2″ wider and 2″ higher than the largest chart to be filed.

Use ¾″ x 2″ hardwood stock for the frame, and cover on both sides with ⅜″ marine plywood. For the best appearance, the frame can be rabbeted so that no plywood edges are exposed. Glue and nail or screw the plywood in place; do not use fasteners longer than ¾″. Now you have a completely closed box, which is cut in half with a rip saw blade. This assures matching parts, and if you have the equipment, easier construction.

If necessary, make up two separate frames of ¾″ x 1″ stock, and fasten one plywood panel to each frame.

The two halves then are hinged at the bottom with a piano hinge or three narrow butt hinges. Jointed adjusters, fastened inside the frame, limit the extent the case can be opened. The case can be held closed by snap fasteners, or hooks at the sides.

Rear chart support pins are made up of $^3/_{16}$″ or ¼″ brass tubing riveted and soldered to plates which are screwed to the back panel. Two pins are used, set in about 4″ from the sides, and at a height that will allow the largest chart to hang clear of the bottom.

Front support pins are made up of wire or rod, and are fastened to the front panel so that they center on the hollow rear pins, and slide into the rear pins when the case is closed. The jointed adjusters are attached so that when the case is open as far as it will go, the pins are separated by about ¼″.

The whole case is mounted against a bulkhead with three butt hinges. These should be mortised for their full thickness into the back panel. Jointed supports, of the type used on card table legs, are mounted at the sides to hold the case up when it is used as a work table.

To finish off the project, install ¾″ stock strips to

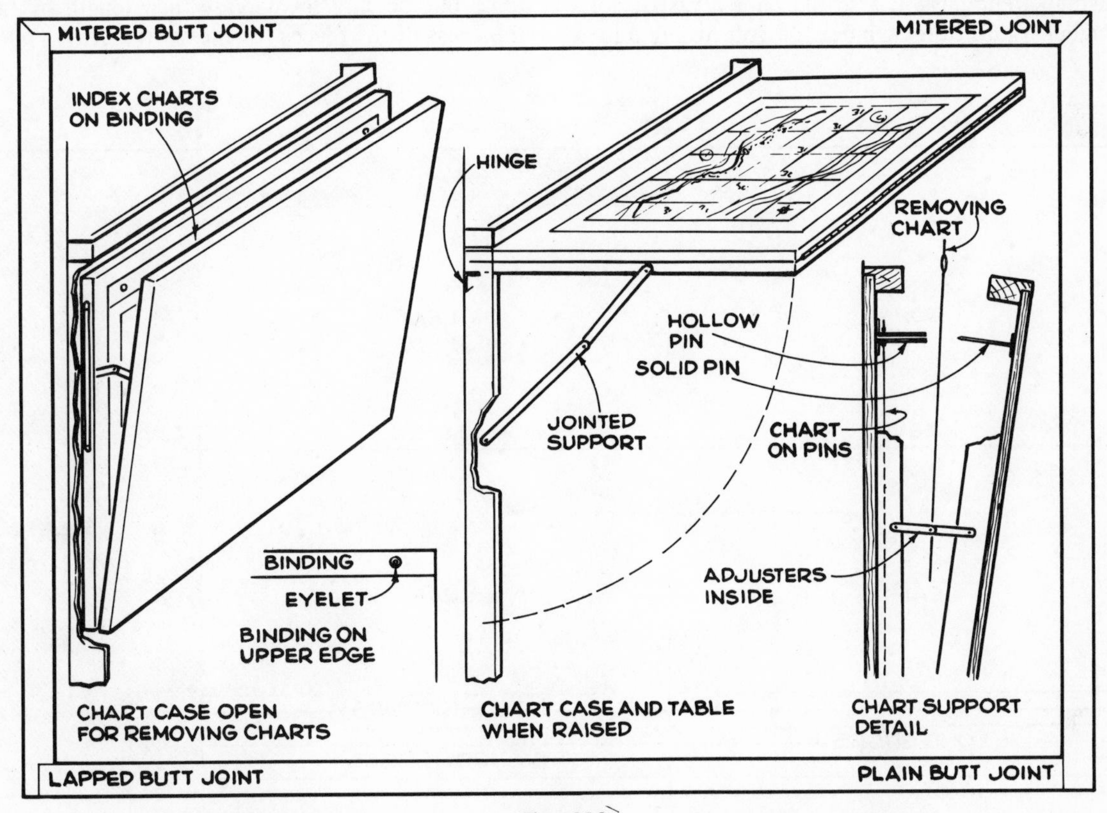

Fig. 218

the bulkhead along each side of the case, and one across the top. A lip around the edge of the top strip makes it a handy place to keep pencils, dividers, parallel rule, etc.

Now reinforce the top edge of each chart to be filed with gummed cloth tape folded over the edge. Holes are then punched through the reinforcement; additional strength can be added with use of the little notebook reinforcement circles that are available at the stationery stores. Use a magic marker type pen to write the chart number on the front of each reinforcing strip.

Arrange the charts in succession, as most used, hang them on the rear support pins, and close the case. To remove a chart, open the case until the pins almost are separated, then slide charts from back pins to front pins until the needed chart is reached. Open the case fully, lift out the chart, and close the case. Then the case can be flipped up to the table position.

Applying Laminated Plastics

Formica, or one of the similar decorative laminated plastics, makes an excellent surface on all of the table tops in the foregoing projects, and it can be used on counter tops, even on bulkheads, to good advantage. Its application certainly is within the scope of anyone reasonably handy with tools.

The instructions and photos provided here come from Leo J. Carling, Jr.:

"First of all, power tools are unnecessary. To be sure, their use could make parts of the work go faster, but the end result will be exactly the same. All you need is a cross-cut saw, 6′ straight edge, hip and rafter square, ruler, scriber (an awl will do), pair of dividers or draftsman's compass, coarse file (not a rasp), soft-faced mallet (substitute a block of soft wood and a hammer), scissors, pencil, sandpaper, and a cheap paint brush.

"In addition to the DLP (decorative laminated plastic), you will need the type of contact cement that's supplied by U.S. Plywood Corp., and some brown wrapping paper. Get enough paper to completely cover the area involved, and try to keep it in a roll rather than folded, as creases could cause trouble.

"Basically, there are two kinds of project, the simpler being an application to a free-standing area such as a table top. A slightly more difficult job involves a piece which must be fitted to one or more fixed boundaries.

"First we will show how to make a free-standing unit — a table top with what is known as a 'self edge.' In the choice of plastic, give some thought to the satin-finish surfaces, as the absence of glare may be most welcome. Make a sketch approximately to scale of a 4′ x 8′ sheet of the material, and lay out the pieces you will require. The sketch should include principal dimensions, and the direction of the grain or pattern if this is a factor. See *Fig. 219*: you will note the order in which major saw cuts are to be made. The first and second cuts will quickly reduce the large sheet to manageable pieces. If you are using a hand saw, the work must be well-supported as close as possible to the line of the cut.

"The dimensions shown in the sketch are about a quarter-inch oversize. This is a little generous; an eighth will do if you are sure all the edges of the table top are perfectly straight, and all corners are exactly 90 degrees. If in doubt, make the pieces a little larger; it will necessitate a bit of extra filing and sanding later, but it's better than having a piece a bit too short.

"In laying out the edge pieces for the long sides of the table, be sure to increase their length by twice the thickness of the pieces for the short sides — about 1/8″.

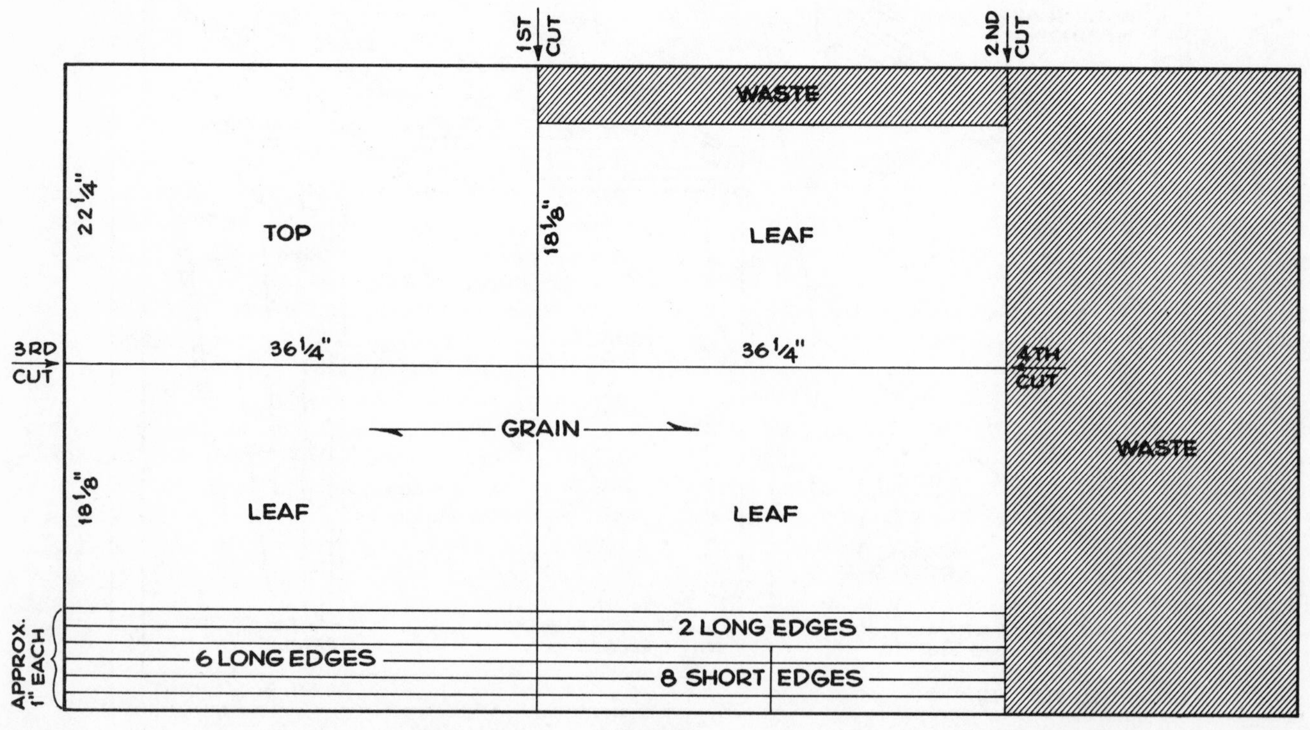

Fig. 219

"A crayon pencil, ball-point, or felt-tip pen can be used to lay out the cutting lines, but try first in a scrap area to be sure the marker does not leave a permanent stain. On high gloss surfaces, you may have to use a scriber or scratch awl for accuracy, but take care to avoid scratches where they're unwanted.

"The edges of the plastic panel should be straight, and the corners square. Check them anyway. If they're true, your layout work is simplified. If not, strike a couple of lines, such as cuts #1 and #3, far enough in from the edge to allow the waste to fall outside the required pieces.

"Use of a hip and rafter square is suggested because its 16″ and 24″ legs make for considerable accuracy. With care, the 24″ leg also can be used in place of the 6′ straight edge by making a series of marks about 20″ apart and connecting them with a line drawn along the long side of the square.

"When you have finished the layout and checked to be sure all pieces are accounted for, you are ready to saw. A cross cut hand saw, preferably 10 point or finer, will do nicely. If you are using a portable circular saw or a saber saw, choose a very fine-tooth blade as these machines cut on the 'up' stroke, and coarse teeth plus fast feed will shatter the plastic's surface, perhaps beyond the 1/16″ per cut you must allow for final finishing. Such blemishes cannot be removed. I have used a standard 10″ cross-cut blade on my table saw successfully.

"After making the major saw cuts, cut the strips for edging, as it is easier to manage them from a fairly wide piece of material than one only a couple of inches wide.

"Before applying the laminate, make sure all surfaces of the table or counter top are smooth. Small nail holes and similar indentations are no problem, but a missing knot or a large void in the edge of a piece of plywood could result in the plastic being fractured should that spot be struck sharply when the table is in use.

"Questionable areas can be filled with wood dough or some similar material, or you can whip up a mixture of epoxy resin and sawdust. Whatever is used, sand the patch smooth after it has hardened, and use a sanding block to insure a level surface.

"Now you are ready to apply the cement. Follow the instructions on the can. Usually two coats are required on all surfaces to be bonded, both the plastic and the wood. If the project is large enough, by the time the last piece has been coated, the first is dry and ready for its second coat. The final test for dryness is made with brown wrapping paper, a piece of which should not stick to the cement coating. On your first project, it might be prudent to coat only the edging surfaces first, and apply the cement to the main surfaces only after the edging is in place.

"In any case, apply the edging first. Start with a short side. It is best to put the work in a vice, or have someone hold it firmly on end for you. Hold the edging material between thumb and forefinger of each hand, by its edges, and bring one end down in light contact with the edge of the panel. Allow about 1/8″ of the strip to overhang at that end; it should also overhang the top and bottom surfaces by 1/8″. 'Aim' the strip with care down the length of the panel edge, and ease it into place with a sort of 'rolling' motion from one end to the other. Do not let it buckle and skip a section, only to make contact up ahead with an air gap in between. Should this happen, you will have to cut the buckle to bring it down to the panel, as the laminate cannot be slid once contact is made.

"This is not a disaster, but it will give you an unwanted joint. Now apply the edging to the side opposite the one just done.

"With the panel standing on edge on a smooth, firm surface, with one laminated edge down and the other up, tap the upper edge with a rubber mallet, or a hammer using a soft pine block for a cushion. Take extra care to avoid striking so hard that the overhanging edges and ends of the strip are fractured. It takes just enough pounding to insure a solid bond. Flip the panel edge for edge, and repeat.

"Trim the excess from both ends of each edge piece, using a coarse file. Lift the file clear of the work after each cutting stroke. At the start, cut the plastic at an angle of 30 to 45 degrees, then gradually decrease the angle. Make the last cut or two almost, but not quite, parallel to the adjacent panel edge. See *Fig. 220.*

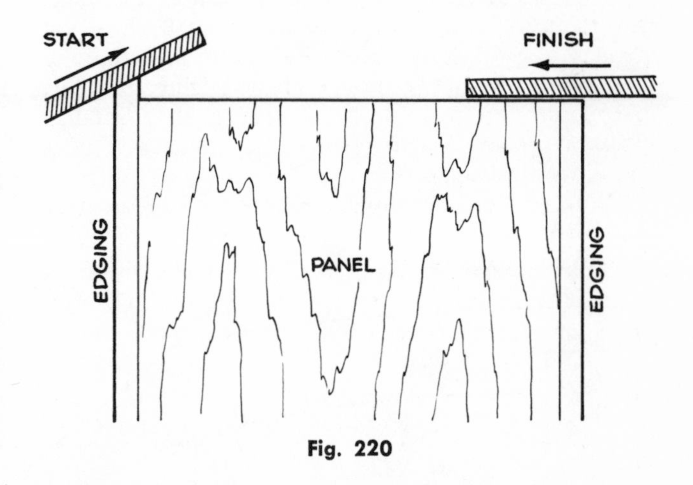

Fig. 220

"Now apply laminate to the two remaining edges, using the same procedure. After the ends have been trimmed, you are ready to dress the upper and lower edges. Maintain the bevel cut down to 1/16″ of the panel surfaces, then drop the front end of the file into contact with the surface for the final couple of passes. The file can be worked along the edge as each cut is made, using the edge-milling of the file somewhat in the manner of a saw. See *Fig. 221.*

"The top is the last piece to be applied. Before actually putting it in place, experiment with the handling of it. Is it so large it sags badly in the middle when held by its edges? If it does, or if you have any doubt about your ability to control it well, don't risk a serious blunder. Make a wrapping paper 'sandwich.' Cut a sheet of the paper several inches larger than the surface to be covered, and lay it over the wood surface after the contact cement has been allowed to dry. Now you can set the plastic laminate panel down on top — after its contact cement has dried — and slide it about to get a uniform overhang on all sides. Then, while

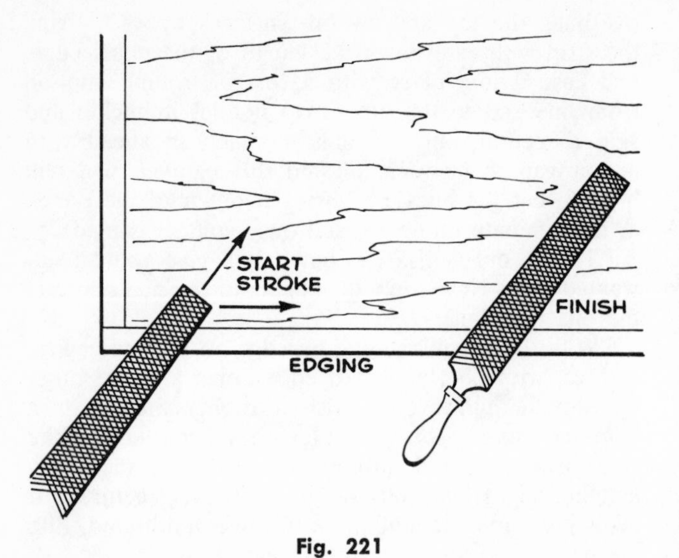

Fig. 221

you hold it in position carefully, someone else can slide out the wrapping paper. Rap the top down firmly with a rubber mallet, or hammer and soft pine block, working from the center outward toward all edges.

"The excess is trimmed from the top in the same way as from the edges, but in this case the final cut is made at a 45 degree bevel. Be sure to stop short of cutting into the upper surface of the edging: See *Fig. 222*. Finish up with #120 sandpaper on a sanding block. Work the length of the edge, not across it as you did with the file.

"Now for a counter top job where curves or irregular shapes are involved: Preparation of the wood, planning the project, tools, quantity of material, and order of

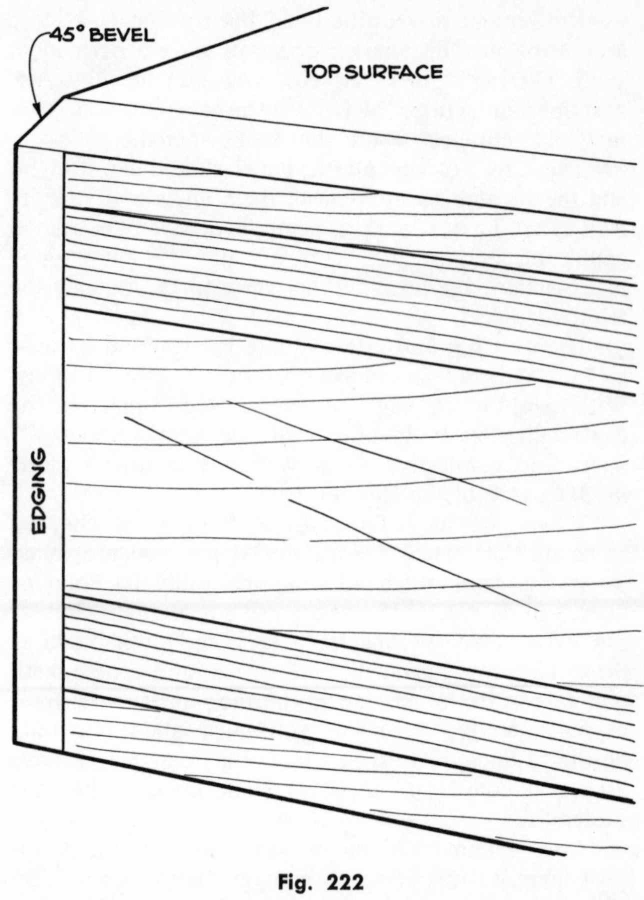

Fig. 222

applying the pieces are all the same as for the table top job. The big difference comes in cutting the laminate for the top. It must fit against the bulkhead or other parts of the boat accurately. This fitting must be done *before* any cement is applied.

"Again, wrapping paper is used. This time cut out a piece which, when spread flat, will leave an inch or

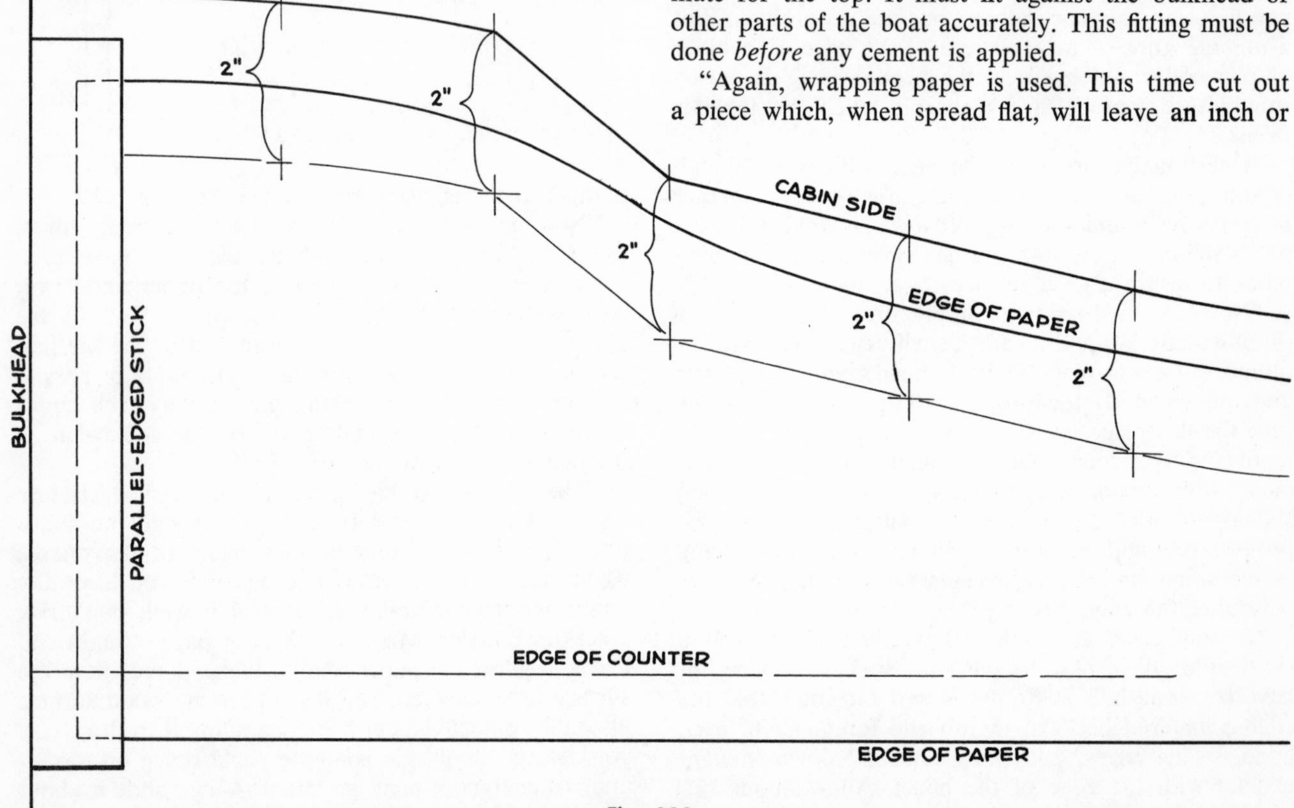

Fig. 223

so of bare wood showing adjacent to the fixed boundaries of the counter area. Use a few thumb tacks to hold the paper in place.

"Set the legs of a drafting compass for any convenient span, such as 2". With the pointed end set snugly at the junction of the fixed bulkhead or cabin side and the counter top, strike a very short arc with the pencil end, at approximately a right angle to the fixed member: See *Fig. 223*. If the member is curved, strike as many arcs as needed to produce a smooth, representative curve on the paper. If the adjacent member is straight, such as a bulkhead would be, the compass method is not needed. A stick with a parallel edge laid against the bulkhead will allow you to transfer the line to the paper with a single pencil stroke. Another method calls for a short block of wood to be slid along the bulkhead with the pencil point held in contact with the block and the paper.

"In the case of intricate details, a small square may help in projecting points to the paper. Don't hesitate to write reminders of special features in the appropriate places on the paper you are developing.

"When the pattern is complete, lay it on top of the laminate. Hold it in place with masking tape. With the same compass setting, or the same parallel-edge stick, transfer the marks back to the laminate.

"There are several ways the laminate can be cut to the lines now drawn on its surface. The choice will depend on the fineness of detail to be carried out, and your skill with the tools available. Naturally, straight cuts will be handled in the usual way. 'Slow' curves may also be cut to ⅛" with a hand saw; a compass saw will be needed on 'tighter' curves, again leaving ⅛" for final trimming. Fine detail may have to be done with a jig saw, either hand or power. Experiment on some scrap laminate first, to see how your saw leaves the edge. Very fine-toothed jig blades should require no final finishing with file or sandpaper. The finished edge should be a snug fit against the bulkhead or other fixed member. A gap of more than 1/32" or a shattered surface will be unsightly, so take your time and check the fit frequently.

"When you are satisfied with the fit against all fixed members, it is time to treat the "open" side or sides. If you have not already done so, apply the laminate to these edges, finishing them flush with the top and bottom surfaces of the counter. Place the plastic top panel in position, and on its underside mark the location of the "open" edges. Allow ⅛" for trim, and make your cuts.

"Now use the laminate as a template, place it on a sheet of wrapping paper, and draw its outline on the paper. Cut the paper to the outline, leaving a generous overhang at the "open" side. Apply contact cement, in two coats, to both the counter top and the under side of the laminate. When the second coat is dry, set the paper on the counter top, exactly in position. It should completely cover the top, and overhang only at the open edge. Place the plastic laminate in position over the paper. When you are satisfied that it is exactly in place, lift the open edge slightly, and have your helper carefully pull out the wrapping paper. Then follow the same steps as for the table top.

"With either the counter top or table top installations, you may find the glue lines show up in an objectionable manner. They will show up rather prominently particularly if the plastic is dark. You can hide this glue line with wood stain, such as a medium mahogany. Don't leave it on too long, and avoid letting it slop over onto the plastic surface. A rag moistened with turpentine will remove any excess stain from the laminate, yet leave the glue line materially darker."

CABIN COMFORT

Cool It Yourself

Air conditioning is a real blessing on those hot days when the sun just seems to cook everything in the cabin, and on those warm evenings when you want ventilation without the open doors or windows that provide ready access for all the insects in the area. By using a number of readily-obtainable components, you can install your own air conditioning system at a reasonable cost. The source is given at the end of this project description.

The basic system operates on 110 volts, either the boat's generator or shore current. The components required are: a compressor with an electric clutch, a 110 volt motor, a dryer/receiver unit, a condenser, a sea-water pump, and the necessary hoses. It is important that all components be compatible, and although it is possible to purchase used items, it is best to buy all new gear.

Although all the components can be mounted in a single unit in the cabin, it's best to mount just the evaporator in the cabin (This is the unit that provides the cool air), and the rest in a "remote" location: forepeak, engine compartment, etc. This way the whine of the compressor's motor, and the thumping of the compressor itself, are not right on top of you.

Start by mounting all units except the evaporator on a base of ⅞" marine plywood, about 15" x 20" in size. The compressor and the motor are bolted to the two opposite front corners. Be sure that the pulleys or sheaves are in exact alignment. Space these units so the belt is fairly tight; the final tightening is done by adjusting the motor on its base, using the slide holes provided in the base for this.

Fasten the condenser coil, the receiver/dryer, and the electric water pump behind the two front units, in any convenient manner (*Fig. 224*). Straps are supplied for this purpose, or you may improvise some other mounting methods. Just be sure everything will remain in place, no matter how rough sea conditions may become.

Component hookup is done by a special synthetic hose that fits over barbed fittings. Clamps over the hose seal the couplings, and make them impervious to the high pressure that may be developed in the system. Note that the connections on the condenser are for flared copper tubing, so special fittings (*Fig. 225*) are needed to make the transition from the hoses.

Three sizes of hose are required: #6, #8, and #10 (the designations refer to the number of sixteenths of an inch of bore diameter). The #8 hose runs from the

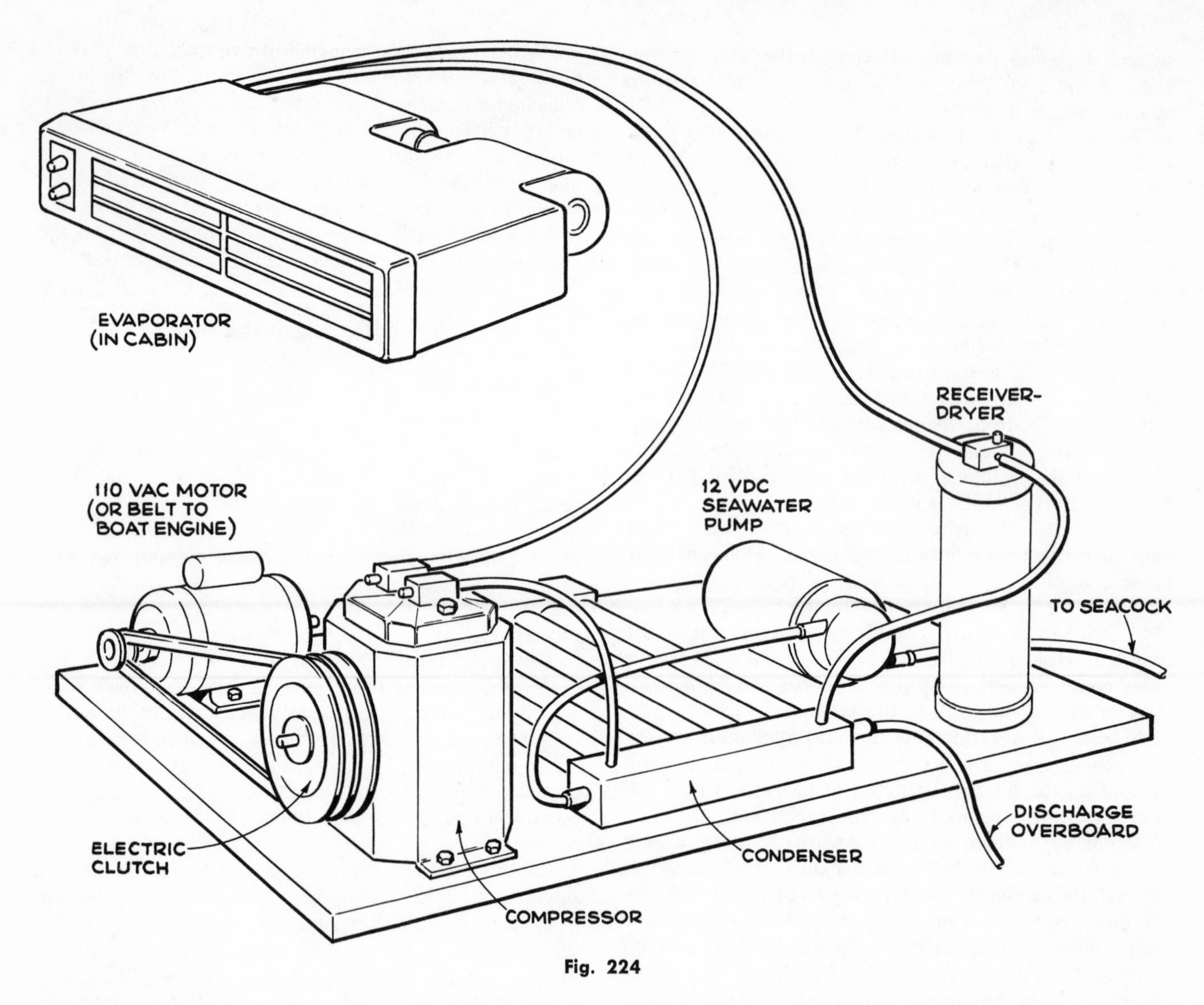

Fig. 224

compressor discharge port to the condenser, and from the condenser to the receiver/dryer inlet. The #6 hose runs from the evaporator to the receiver/dryer; #8 hose runs from the evaporator to the compressor intake. Use the #10 hose for the seawater pump connections.

When making hose connections, use refrigerant oil on all mating threaded and sliding surfaces. Be sure to use refrigerant oil, and no other kind. Guard against moisture, dust, or dirt entering hoses, ports, or any other part of the internal system; keep all openings plugged or capped until hooked up. This applies especially to the two evaporator hoses, which may have to be snaked under the cockpit or behind bulkheads or ceilings.

Wiring is done in accordance with *Fig. 226*. Note that the seawater pump and the motor for the compressor are hooked to the 110-volt AC circuit, and the evaporator and electric clutch on the compressor are in the 12-volt DC circuit.

The electric driving motor for the compressor draws its heaviest load — its starting current — only the first time you turn on the air conditioner. This motor then keeps running while the electric clutch starts or stops the compressor in response to thermostat demand. The unloaded motor draws negligible current, permits a smaller motor to do the job, and prevents flickering of lights when the conditioner kicks on.

When everything is hooked up on the plywood board, it can be mounted in a convenient spot outside of the cabin to be air conditioned. A forepeak or galley locker are fine; the engine compartment is usually used, but it must be large enough, and well-ventilated. Keep in mind that the electric motors may spark in operation, and gasoline fumes may be present in the bilge!

The evaporator unit is mounted in the cabin to be cooled, preferably as high as possible, with its grill protruding from a shelf or the top of a locker. Its drain hose should run overboard.

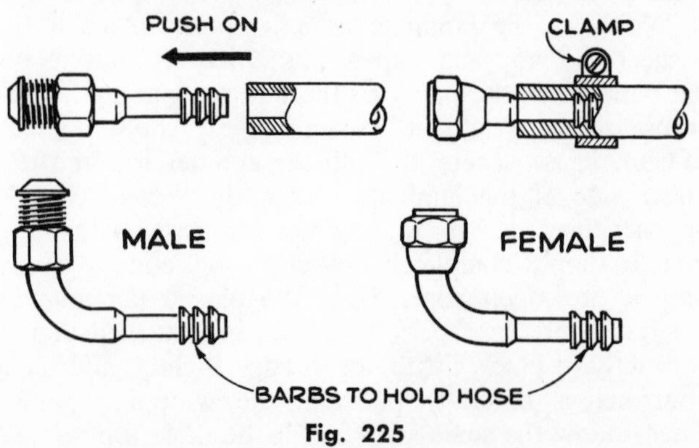

Fig. 225

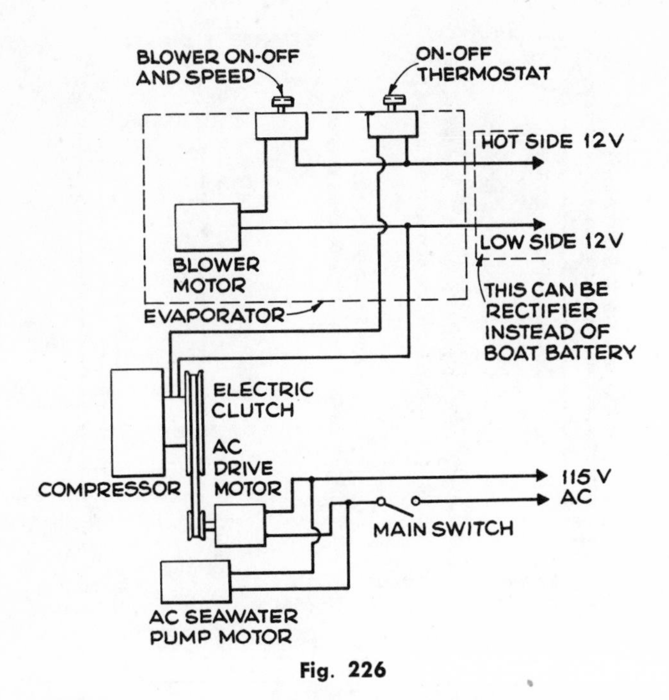

Fig. 226

Now, with the hoses hooked from evaporator to the compressor assembly, you are ready to charge the unit. The recommended way is to have your local refrigerator service man bring his equipment to the boat, and do it for you.

There is a way you can do it yourself, but it will waste about a half pound or so of the Freon refrigerant. Attach the tapping valve and its charging hose to the Freon can, and connect the hose to the discharge valve service port on the compressor. Hold the Freon can *upside down* so that you will be charging with *liquid* Freon. Slowly open the can valve, and allow half or a little more of the contents to be fed into the system. You can judge the level of the can's contents by its weight, and the frost line that develops on it. The unit should not be running.

The Freon will flow into the condensor, the receiver/

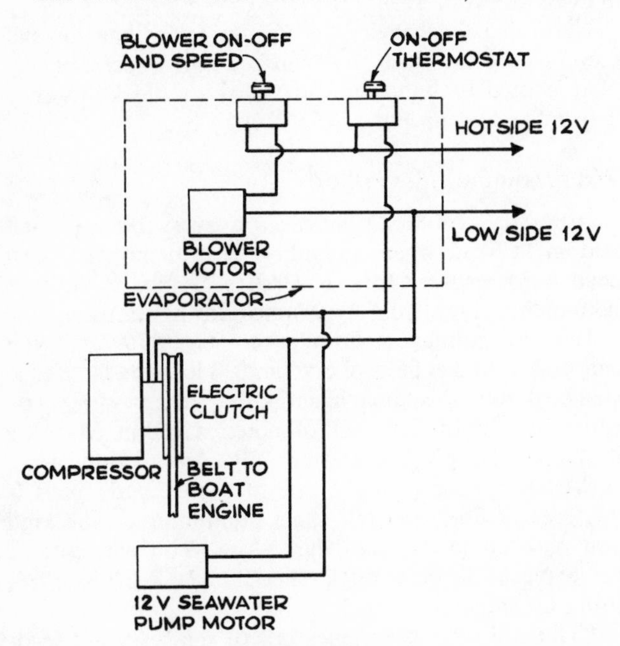

Fig. 227

dryer, on through the expansion valve into the evaporator, and then back to the compressor, pushing the air ahead of it. Crack the suction port open a bit to allow the air to escape. Let most of the Freon out because it will take any moisture out with it.

Close the valve on the Freon can, disconnect the hose from the discharge valve service port on the compressor, and reconnect it to the suction service port. With the compressor running, open the can valve. You will see a parade of bubbles in the sight glass at the top of the receiver/dryer. When the bubbles cease and the flow becomes a constant stream, the unit has had enough.

While handling Freon, wear goggles, and keep it from getting on your skin — the result may be frostbite. You may have to coax the last of the Freon out of the can by applying moderate heat. Use rags soaked in hot water; do not use a torch of any type.

If you have neither an on-board 100-volt AC generator, nor access to 110-volt AC shore power, you can substitute a 12-volt seawater pump for the 110-volt one, and your boat's engine for the 110-volt electric motor that drives the compressor. In this case the compressor must be mounted solidly with its sheave in line with the engine's power take off, and an idler pulley may be necessary to preserve belt tension. On some engines, the compressor can be included in the alternator loop with proper mounting and a longer belt. The compressor can rotate in either direction.

The compressor sheave, again, incorporates the electric clutch that engages and disengages the unit in response to the switch in the evaporator thermostat. The necessary wring is shown in *Fig. 227*.

A further refinement would be to add a double sheave to the electric clutch on the compressor. The inner sheave would run by a belt off a 110-volt electric current; the outer sheave would connect to the engine. Thus you can have shore-power air conditioning while docked, and engine-power air conditioning while cruising.

All necessary parts, including hoses and fittings, can be ordered from the manufacturer: Vornado Division, Automatic Radio Corp., Melrose, Mass. 02176.

Radiant Heat Panel Installation

On some small boats, you can take the chill off the air in the cabin by lighting up the galley stove on those raw spring or autumn days when you're aboard either for cruising or to work on the boat. On large yachts, an elaborate and costly heater system may be present.

But if you have a medium-size cruiser or sailboat, the galley stove won't put out enough heat, and the normal heating system would be too expensive. A simple, effective, inexpensive and popular heater is still the charcoal burner of the Shipmate type. These are simple to install, but consideration must be given to proper ventilation, fire safety, and the "chimney" itself.

A newer alternative is the radiant heat panel manufactured by the 3M Company. These are made for use in homes with 240 volt operation, but the wiring can be changed for use with 110 volt systems aboard boats. This means the units can be used only where a ship-

Fig. 228

board generator or shoreside power provide the needed voltage. The units draw 500 watts.

The radiant heat panel measures 2′ x 4′, and has a depth of about 2″. It can be suspended from the overhead (*Fig. 228*), or if space permits, recessed into it. In the latter case a hole must be cut in the overhead, using the template supplied. If the overhead is fabric or some other light material, frame out the opening to provide a solid base for attaching the panel.

Install the mounting brackets, which also are located by use of the template, and attach the heating unit to the brackets. The whole panel then can be swung up and latched into position.

Note that this is not a plug-in unit. A junction box must be used in conjunction with it, and all wiring must be in accordance with applicable insurance, local, marine, and national electrical codes (See Article 250 of the National Electrical Code).

Locate the unit as far from cabin sides, and/or forward and after bulkheads, as possible. Most cabins are not insulated, and if the heating panel is placed near a bulkhead, much of the heat will go right on out before it does much good in the cabin. In most cases, the middle of the cabin overhead is the best spot.

A standard code-approved fuse or breaker-type switch panel will be required to connect up the heater to the boat's on-board or shoreside 110-volt system, if an extra position is not available on your present board, one will have to be installed.

MISCELLANEOUS CABIN PROJECTS

Furniture Fasteners

Many cruisers, especially larger ones, are furnished with large chairs, sofa-beds, and coffee tables similar to those found in homes. In most cases, these will stay put, but in rough weather, they could slide about the cabin and cause considerable damage if there's no way to keep them in place.

Shown in *Fig. 229* are some suggestions for rigs that range from easy-to-make-up straps for lighter-weight items, to machined fittings for heavy furniture. In addition to those shown, you'll probably figure a way to use shock cord for many hold-down applications.

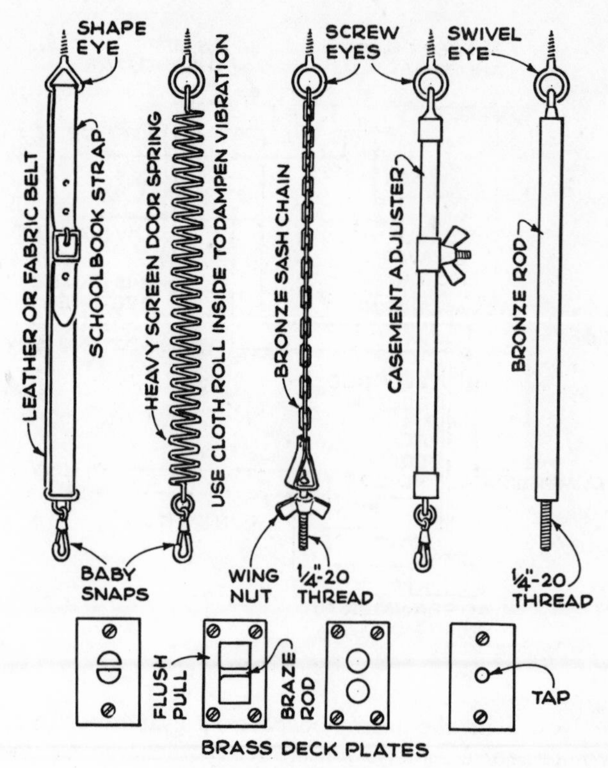

Fig. 229

In each of the rigs illustrated, a screw eye must be installed on the furniture item, and the belt, spring, chain, or rod is fitted to the screw eye. The heavier the furniture, the larger the screw eye (or bolt, if necessary). Where the lower end of the strap, spring, chain, or rod has a hook fastener, a deck plate must be supplied that will accept the hook; three types are illustrated.

The bronze rod with one end threaded to screw into a floor plate is a real machine shop project, but its use will guarantee that the heaviest sofa bed will stay put in even the worst seas.

Naturally, the heavier the furniture, the heavier and more secure the deck plate must be. If necessary, the plate should be bolted through backing blocks to keep it from pulling up out of the deck.

Wall-Mounted Memo Pad

A minor item that's needed on every boat — but seldom at hand when wanted — is a memo pad. You need it for grocery lists, reminders of jobs to do, appointments, even "log" type notes during a cruise.

Here's a permanent installation (*Fig. 230*) that you can easily make in a short time. This "pad" uses a standard roll of adding machine paper, on which you can write up to 225 feet of notes! Gordon Manning developed the project, and he tells how it's done:

"All you need to make one of these handy pads is 3 pieces of do-it-yourself sheet aluminum — the kind you pick up in any hardware store. You can cut the three pieces from a single sheet that's 8½″ x 4½″, using tin snips.

"The roll of paper comes out of the wall and feeds through the ⅛″ slot near the top. The standard 2½″

Fig. 230

wide adding machine tape then tucks under the top and bottom cross pieces. You write between upper and lower, and to remove a note, pull it down and tear it off against the bottom piece.

"Easiest way to cut the slot in the aluminum is with a series of holes, connected with a metal saw, and finally filed smooth.

"Note that the ends of each cross piece turn under themselves for ⅜", thus making a spacer for the paper to slide between. Be sure the width between these ends is the same 2¾" of the slot. This is just right for the 2½" paper to slip through easily.

"Escutcheon pins will fasten the plate on the wall, at the same time hold the two cross pieces in position.

"In mounting the pad, select a bulkhead or locker surface that has room behind it for the roll of tape (approx. 2½" x 3½"). This roll needs little support

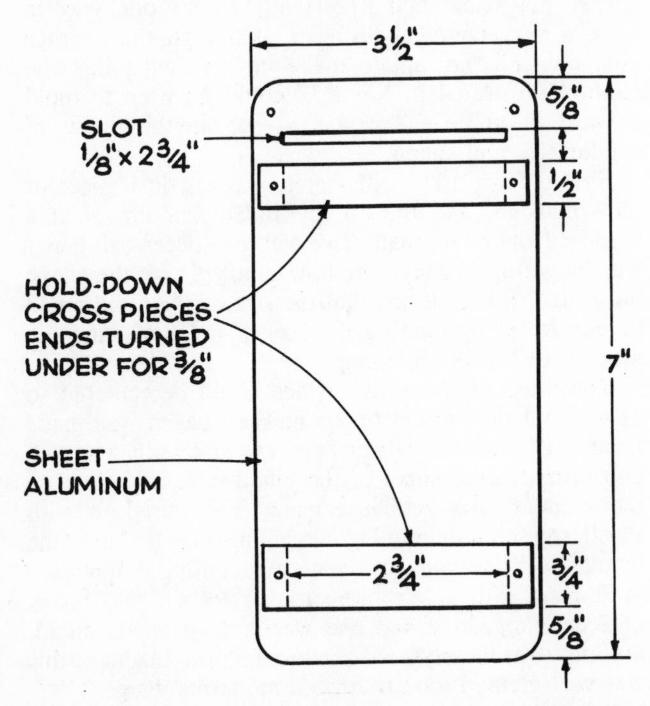

Fig. 231. Paper feeds out through slot at top of plate, and through two slides, top and bottom, that hold it flat against the plate.

Fig. 232. Slot is cut by drilling series of holes, filing smooth.

— it can rest on a handy shelf or be held up by a dowel or wire through its center.

"Locate the spot, then cut the slot through the bulkhead a little larger than the metal slot. A good size is ¼" x 2⅞". Be sure the edges are well-sanded and smoothed so that the paper cannot catch or tear as it is pulled through the wood and metal."

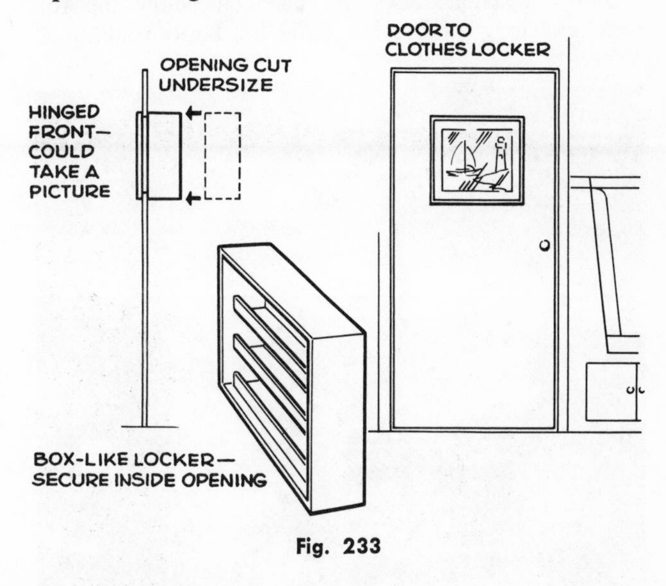

Fig. 233

Build a Door locker

Here's a suggestion from Jim Emmett for a little locker that's built right into a door. It can be set up as shown in *Fig. 233*, with its own door doubling as a picture plaque or frame. Or if the door is strong enough, and space permits, you can make it an open-fronted locker with shelves for paperbacks or other small books.

Rod and Magazine Racks

Wasted cabin space under side decks can be put to good use, as these Gordon Manning photos of a combination fishing rod and magazine storage racks show. As can be seen in *Fig. 234*, a finished panel backs this storage unit, and serves as a base to which the rod holder blocks are attached. There are holes in the blocks at each end of the rod rack, so those extra-long rods can be accommodated. A length of piano hinge

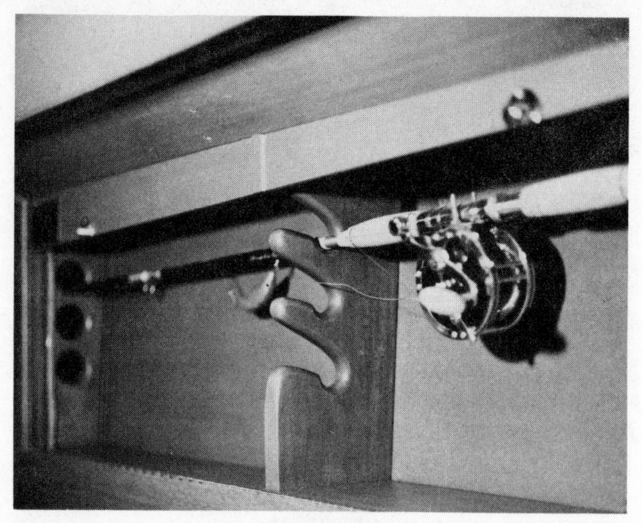

Fig. 234

runs along the bottom edge of the front panel, which can be held in the closed position by a turn button or mechanical catch.

Two magazine racks are installed below the rod rack, and they too are hinged at the bottom, although

Fig. 236

those in the photo (*Fig. 235*) use internal hinges, not external piano hinge as for the rod rack.

In the installation shown, existing wall panelling was cut, very carefully, and the cut-out panel was used for the doors. Of course if your boat does not have wall panelling, you can surround the storage unit with framing and panels to match whatever you have chosen for the doors.

Fig. 235

Split Companionway Hatch

On many contemporary cruisers, the hatch leading into the forward cabin is a single unit, hinged in the front. When open it blocks the helmsman's vision through the center sector of the windshield.

A simple solution, shown in the Gordon Manning photo (*Fig. 236*) is to cut the hatch in half, and install a piano hinge along the cut edges. With this arrangement, the back half of the hatch folds forward onto the forward half. A hook and eye holds the folded hatch to the windshield center post, and the top of it now is well below eye level.

Home Made Marine Toilet

We came across this in Britain's *Practical Boat Owner* magazine, and it certainly shows one way to solve a very complex problem. Although the average boat owner is not apt to make up his own toilet, the method illustrated in *Fig. 237* could be used to mold a wash basin or galley sink — or anything else of similar size and shape.

First a hole, 10″ in diameter, was cut in a piece of ⅜″ plywood, and the edges sanded smooth. Next a bladder from a "football" (we call it a soccer ball here) was blown up, through the hole, until it took the shape illustrated. It is assumed that the size of the mold could be controlled by altering the size of the hole, and the amount of bladder inflation.

The mold for the drain, which could be centered so as to be at the bottom of the finished basin, was made from a 1″ diameter dowel, tapered, and shaped at one end to match the curve of the bladder. It was glued to the bladder with rubber cement, and faired in with Plasticene (non-hardening modelling clay). Then the whole works was given a generous coating of grease.

Starting with a fairly generous gel coat, two layers of 2 oz. chopped strand mat was laid up on the mold, and out over the plywood surrounding the bladder (this was well-greased too) to form a mounting flange.

After the resin had cured for 24 hours, it was found to be a bit flexible, so another two layers of mat were laid up over the roving, and extra layers were applied

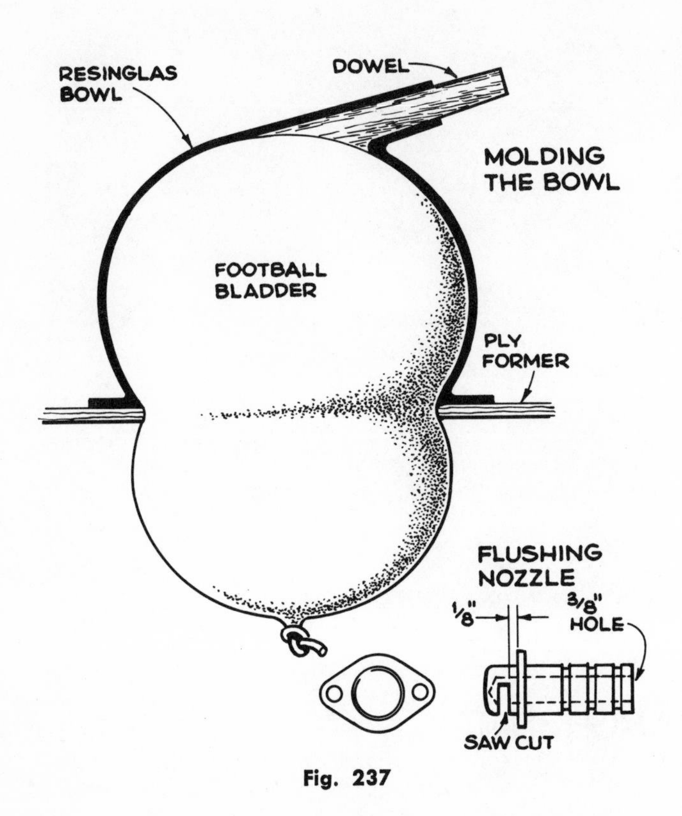

Fig. 237

around the mounting flange. Total thickness came to about 3/32", and the cured bowl had satisfactory rigidity. Of course, all the layup could be done at once, eliminating the 24-hour cure of the first two layers prior to addition of the rest.

When everything had cured, the bladder was deflated and removed. Then the inside of the bowl was rubbed down with successively finer grades of wet-or-dry production paper before painting with four coats of a white marine polyurethane enamel.

The flushing nozzle was made up from a short length of ½" brass rod, domed at one end and drilled ⅜" in diameter almost through from the other end. Three grooves were turned in the open end to provide a good grip for the hose from the pump. Then the rod was silver-soldered into a flange cut from 1/16" brass sheet, and a saw cut was made about half way through the domed end, so water is forced out in a fan shape through the slot. The nozzle then was inserted through a hole drilled in the edge of the basin, and bolted in place through holes drilled through both the basin and the flange.

The unit was installed in the forepeak, as illustrated in the cutaway drawing, *Fig. 238*. Note that all pump components are accessible. Flexible polyvinyl chloride hose worked well to hook up the units and the inlet and discharge fittings.

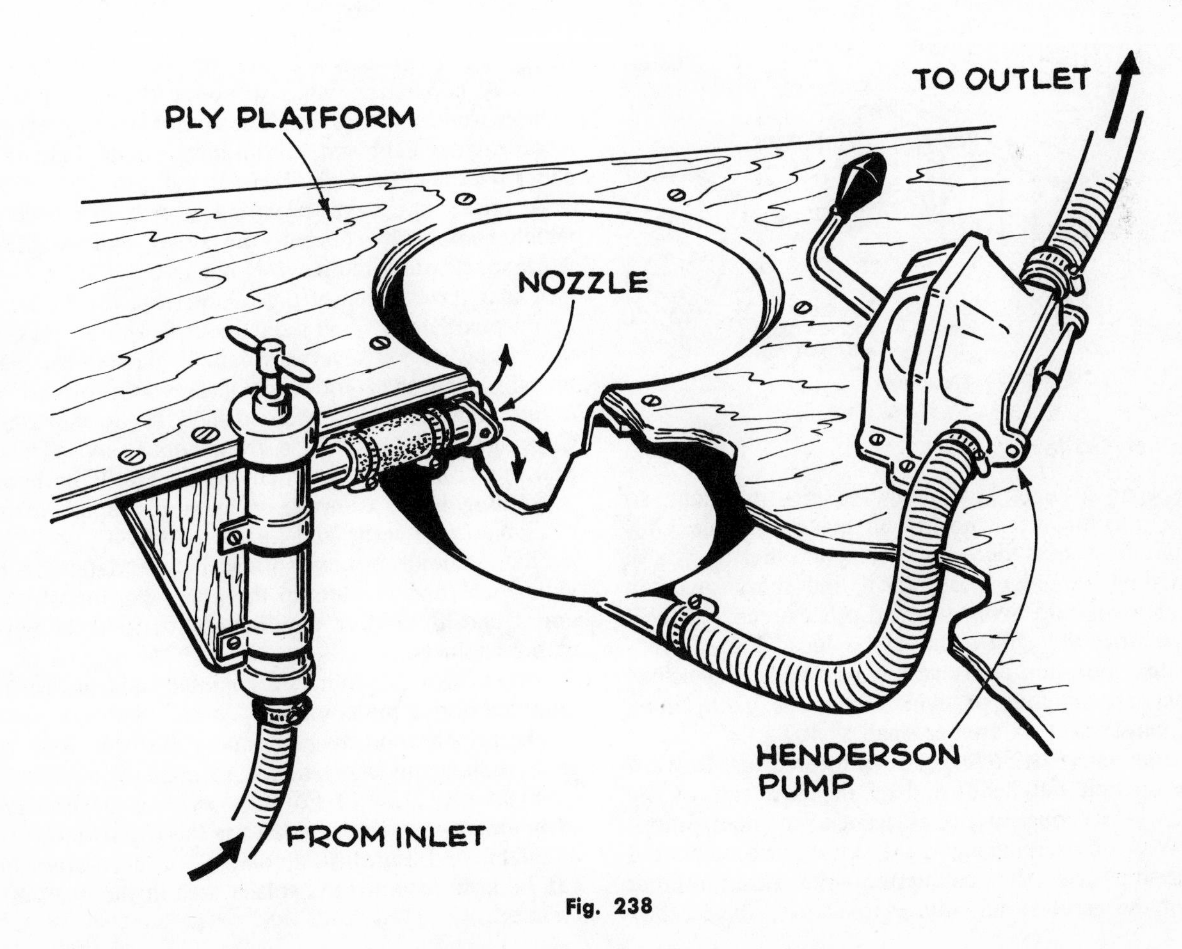

Fig. 238

3. GALLEY

GALLEY ARRANGEMENTS

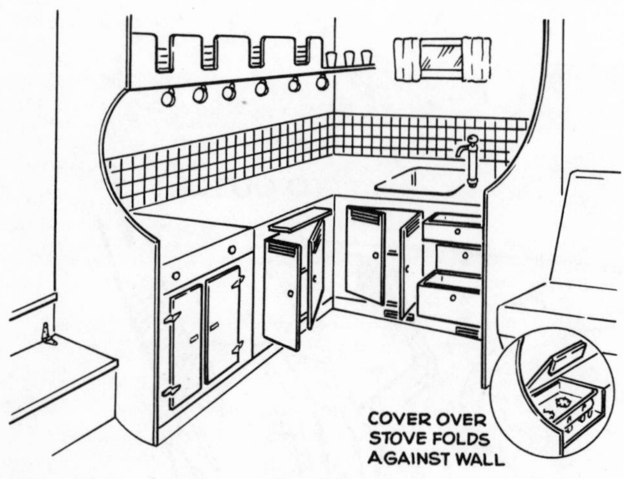

Fig. 301

A Corner Galley

Space on a small boat is always at a premium, so you have to make the most of all space available. Galleys on most new boats are compact, but if you're remodelling an older boat, you'll find space saved in the galley will add living space to other areas.

Of course the galley should be located in a well-ventilated spot, and easily accessible. While dimensions will depend on your particular boat, the galley illustrated can occupy an area as small as 40″ x 46″.

This galley (*Fig. 301*) is shown located just forward of the cockpit bulkhead, and on the port side of the cabin, with its inboard end adjacent to the companionway. With this arrangement, the stove can be mounted athwartships on the countertop—the position that gives it the greatest stability. Place it over the ice box (or refrigerator), next to the companionway partition. The roll of the boat is least here, and the partition eliminates the danger of anyone falling onto the stove.

The sink and drainboard are located along the side of the cabin between a partial partition and the bulkhead. A good-sized window above the sink provides light as well as ventilation. The companionway entrance also provides light and ventilation; a dome light in the cabin overhead provides light at night.

A cover has been provided over the refrigerator which completely conceals the stove, and doubles as work space when the stove is not in use.

Under the balance of the countertop, there's a small bread board, two good-sized lockers with shelves, and three drawers for silverware, small glasses, and galley utensils. The shelf for large glasses is provided with a false bottom, with holes drilled to fit the glasses. Cups should be suspended from hooks, and so placed that they cannot touch when the boat rolls or pitches.

By hinging the companionway step, a space is made available for utensils and linen—or tools.

Note that all lockers should be ventilated by providing screened air slots in the upper portion of locker doors, and in the floor molding sash strip at the bottom of the cabinets.

Shown with this unit is a compact built-in dish rack mounted above the counter.

Marine plywood is best suited for this type of a galley unit, painted or stained to match the rest of the cabin interior. Use of Formica, or even a good grade of linoleum, is recommended for the top surface of the counters, and Formica, linoleum, or decorative tiling can be used to finish the splash area at the back of the counter.

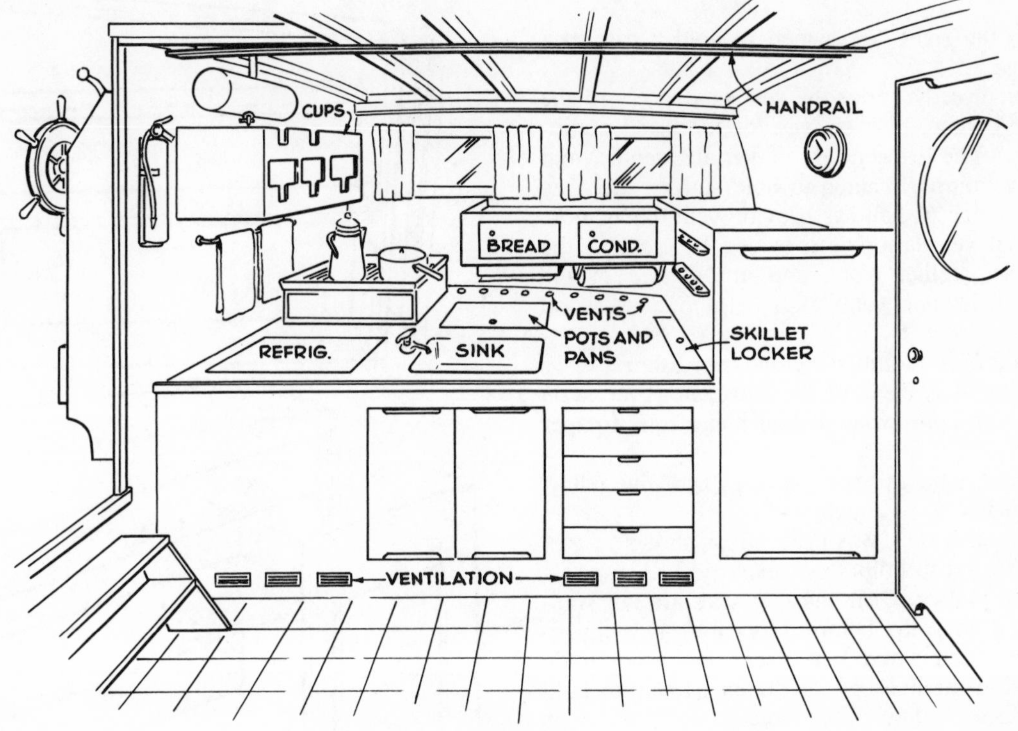

Fig. 302

Galley For Six

On the average small cruiser, of 30′ to 40′ in length, a galley should have provision for serving a maximum of six persons (other than for snacks served on afternoon or evening outings). *Fig. 302* shows how one galley was set up on this basis. It was done during the World War II years, but we have added some modern improvements.

The perspective drawing shows the layout clearly. The galley occupies the port side of the cabin; the starboard side is used for bunks and stowage—or for a convertible dinette arrangement.

Bread and condiment lockers are shown against the cabin wall, just beneath the windows. Since most windows come down close to the counter top level on newer boats, alternate locations would be on the forward bulkhead above the hanging locker shown, or on the side of the hanging locker itself.

If the space above the hanging locker can be kept clear, leave its top recessed slightly below the door frame and locker side panel. This leaves you with a shelf surrounded by a lip on the open sides. Dishes placed here during meal preparation won't slide off.

Glass racks are shown attached to the hanging locker side panel. Of course the glasses used must be tapered so they will slide down into, but not through, the holes.

The counter top is of marine plywood, covered with linoleum. The front edge is faced with a mahogany strip that also acts as a low rail. A Formica-topped counter is more work, certainly, but will last longer with less upkeep (see "Applying Laminated Plastics" in the preceding section).

The stove is of the two-burner alcohol type, with gravity feed from a tank mounted above the dish rack. The tank fill goes up through the cabin overhead. Many alcohol stoves are the pressure type, with self-contained tanks now, and your arrangement will depend on the type of stove you have.

Note that the stove is set well back, behind the ice chest. A folding "Dutch" oven can be used with it; the oven is stowed in the locker under the sink when not in use. Two points can be made here:

First, if your stove is a combination of range top and oven, it will have to mount at the front of the counter, and the hanging locker at the right will have to give way for the refrigerator. Or put the stove at the forward end of the galley and leave the refrigerator to the left.

Second, there's almost no excuse for carrying ice on a boat, with the electric refrigerator units now available. If you have an ice chest, we'll show you how to convert it to an electric refrigerator in a following project in this section.

If the stove is mounted at the forward end of the galley, add a second fire extinguisher on the bulkhead there.

Counter well lockers are provided here, one behind the sink and one to the right, alongside the hanging locker. Pots and pans are stowed behind the sink, and

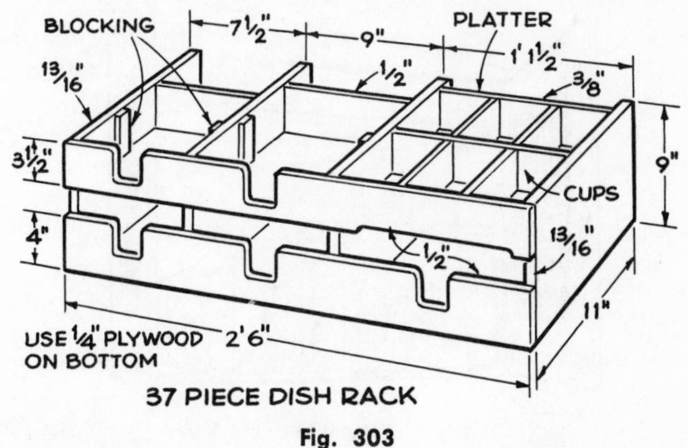

37 PIECE DISH RACK

Fig. 303

the locker to the right is designed to hold a cast iron skillet on edge.

The locker directly under the sink has access to the plumbing, of course, plus shelves for food and equipment stowage. The drawers are of various depths, and the top one is compartmented to hold cutlery, etc. The slots used in place of handles provide ventilation; note that additional ventilation is provided by slots at the bottom of the cabinet front, and at the rear of the counter top. Adequate ventilation helps prevent wood rot.

A towel rack is mounted below the dish rack, as shown. Be sure it is clear of the stove, however. You can substitute an appropriate holder and a roll of paper towels here.

An overhead hand rail runs the length of the galley, a real asset if it's at all rough.

Finally, the dish rack was made up as shown in *Fig. 303*. It is designed to hold six of each type of dish, six cups, and one platter. Dish and cup sizes are not standard, so check on yours before duplicating any dimensions shown. Small wood blocks can be glued in on each side and at the back of each compartment to hold each tier of dishes snugly.

LOCKERS & SHELVES

Galley Food Locker

Do-it-yourself aluminum materials available at hardware stores and lumber yards can be used in a variety of ways aboard boats, as Gordon Manning demonstrates. Here's another of his projects; this one uses both decorative ventilation grill stock and aluminum piano hinges.

Of course dimensions will have to be adjusted to suit your boat. The cabinet illustrated in *Fig. 304* is 5″ deep, so all the shelves were cut 5″ wide from a ⅜″ thick panel of marine plywood. Note that one end is higher than the other, in order to fit snugly under the cabin overhead.

Start by assembling the two ends to the bottom shelf and the top panel. Note that the top panel must be cut about 1″ longer than the bottom piece, because it runs

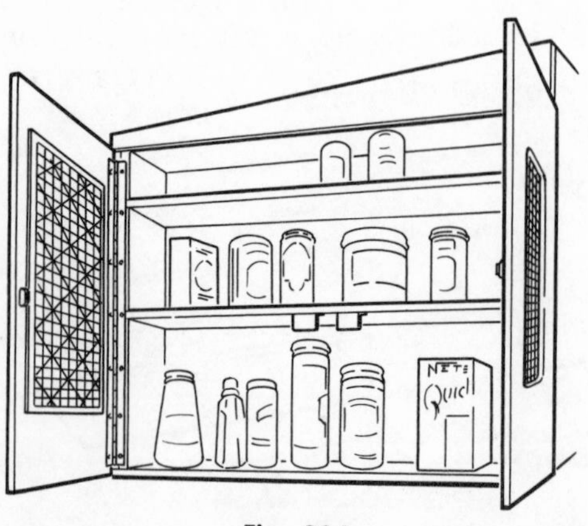

Fig. 304

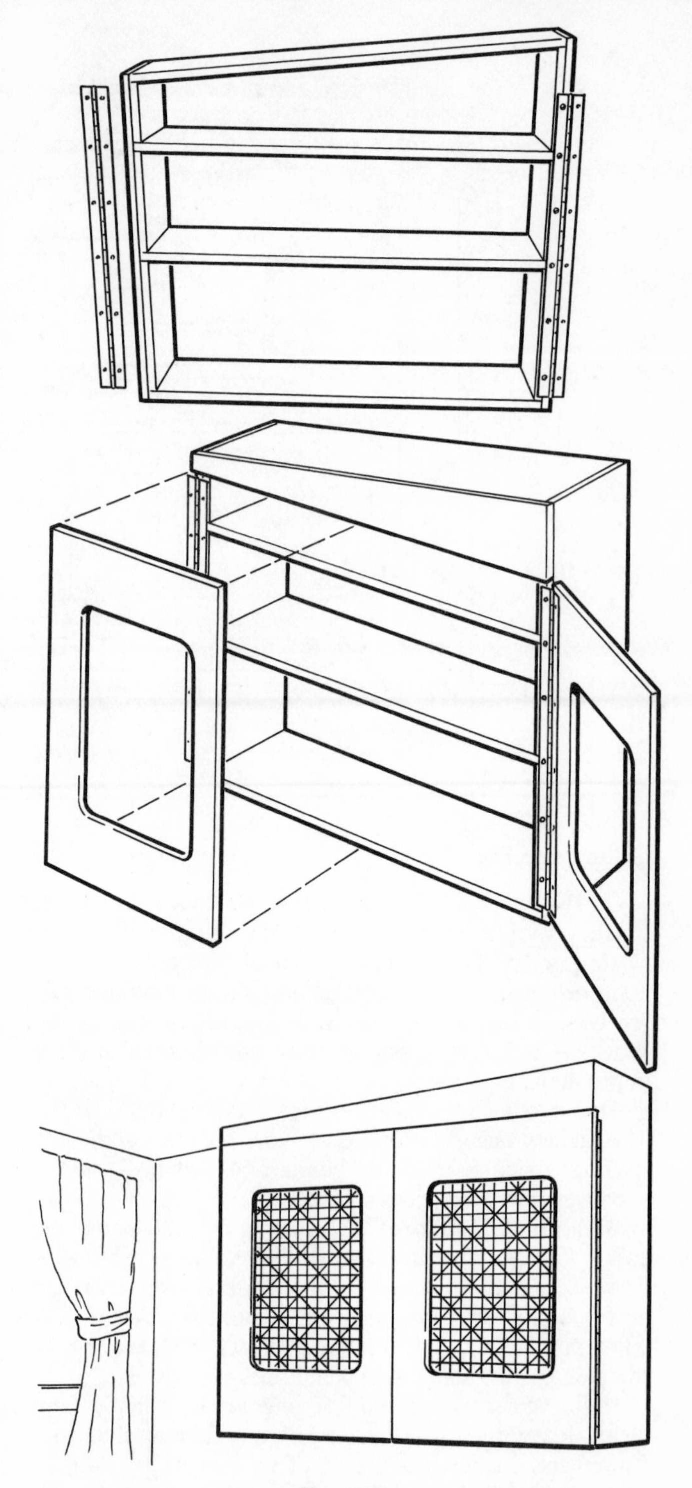

Fig. 305

on an angle. Be sure to trim each end to the proper angle to insure a tight fit against the sides. See *Fig. 305*.

Next cut out the three shelves (or however many you need), and the shelf supports. With the supports in place, total side width is ¾″. The supports are glued in place, and fastened with ¾″ brass wood screws, driven from the inside. The shelves themselves, and the top and bottom panels, are glued, and fastened with small galvanized brads.

A piece of ⅜″ plywood is cut to fit between the top of the doors and the headliner. This may need a slight curve in many installations. It is glued and nailed with brads to the top and end panels.

The two doors are also ⅜″ marine plywood. After the center sections are cut out and sanded smooth, they are backed with the decorative aluminum grill. Gordon Manning used grill that was anodized gold in color, which was very effective with the mahogany-faced plywood. The doors are attached with two lengths of aluminum piano hinge, and the necessary catches are installed. He used magnetic catches, which are good if they hold well, and they are well away from your boat's compass.

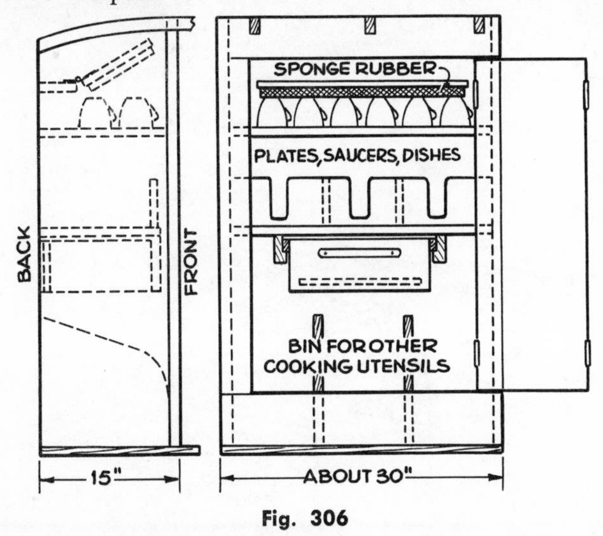

Fig. 306

Dish and Utensil Cabinet

Here's a way to combine dish, cup, utensil, and even pan storage in a single, neat cabinet, and it can easily be set up as a variation on Gordon Manning's galley food locker, above. Use the same materials and method of construction, and the two matching units will provide most—if not all—of your galley stowage requirements.

The top shelf in this cabinet is used to hold cups. A small block of wood, about ½″ thick, is cut to fit loosely inside each cup, and is fastened to the top shelf. These blocks center each cup in its particular place. To hold them in place, there's a hinged cover, faced on its underside with a sponge rubber or polyurethane foam pad. When this is lowered and secured, the cups can't shift around.

A panel across the front of the center shelf is slotted so dishes can be lowered into place, or lifted off the shelf. Full length dividers keep dishes from sliding from side to side. Dimensions must be worked out to suit your dishes, of course.

Guides are mounted on the underside of this shelf to take a small drawer for silverware and utensils. Runners attached to the upper edges of the drawer's side pieces slide in the guides. The drawer can be compartmented as desired.

Space-Saver Dish Rack

Special aluminum corner posts make construction of this little dish rack simple, and they give it a very professional look. Gordon Manning designed the rack to mount flush against a bulkhead, up near the cabin overhead where it will be out of the way.

The corner posts, made by Reynolds Aluminum, are available at many hardware stores and lumber yards, and they are slotted so that ¼″ plywood back and side panels slip right into them. Drill three ⅛″ holes through each inside edge of each post, and use ⅜″ long metal screws to hold the panels in place during the final assembly.

Your best bet, for the sake of appearances, is to select plywood with a veneer that matches other woodwork in

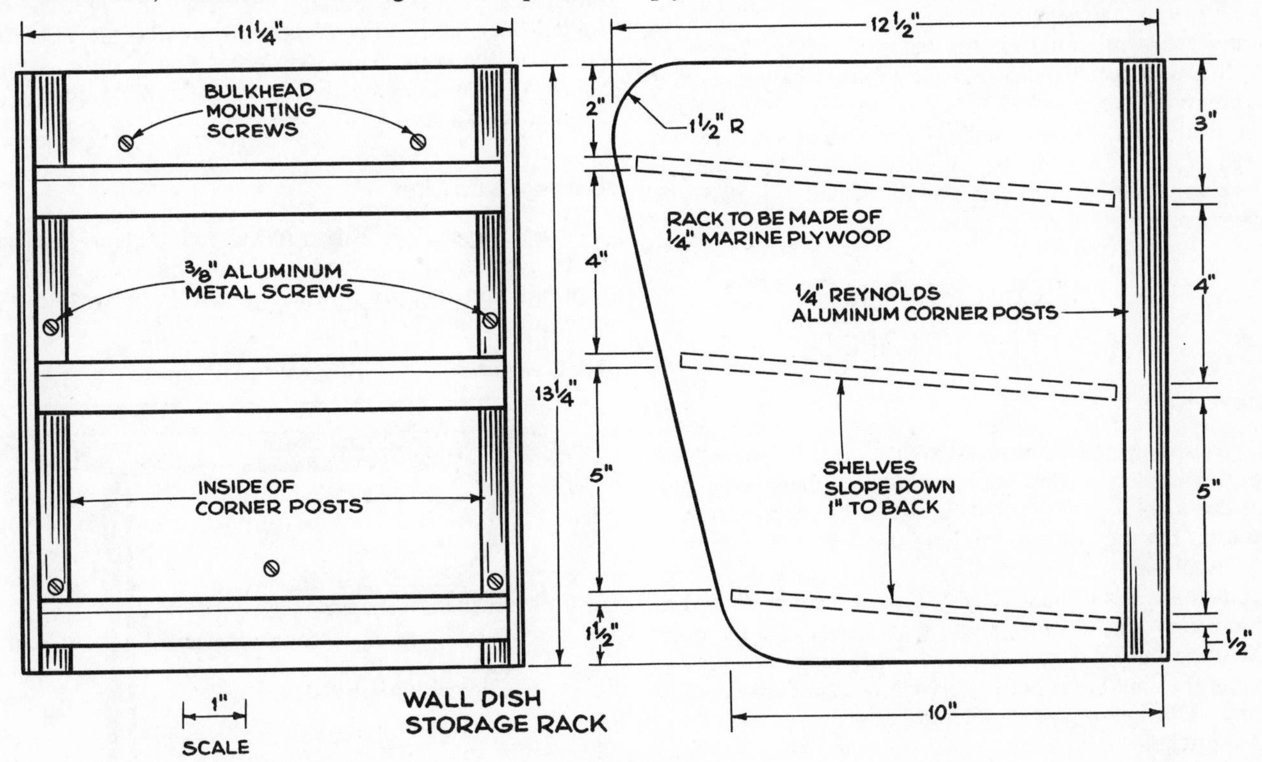

Fig. 307

your galley or cabin; Mahogany is the wood used most commonly. All pieces can be cut from a single 2′ x 3′ panel, if you use the dimensions shown in *Fig. 307*. Assemble the back and sides temporarily, and measure between the sides to determine the exact shelf width.

Shelves are cut and trimmed to a snug fit, and they are fastened in place with epoxy glue and 1″ brass or stainless escutcheon pins. Note that depths of the shelves vary: the top shelf is 11″, the middle 10″, and the bottom is 9″. Each is inset about ½″ from the front, and there's clearance at the back for the corner posts.

Before final assembly, coat all mating surfaces with the epoxy glue, including the edges of the plywood panels that slide into the corner posts. For a finishing touch, you can cover the exposed edges of the side panel with the flexible wood tape that's sold for this purpose.

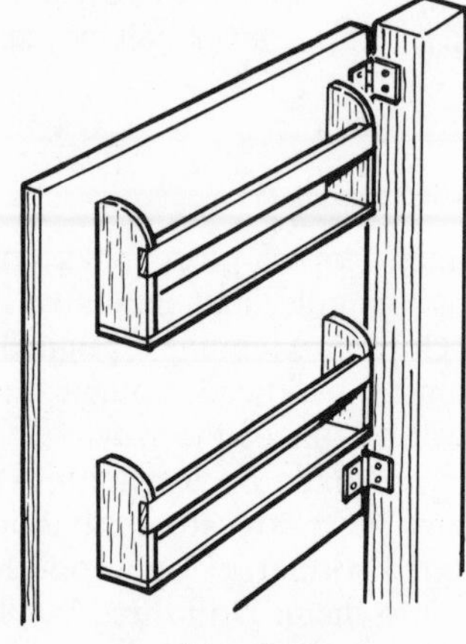

Fig. 308

Galley Space Saver

Here's a simple variation (*Fig. 308*) on Jim Emmett's door-storage arrangement (See *Fig. 232*). These are small racks mounted on the back of cabinet doors in such a way that they do not hit cabinet shelves, or the contents on those shelves. They do provide storage space for those small items such as spices that tend to get lost, or fall over, on the larger shelves. Mike Witney developed the idea, and it was illustrated in England's *Practical Boat Owner* magazine.

MISCELLANEOUS GALLEY PRJOECTS

Stove-Hole Bar

According to Gordon Manning, many owners of sportfishermen or day cruisers find they have little use for the alcohol stoves often furnished by the stock boat builder, but they do seem to have use for a portable bar.

His photo (*Fig. 309*) shows a unit devised by one yachtsman. It's a mahogany tray with deep sides and a trim rim around the top, and it seats neatly into the hole left when the stove was removed. The unit has compartments that hold two bottles, six glasses, and an ice container. Chrome-plated handles are attached to each end, so the whole unit can be lifted out and taken into the cockpit for the cocktail hour.

Fig. 309

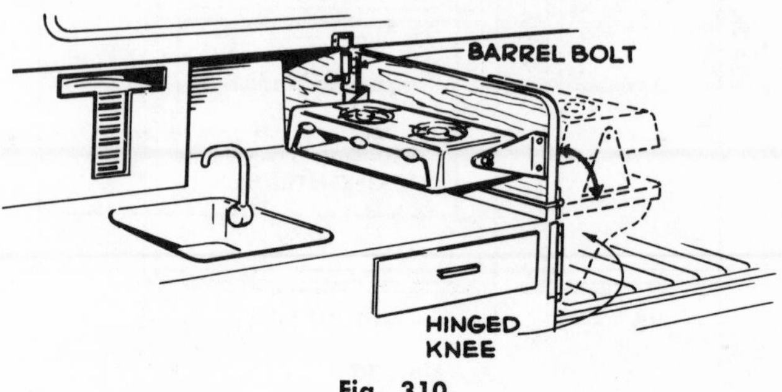

Fig. 310

A Moveable Feast

Rosemary Wilson came up with this idea in England, and submitted it to *Practical Boat Owner* magazine there. In this arrangement, the galley stove is hung in "gimbal" brackets mounted on a hinged panel. The panel can be locked upright, as shown in *Fig. 310*, or folded back onto hinged knees to provide more workspace on the countertop. She notes that a stove swung this way is not intended to help in cooking aboard a sailboat that's heeled!

Barbecue Bracket

Strictly speaking, this isn't a galley item because C. G. Rockwood designed it to hang out over a boat's transom. But it is used in cooking, it's handy, and it's extremely simple.

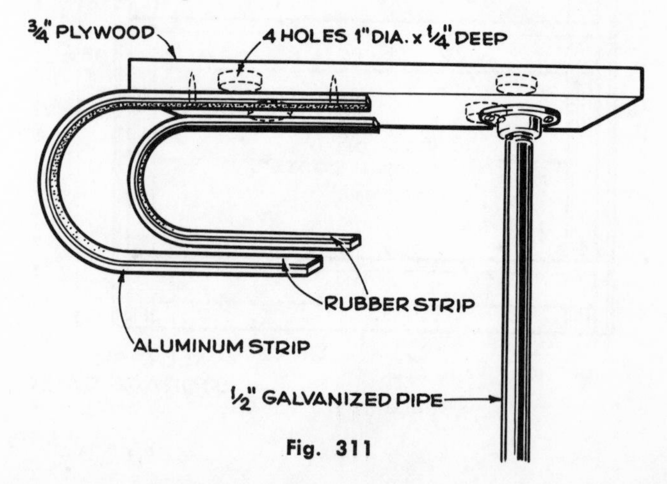

Fig. 311

The unit shown in *Fig. 311* was cut from a section of Formica-plywood laminate that had been cut from a kitchen countertop for a sink installation. Regular marine plywood, about ½″—¾″ thick, will do as well, but the Formica surface is really easy to keep clean.

The shelf is set up to hold the hibachi type barbecue stove, so its dimensions will depend on the size of your stove. Note the four holes drilled part way through the laminate. The legs of the hibachi set into these to prevent it from sliding about.

Aluminum strips were used to make the two brackets. These were screwed to the under side of the shelf, and they were covered with rubber stripping to prevent any marring of transom rail finish. The support leg is a length of ½″ galvanized pipe that screws into a flange plate mounted under the shelf, and it can be unscrewed easily so the whole rig takes very little storage space. Use a rubber crutch tip on the base of the leg to prevent scratching your deck.

Refrigerator Conversion

Although more and more new boats are furnished at the factory with electric refrigerators, there are many new ones—and even more older ones—with nothing more sophisticated than an ice chest.

Fig. 312

Most ice chests can be converted to electric refrigerators with just a little time and effort, and you do away with the mess and inconvenience of ice. Conversion units, such as those supplied by General Thermetics, are available for front opening or top opening ice chests, and with either 12-volt DC or 110-volt AC operation, to suit the boat's electrical system. See *Figs. 312, 313, 314.*

Fig. 313. AC Condensing Unit.

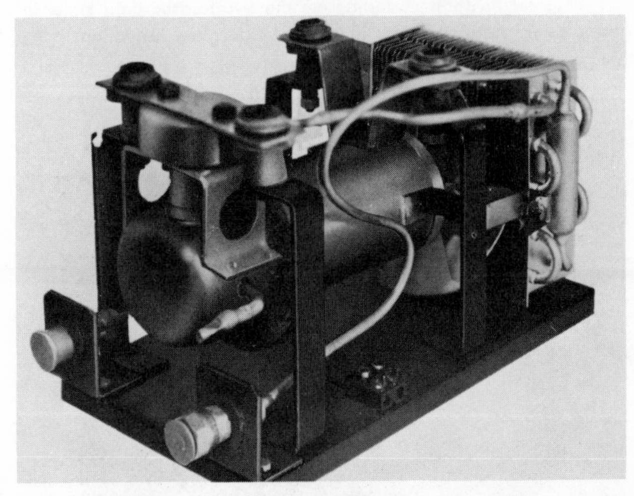

Fig. 314. DC Condensing Unit.

While most ice chests are suitable for conversion, those with chipboard, Celotex, and other building board materials used as insulation should not be considered. These materials really provide very little insulation, and will cause excessive running time for the compressor, and sweating of the box in hot or humid weather. Insulation of fiberglass, rock wool, Styrofoam headboard, and cork, all in 2″ thickness, are acceptable; urethane foam, 1″ thick, also is acceptable.

Two major components are supplied for the conversion: an evaporator (ice tray compartment), and the condensing unit. Locate the condensing unit so it will be within reach of the tubing (supplied) that runs to it from the ice chest.

The engine room and bilge are acceptable locations. If the unit must be placed in a locker or other small compartment, you must provide air intakes and outlets, each with an area of at least 36 sq. in. When running, the condensing unit gives off heat equivalent to a 150 watt light bulb.

Some marine ice chests are set up to take conversion units. On these, just remove the plastic plugs at the rear of the cabinet. For other boxes, note where the tubing leaves the evaporator unit, and drill a 1″ hole through the rear or side of cabinet in the matching location (See *Fig. 315*).

Leave the plastic caps on all fittings on the evaporator. Unroll the coil of tubing completely, and start it through the hole at the rear of the cabinet. Snake the tubing toward the condensing unit until all excess tubing is out of the cabinet (*Fig. 316*). On those chests that have provision for conversion, remove the mounting screws, set the evaporator into position, and replace the screws. Use plastic spacers between the evaporator and the chest.

On chests without such fasteners, use the $^{10}/_{32}$ brass mollies that are obtainable in most hardware stores (*Fig. 317*).

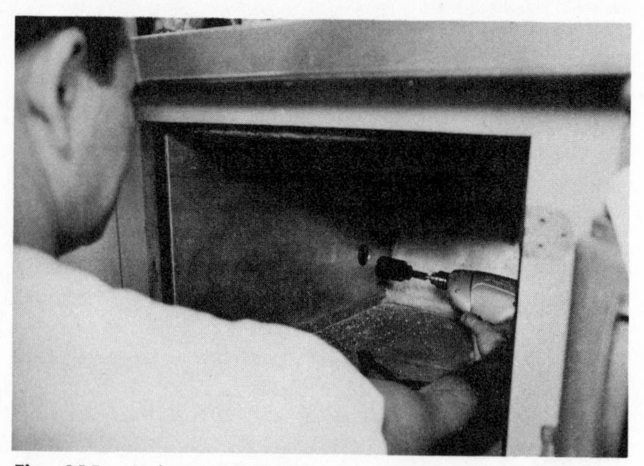

Fig. 315. Hole is drilled through side or rear of cabinet, depending on location of tubing on the evaporator unit. Hole saw goes easily through metal lining and fiberglass insulation.

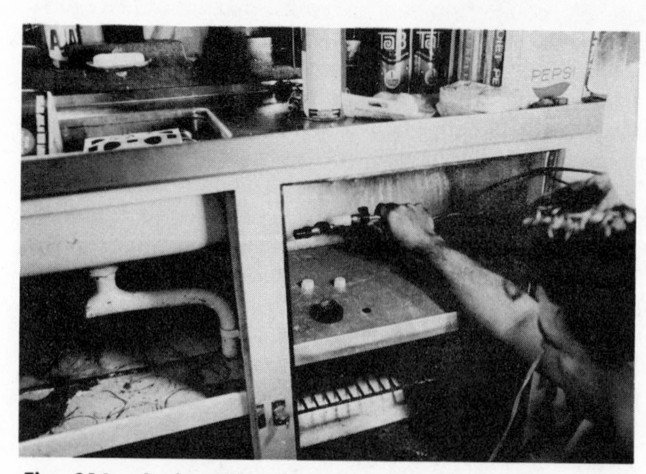

Fig. 316. Snake tubing through the hole, toward the condensing unit. Be sure all excess tubing is outside the cabinet, and that it is free of kinks or sharp bends.

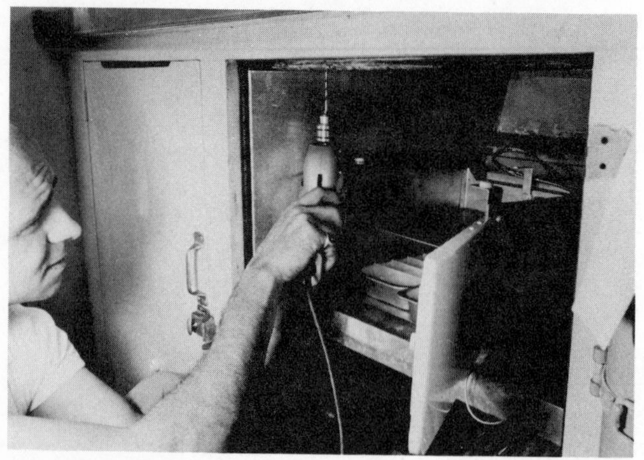

Fig. 317. Evaporator unit is positioned in the box, and the necessary holes are drilled to mount it to the top or side, depending on the unit.

Fig. 318. Thermostatic control is wired in and attached in any convenient location inside the box.

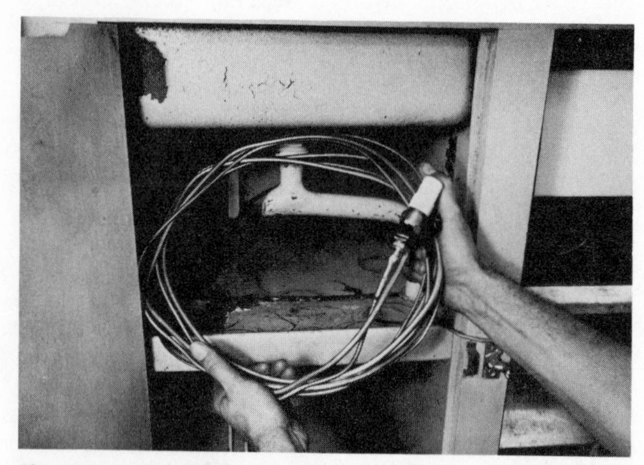

Fig. 319. Lead tubing to the condensing unit; support it with clamps where necessary, and coil any excess as shown. Do not remove any caps or fittings until you are ready to hook up the condensing unit.

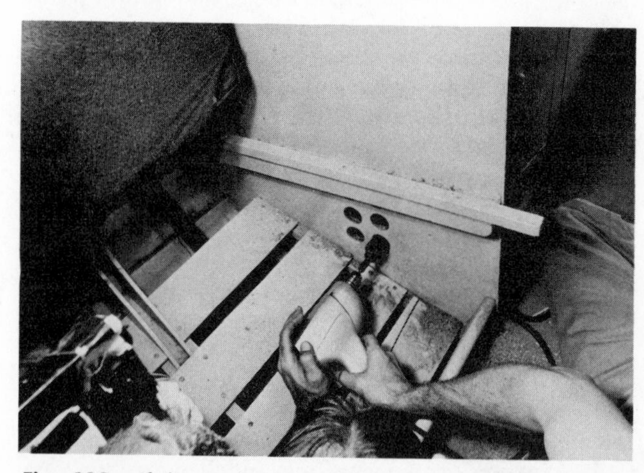

Fig. 320. If the condensing unit, with its compressor, is located in an enclosed space, drill holes or otherwise provide ventilation. A flow of fresh air is needed to keep the compressor cool.

Attach the cold control housing to the side or back of the chest as convenient, using stainless steel sheet metal screws (*Fig. 318*). Seal the hole around the tubing with the mastic provided.

Now follow the tubing back to the condensing unit, supporting it with clamps as needed to keep it out of the bilges. Any excess tubing should be formed into an 18″ diameter coil (*Fig. 320*). Be sure there are no kinks in the tubing!

The unit is fully charged at the factory, which means that refrigerant will escape when the plastic plugs are removed prior to coupling the tubing to the compressor. Get everything ready first, and connect one tube completely before starting on the second, using the following procedure:

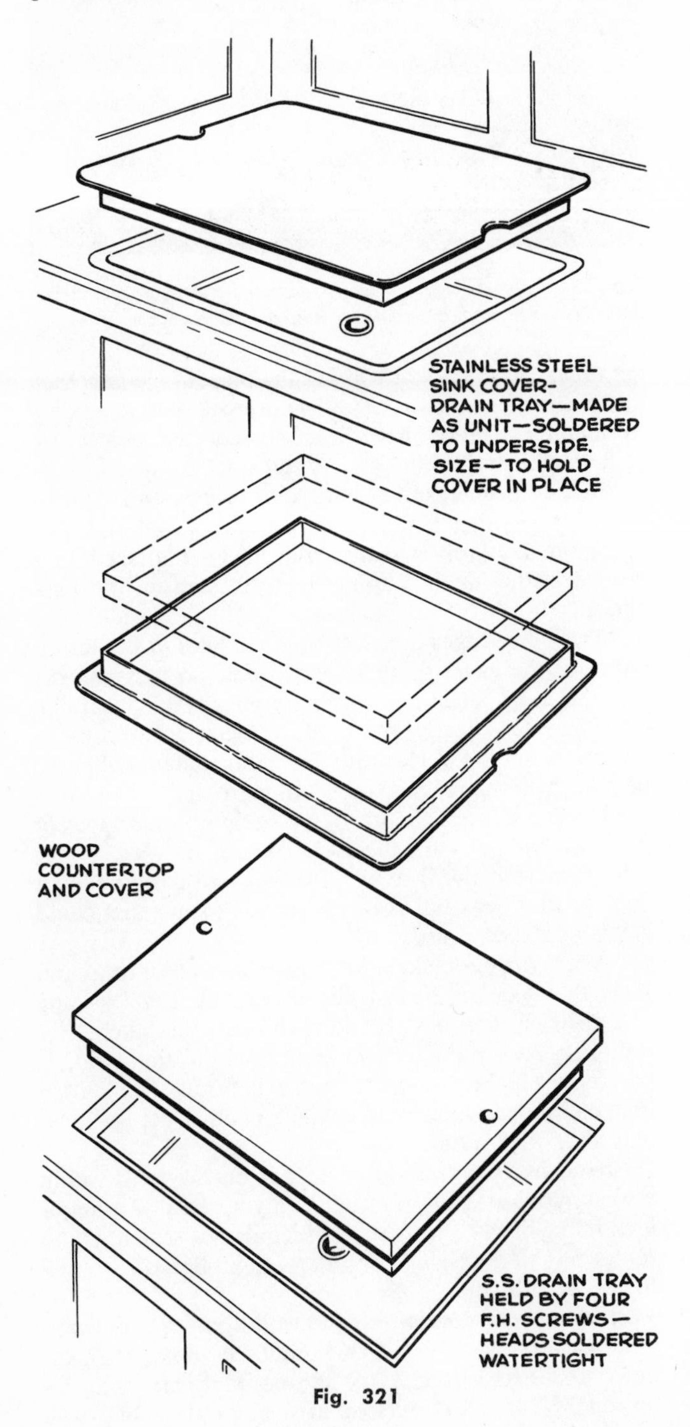

Fig. 321

Loosen the condensing unit mountings, and shift it so the couplings can be attached with a minimum of tube bending. Make sure the couplings are dry, remove the plastic plugs, and connect the male fitting to the female fitting on the compressor unit. Hand tighten one turn, then use an open-end wrench to tighten the fittings. Turn only the swivel nut on the female fitting; hold the male fitting fast and don't turn it. Work rapidly to minimize escape of refrigerant.

Finally, insert the end of the thermostat wire from the evaporator through the "strain relief" on the side of the junction box on the condensing unit box. Tighten all mounting bolts or screws, and hook up the wiring as specified for your unit.

If you have a 110-volt AC system, a couple of points should be noted. It is imperative that the green ground lead of the refrigerator be wired to the green ground lead of the shore receptacle, *not* to the neutral buss bar of the AC panel. AC neutral must be isolated from ground on the boat.

Power from the AC source should be run to the junction box with three wire #16 cable, and a 15 amp circuit breaker should be installed in the *hot* lead.

If your boat has a metal hull, with a 110-volt AC system, it is recommended that you use the services of a qualified marine electrician.

Drop-In Sink Cover

In place over the sink, this cover provides additional counter space when a meal is being prepared. Flip it upside down alongside the basin after the meal, and it's a drain tray.

As designed by Jim Emmett, it can be of fairly stiff stainless steel, or of teak (*Fig. 321*). If stainless steel, the band of light gauge stainless steel that forms the drain tray is soldered in place. If wood, the band is flanged, and screwed to the wood, and the screw heads are soldered over to keep them watertight.

In either of these arrangements, water that drains into the tray just collects there, and must be sponged out. An alternative would be to make a three-sided tray that can be arranged to drain directly into the sink.

Also, as a substitute for the stainless steel or teak cover, you could make up a Formica-faced plywood cover, perhaps with the Formica on both sides, and with wood battens to form the sides of the drain tray.

Make Your Water Tank from Wood

Many of the smaller cruisers and auxiliaries have a really limited capacity for freshwater storage, and suitable tanks of fiberglass, stainless steel, copper, rubber, or plastic are quite expensive.

A solution is to make a wooden water tank with a waxed interior surface. It's inexpensive, long-lasting, can be designed to fit snugly in an existing space, and it imparts no taste to the water. Photographs and text supplied by Gordon and Janet Groene tell how to make one:

"Basically, you'll get the strength you need by using sturdy boat-building construction. The baffles you build in to prevent weight transfer in rolling and heeling will also add structural strength. Ours is fitted with a

Fig. 322. Cut out individual pieces from plywood, using a sharp, fine-tooth blade to make sure that edges do not splinter.

Fig. 323. Fit all corners carefully, especially where the panels must be joined at an angle.

fore-and-aft baffle, with a bottom opening only as large as the feed. At the top of your baffle, plan a slightly larger hole, depending on your filler size.

"First, carefully measure the space available for your tank, including clearance for inlets, outlets, vents, and supports. Make scale drawings to determine the amount of material you'll need. Then shop for ⅜″ inch marine plywood, fir for corner strips, galvanized screws, and a good grade of two-part waterproof glue.

"After inspecting the plywood carefully for flaws, lay out a pattern according to scale drawings. Then cut out individual pieces including baffles and an access hatch that you can work through to finish the tank, and for cleaning and repairs later.

"Make a rough assembly of four sides, then plan and cut corner strips. Now make a rough assembly of all sides, and finish the outside corners. At all seams, check and adjust for perfect fit.

"Now take it apart and sand the insides of all pieces to make a smooth surface to receive the wax. Where two pieces join, lightly countersink all screw holes. Plan

Fig. 324. Use of a guide on the sander help to provide a flat, accurate edge and a maximum adhesion surface for glue.

the order in which you will put the pieces together, then make a final assembly, using waterproof glue according to manufacturer's instructions. Screw the pieces together tightly while the glue is still wet.

"Make up inlet, outlet and vent fittings, and seals of neoprene or other long-lasting waterproof material. The hatch on this tank is sealed with an O ring, set into a groove in the hatch, putting light pressure on the tank flange.

"Mask any edges that will be glued later at the installation of the last side or sides, so that no wax can get into the joint. Then heat ordinary jelly-making paraffin over very low heat. (We used an electric hot plate at its lowest setting.) Hot wax is highly inflammable, so be sure it never reaches the smoking point.

"Using a clean, soft brush, 'paint' interior surfaces of the tank with a smooth, even coating of wax. Cover thoroughly but not heavily. At edges and corners, lay a good bead of wax but again, avoid thick spots that could crack in extreme cold.

"After waxing, make a final installation of fittings and seals, then glue on the last side of the tank. Final waxing and clean-up can now be done through the hatch. For testing, block up the tank in its normal position with air vent at its highest point. Support it firmly (remember that the water alone weighs eight pounds per gallon), and fill it with water.

"If no leaks or wet spots appear on the tank within a week, you're ready to install it in your hull. If a major leak immediately shows that a seam is not sealed, try to re-open it and re-glue, or inject glue. But do not fill the void with wax.

"If wet spots develop on the wood, indicating a pinhole leak, mark the area and drain the tank. Then remove the access hatch to let the tank air and dry thoroughly. If the suspicious area had only a thin wax

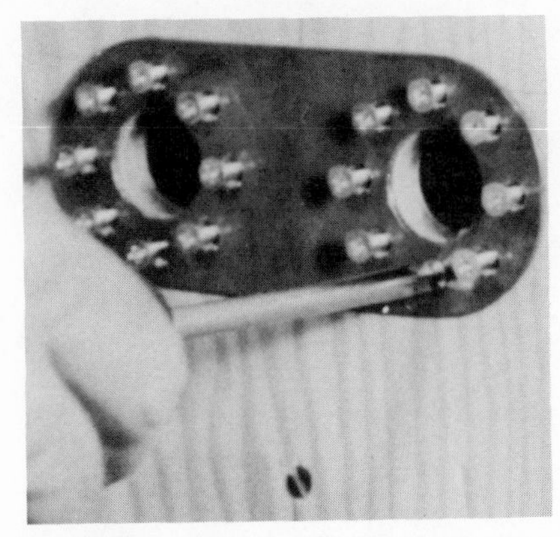

Fig. 325. Make a trial fit of inlet and outlet fittings before waxing the interior of the tank.

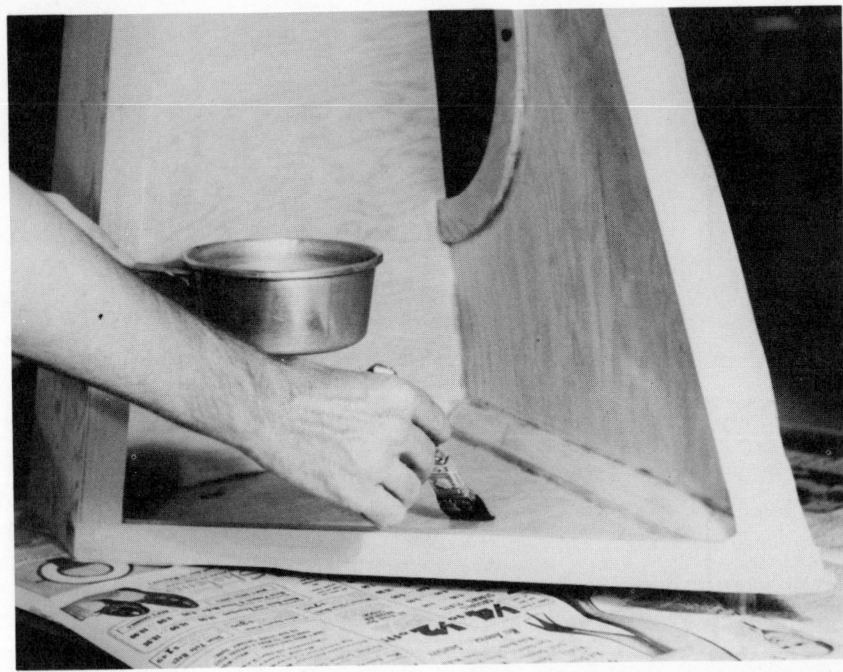

Fig. 326. Right: Tank interior is painted with warm, liquid wax. Flow the wax over the wood in a thin, even coat.

coating, it can be rewaxed. If the wax is thick in the area, scrape and wax again. Repeat this week-long test until the outside of the tank stays dry.

"Now you are ready to plug fittings, sand the outside, and paint the tank with a good marine waterproof paint. This sealer is important because of condensation that will form in hot, humid weather.

"Before mounting the tank permanently, compute what it will weigh filled, and anchor it accordingly to make sure it won't break loose in roughest seas.

"Water from your wax-lined tank will not take on flavors, as it might in rubber, plastic or fiberglass tanks. And this type tank is reportedly less conducive to scum growth than metal tanks, especially copper. For low cost, easy maintenance and stalwart service, a wooden water tank might be the answer for you, too. Ours has proved to be the smartest bargain aboard."

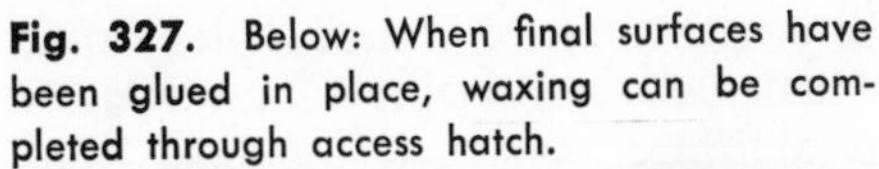

Fig. 327. Below: When final surfaces have been glued in place, waxing can be completed through access hatch.

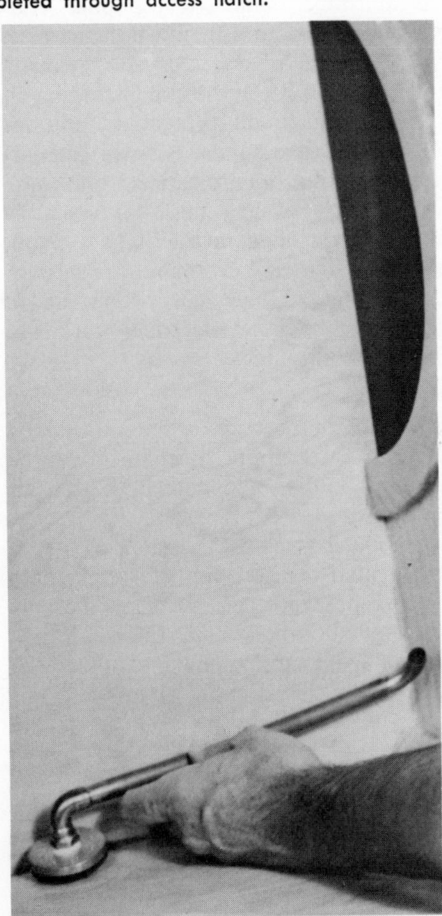

Fig. 328. In testing tank, make sure supports are adequate for weight of the tank when it is filled with water.

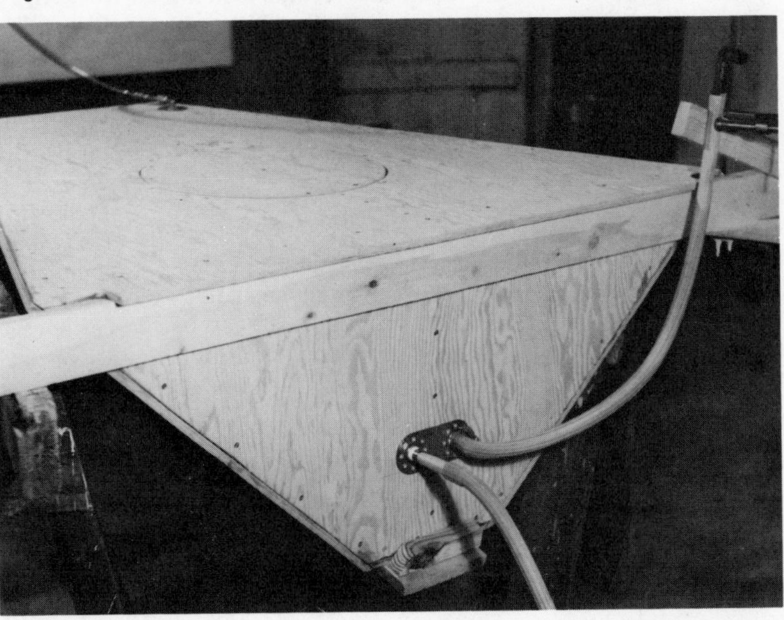

4. ELECTRICAL SYSTEMS

ELECTRICAL SYSTEM DESIGN

Design and installation of a complete electrical system for a boat is best left to a professional electrical engineer who is familiar with the special requirements of marine service. This is true whether the system is based on a 12-volt direct current (DC) battery, or on 110-volt alternating current (AC) supplied by shoreside power, a shipboard generator, or both.

However, you may find it necessary to modify, or add to, an existing system. The qualified marine electrician is still your best bet, but if you do the work yourself, you should follow the best advice available: the standards and recommended practices for electrical systems established by the American Boat & Yacht Council, Inc. This organization includes technicians of the boating industry, insurance underwriters, representatives of safety-standard and testing organizations such as the National Fire Prevention Bureau and Underwriters Laboratories, representatives of the United States Coast Guard, and individuals whose specialized knowledge is instrumental in establishing standards for boat construction and installations that are in the best interests of the consumer.

With permission of the ABYC, we are including in full the standards covering circuit protection, and installation of AC systems. Other standards cover grounding of DC systems, wiring identification, and safe installation of DC systems of less than 50 volts. In tentative form, they are included in the ABYC book, *Safety Standards for Small Craft*, available for $10.00 from ABYC at 15 East 26th St., New York, N.Y. 10010. If you plan on doing any extensive electrical work, use the ABYC standards as your guide!

Recommended Practices and Standards Covering
The Protection of Electrical Circuits
(ABYC Project E-5 [Proposed])

1. SCOPE

Wherein safety standards and recommended practices apply to the means whereby electrical wiring and equipment of both AC and DC circuits on small craft can be controlled and protected against overload and short circuits.

2. DEFINITIONS

a. *Trip-Free Circuit Breaker*—A thermal or magnetically operated overload protective device so designed that the operating handle *cannot* be manually held in to override the circuit-interrupting mechanism.

b. *Non-Trip-Free Circuit Breaker*—A thermal or magnetically operated overload protective device so designed that the overload-circuit-interrupting mechanism can be bypassed by manually holding the control button or handle on the "on" position.

c. *Circuit Protection Device*—A device, such as a fuse or circuit breaker, located at the point of supply of a circuit and designed to break the circuit when the current flow exceeds a predetermined value. Overload protective devices integral with equipment and others not located at the source of supply for the circuit will not be considered circuit protection devices.

3. GENERAL

a. *Protection of Ignition Sources*—Circuit protection devices, switches, and other devices intended for installation in machinery spaces or other potentially hazardous locations shall be so designed and constructed as to prevent the ignition of flammable vapors or gases and shall be approved for marine use.

b. *Marking*—Each switch and circuit breaker shall be clearly identified with a permanent label to indicate the circuit controlled. Each fuse holder shall be marked to indicate the circuit and current rating of its fuse.

c. *Protection of Current-Carrying Parts*—Current-carrying parts of all switches, circuit breakers and fuses shall be so installed as to be protected against accidental contact or damage.

d. *Types of Overload Protection*—

(1) Each circuit breaker, where used, shall be specifically designed, in regard to ambient temperature and demand load, for the type of overload conditions to be encountered in its particular circuit.

(2) A thermal circuit breaker without a manual reset device may be used as an integral part of an electrical device only and shall be backed by a second, trip-free circuit protection device, or fuse at the main switchboard or distribution panel.

e. *Reduction of Wire Gage*—Where for any reason the gage of wire is reduced at a junction, a fuse or a trip-free circuit breaker shall be installed to protect the lighter gage wire unless the current-carrying capacity of the smaller wire equals or exceeds the rating of the circuit protection device.

4. a. *NOTE: There remains an unresolved conflict with respect to the requirements for a battery disconnect switch. Therefore both views are published herein as alternates.*

Master Battery Disconnect Switch

(1) An approved master battery control and emergency disconnect switch shall be installed close to each battery in each ungrounded lead.

(2) Installation of a master switch as close to the battery as practicable is recommended, but not required in boats under 26 feet in length.

Switches used for this purpose shall comply with Section No. 3. a. and the following:

(1) Battery disconnect switches which also serve as battery selector switches shall be of the "make before break" type to avoid the development of high transient voltages from alternators or generators when switching from one battery to another.

(2) It is recommended that battery disconnect switches incorporate an auxiliary switch to open the field circuit of a generator or alternator when in the "off" position. Battery switches not incorporating an auxiliary field switch shall be marked with a caution *not* to turn the switch off while the generator or alternator is operating.

b. *Main Switchboard Overload Protection*—A fuse or trip-free circuit breaker shall be located on the load side of the master battery switch in each ungrounded power lead to the main switchboard. The overload protection provided shall be rated at not more than 125 percent of the total load of the switchboard.

c. *Distribution Panel*—Fuses or trip-free circuit breakers shall be provided at the main switchboard in all ungrounded power feeds to distribution panels. Where a main disconnect switch is provided for the panel in the main switchboard, the overload protection shall be located between the switch and the load.

d. *Branch Circuits*—Each ungrounded conductor of a branch circuit shall be provided with suitable overload protection at the point of connection to the main switchboard or distribution panel bus. Each fuse or trip-free circuit breaker used for this purpose shall be rated according to the current rating of the smallest feeder conductor between the fuse or circuit breaker and the load or the maximum current rating of the particular device, whichever is less.

e. *DC Motors*—Circuit supplying motors or motor-operated devices shall be protected by overload devices that are responsive to motor current. Each of these overload devices shall not be rated at more than 125 percent of the full-load current rating of the motor it is protecting.

f. *Generators and Alternators*—Generators and alternators having a current rating in excess of 250 watts shall be provided with overcurrent protection to prevent a continuous output of the device in excess of the maximum current specified by the manufacturer. In providing overcurrent protection consideration must be given to the type of device being protected in order to avoid the development of high voltages that will damage the device or its regulator. In such instances, it will generally be necessary to utilize dual circuit breakers or auxiliary contact circuit breakers that will simultaneously open both the output and field.

(1) Third brush generators shall be protected with simultaneous trip or auxiliary contact circuit breakers to open both the armature lead between the generator and cutout relay and the field lead.

(2) Shunt-wound type generators shall be protected with simultaneous trip or auxiliary contact circuit breakers to open the armature and field leads.

(3) Compound-wound generators shall have overload protection in the ungrounded armature lead only. The shunt field should not be separately protected.

(4) Alternators with electromagnetic fields (rotor) shall be protected with a simultaneous trip or auxiliary contact circuit breakers to open both the ungrounded load rectifier output and the field circuit. The manufacturer's recommendations with respect to the location of the field circuit breaker in the circuit should be followed to avoid the development of transient voltages in the regulator.

5. ALTERNATING CURRENT CIRCUITS

a. *Shore Power Disconnect*—Means shall be provided to disconnect simultaneously all current-carrying conductors from shore as close to the boat's shore-power disconnect plug as possible. For a system that is arranged to be powered both from shore and by means of an on-board generator, a dead-front manual or automatic selector switch shall be provided that will prevent both AC power sources from being used on a given circuit at the same time. The switch used for this purpose shall provide an "off" position. Where two or more switches are used, they preferably should be interconnected to provide an off position as an integral part of their operation.

(1) The main disconnect switch handle shall be readily available.
(2) The general requirements of Section No. 3 shall be heeded.

b. *Overload Protection of Shore-Power Feeders*—Each current carrying conductor from the shore-power inlet receptacle to the main AC switchboard or panel, except the grounded neutral of a three-wire, single-phase 115/230-volt AC service, shall be protected from excessive current by a circuit breaker or fuse having a rating equal to no more than 125 percent of the total normal load. Where port and starboard shore-power inlet receptacles are provided, overload protection shall be provided for each receptacle.

c. *AC Generator Protection*—Overload protection shall be provided at the generator in all ungrounded conductors.

d. *AC Distribution Panels*—Fuses or trip-free circuit breakers shall be provided at the main AC switchboard for all current-carrying conductors to distribution panels. Where a main disconnect switch is provided for the panel in the main switchboard, the overload protection shall be located between the switch and the panel.

e. *AC Branch Circuits*—All current-carrying conductors of branch circuits shall be provided with suitable overload protection at their points of connection to the main switchboard or distribution panel bus. Each fuse or trip-free circuit breaker used for this purpose shall be rated according to either the current rating of the smallest feeder wire between the overload protection device and the load or the maximum current rating of the device being served, whichever is less. Up to four 115-volt AC outlets rated at 15 amperes each may be serviced in the same circuit provided that the circuit is fused at 15 or 20 amperes, depending on the current-carrying capacity of the complete circuit (wiring, connectors, etc.). Special-purpose, 115-volt AC outlets rated above 15 amperes shall be wired separately and, provided that the circuit capacity is adequate, each shall be fused at the rating of the receptacle. Thermal overload devices without manual controls should not be used at the power source.

f. *AC Motors*—Each circuit supplying a motor or motor-operated device shall be protected by an overload device that is responsive to the motor current. The overload device shall not be rated at more than 125 percent of the motor full-load current rating.

Recommended Practices and Standards Covering Alternating Current (AC) Electrical Systems On Boats—ABYC Project E-8 (Proposed)

1. SCOPE

The recommended practices and standards in this section are intended as a guide for the design and installation of AC electrical systems operating at potentials under 300 volts on boats.

2. DEFINITIONS

a. *Ground*—Applies to the potential of the earth's surface and is established by a conducting connection (intentional or accidental) with the earth, including any conductive part of the wetted surface of a hull.

b. *Grounded Conductor*—A current-carrying conductor connected to the side of the source which is intentionally maintained at ground potential.

c. *Grounding Conductor*—A normally non-current carrying conductor provided to connect the exposed metallic enclosures of electrical equipment to ground for the purpose of minimizing shock hazard to personnel.

3. GENERAL

a. All component parts of the system shall be designed, constructed and installed so as to perform with safety under the environmental conditions of continuous exposure to vibration, shock, corrosion in salt atmosphere, and high humidity.

b. The system shall be permanently installed in such a manner as to provide maximum protection against electrical shock for persons on the boat, in the water in contact with the boat and persons in contact with the boat and a grounded object on shore.

c. The system shall be so designed that on-board AC generators and shore power cannot simultaneously feed the same circuit.

4. SYSTEM VOLTAGE

Since boats are essentially mobile units, it is recognized that systems utilizing shore power may be subjected to wide variations of input voltage. Accordingly, in order to permit operation of the system from either 120/208 VAC or 120/240 VAC single phase shore service receptacles, it is recommended that the system be designed for a nominal system voltage of 115/230 VAC. However, boats confined to a specific geographic location may be designed for the available nominal system voltage in the area.

5. SYSTEM VOLTMETER

A system voltmeter installed to read input voltage from shore and/or the output voltage of on-board AC generators, shall be provided and mounted in a readily visible location, except that a voltmeter need not be provided for simple systems with straight resistive loads (lighting and heating, etc.).

6. SYSTEM FREQUENCY

A frequency of 60 cycles per second will be considered standard for AC powered systems on boats.

7. SYSTEM MARKING

a. The system frequency and nominal voltage shall be clearly and prominently marked at the main AC switchboard or other readily visible location.

b. It is recommended that the system voltmeter be marked with voltage limit markings plus and minus ten (10) percent of the designed system nominal voltage.

8. AMBIENT TEMPERATURE

a. Motors, generators and other electrical equipment intended to be installed in machinery spaces shall be designed for operation in an ambient temperature of no less than 50°C (122° F).

b. Where equipment is designed for use outside of machinery spaces in cabins or on deck etc., the designed ambient temperature may be reduced to 40°C (104°F).

9. SHORE POWER POLARITY DEVICES

Polarity indicating devices shall not be used with the systems covered by this standard.

10. PROTECTION OF IGNITION SOURCES

All potential sources of ignition, of devices installed in machinery space, fuel tank spaces or other hazardous areas and of all automatically operated devices, shall be so enclosed or otherwise protected to prevent the ignition of flammable vapors or gases which may surround such devices in service.

11. APPLIANCES AND EQUIPMENT

Appliances and fixed AC electrical equipment used on boats shall be so designed that the current-carrying parts of the device are effectively insulated from all exposed metal parts by a dielectric material suitable for use in damp and/or wet locations, depending on the location of the device and its intended usage.

12. RECEPTACLES

a. Receptacles located on deck, in cockpits or other exposed areas, shall be of an approved water-tight design with self-closing water-tight cap.
b. Receptacles provided on the boat for purposes of connecting the boat's shore power cable, shall be of the reverse service, grounding type.
c. All receptacles shall be of the grounding type.

13. SWITCHES

All switches used in the circuit shall be of an approved type that will simultaneously disconnect both current-carrying conductors.

14. APPLICATION OF RECOGNIZED TYPES OF CIRCUITS

a. *Single Phase 115 Volt Shore Grounded System with Grounding Wire*—This system, wired in accordance with the basic circuit outlined in Section 15 of this standard, shall be used on any non-metallic hulled boat with underwater hardware of metal alloys which are galvanically compatible with normal marine bronzes. This system may also be used with metal-hulled boats where no problems with galvanic corrosion are anticipated, or where protection against galvanic corrosion is provided by means of a suitable cathodic protection system or other suitable means.
b. *115/230 Volt Systems with Shore Grounded Neutral Conductor and Grounding Wire*—This system, wired in accordance with the basic circuit outlined in Section 16 of this standard, shall be used on any non-metallic hulled boat with underwater hardware of metal alloys which are galvanically compatible with normal marine bronze. This system may also be used with metal-hulled boats where no problems with galvanic corrosion are anticipated, or where protection against galvanic corrosion is provided by means of a suitable cathodic protection system or other suitable means.
c. *Isolation Transformer System*—This system, wired in accordance with the basic circuit outlined in Section 17 of this standard, may be used with any boat and shall be used on all metal-hulled boats where galvanic corrosion may occur and where other suitable means of protection against galvanic corrosion is not provided.

15. SINGLE PHASE 115 VOLT SHORE GROUNDED SYSTEM WITH GROUNDING CONDUCTOR

This system utilizes directly, the shore grounded and ungrounded conductors, together with both the shore grounding wire and boat's ground to keep the exposed non-current carrying parts of the system at ground potential. See *Fig. 401*.

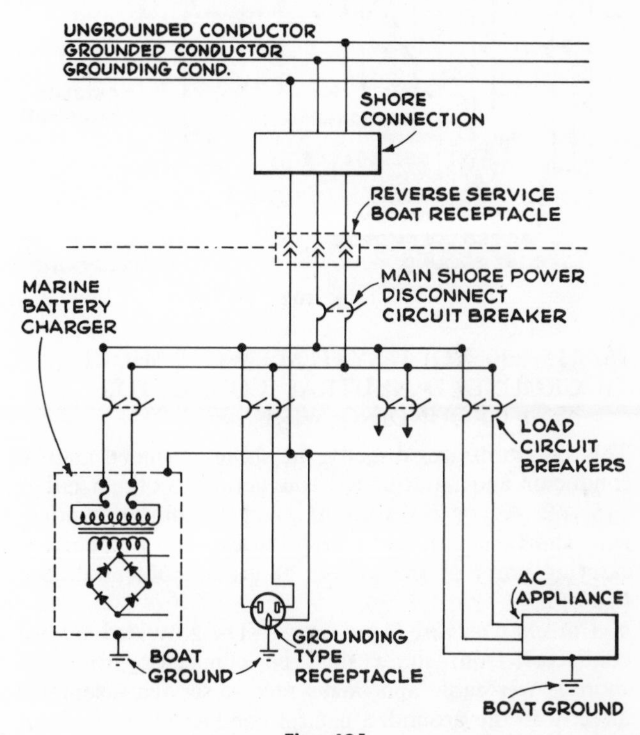

Fig. 401

a. *Current Carrying Conductors*—The grounded and ungrounded shore current carrying conductors shall be connected from the shore power cable and boat's reverse service receptacle to the boat's AC circuit or system, through an overcurrent protective device which simultaneously opens both current carrying conductors. Where the boat's AC electrical system includes multiple circuits, each such circuit shall be protected by simultaneous-trip circuit breakers in accordance with the requirements of ABYC Standard E-5 covering "Overcurrent Protection of Electrical Circuits." Fuses shall not be used. Neither current carrying conductor shall be grounded on the boat.
b. *Grounding Conductor*—The shore grounding conductor shall be connected from the shore-power cable and boat's reverse service receptacle directly to all non-current carrying parts of the AC electrical system and to the boat common ground point without interposing switches or overload protective devices. The boat's ground or shore grounding wire alone will not be considered adequate for purposes of grounding the non-current carrying parts of the AC electrical system.

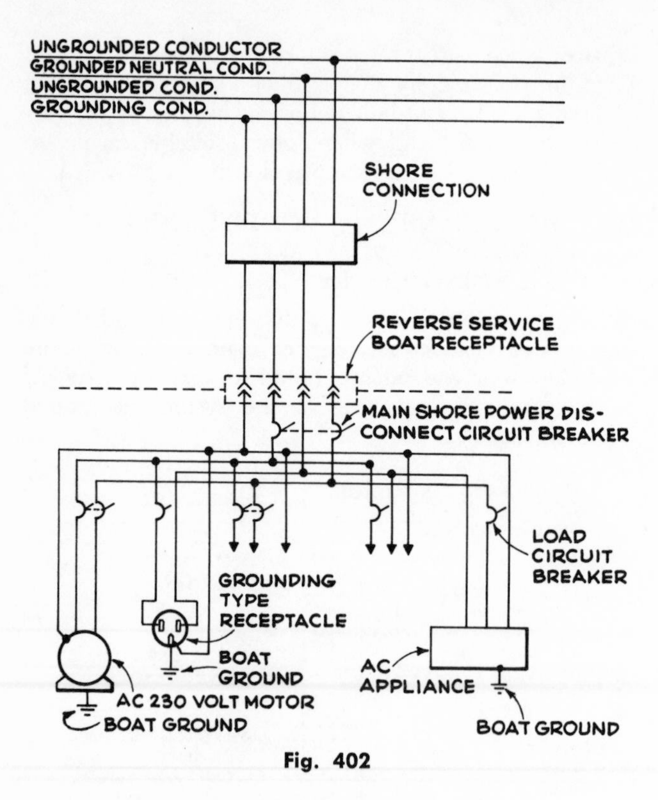

Fig. 402

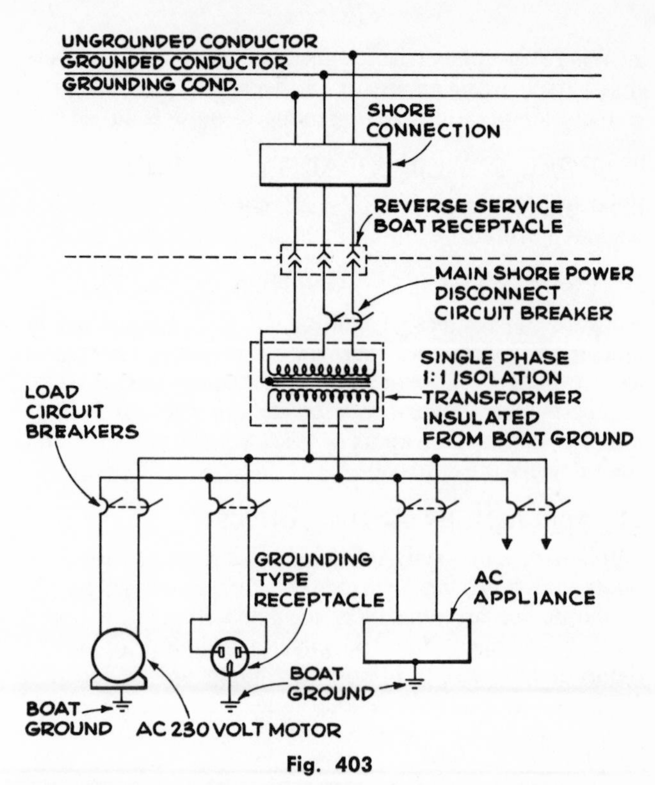

Fig. 403

16. 115/230 VOLT SYSTEMS WITH SHORE GROUNDED NEUTRAL CONDUCTOR AND GROUNDING WIRE

This system utilizes directly, the shore grounded neutral conductor and ungrounded conductors to obtain either 115 volts AC or 230 volts AC, and the shore grounding wire and boat ground to keep the exposed non-current carrying parts of the system at ground potential. See *Fig. 402*.

a. *Current Carrying Conductors*—The grounded neutral conductor from shore shall be connected from the shore-power cable and boat's reverse service receptacle directly to the grounded neutral conductors in the boat AC electrical system without interposing switches or overload protective devices, except as noted in subparagraph (1) below. Each ungrounded shore conductor shall be connected from the shore-power cable and boat's reverse service receptacle to the boat's AC electrical system through a single-pole circuit breaker or fuse in accordance with the requirements of ABYC Standard E-5 covering "Overcurrent Protection of Electrical Circuits." Polarization of conductors must be observed in the shore connections and throughout the entire system. Neither the shore grounded neutral conductor nor ungrounded current carrying conductors shall be grounded on the boat.

(1) An overcurrent protective device may be used in the shore grounded neutral conductor providing the overcurrent protective device simultaneously opens all current carrying conductors in the circuit.

b. *Grounding Conductor*—The shore grounding conductor shall be connected from the shore-power cable and boat's reverse service receptacle directly to all non-current carrying parts of the AC electrical system and the boat common ground point without interposing switches or overload protective devices. The boat's ground or shore grounding wire alone will not be considered adequate for the purpose of grounding the non-current carrying parts of the AC electrical system.

17. ISOLATION TRANSFORMER SYSTEM

This system utilizes an isolation transformer to conductively separate the shore feeder conductors from the electrical load circuits on the boat. The shore grounding conductor is used to ground the non-current carrying parts of the isolation transformer but is conductively separated from the boat ground. See *Fig. 403* and *Fig. 404*.

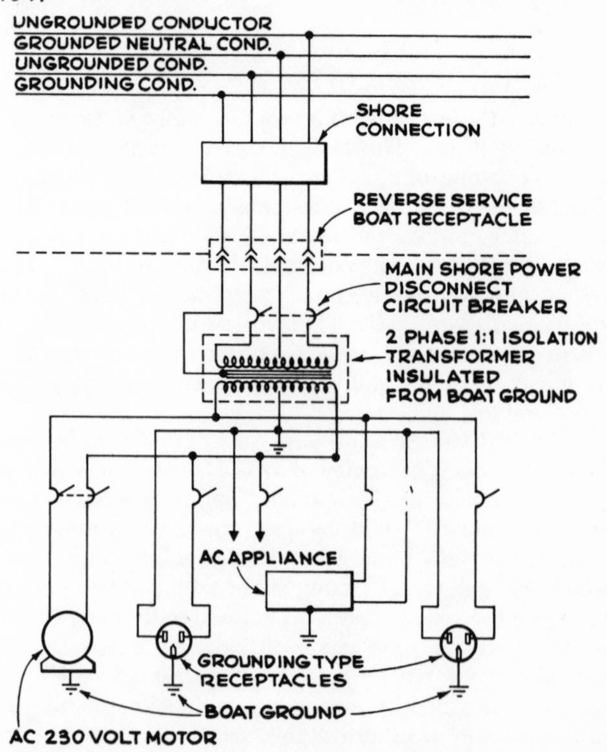

Fig. 404

a. *Current Carrying Shore Conductors*—In 115 volt AC single phase systems, the shore current carrying conductors shall be connected from the shore-power cable and boat's reverse service receptacle to the primary winding of the isolation transformer through an overcurrent protective device which simultaneously opens both current carrying shore conductors. In circuits other than 115 volts single phase, no overcurrent protective device shall be used in the neutral conductor unless the overcurrent protective device simultaneously opens all ungrounded current carrying shore conductors in the circuit. The shore conductors shall not be grounded on the boat. Polarization of conductors must be observed in circuits other than 115 volts single phase.

b. *Shore Grounding Conductor*—The shore grounding conductor shall be connected from the shore-power cable and reverse service shore-power receptacle directly to the non-current carrying parts of the isolation transformer, which in turn shall be insulated from any contact, directly or indirectly with the hull.

c. *Isolation Transformer Secondary Circuit*—It is recommended that the secondary circuit of the isolation transformer used as a power source for the boat's AC system be ungrounded throughout the system, however a polarized system with one side of the circuit purposely held at boat ground potential may be used.

d. *Devices Employing Isolation Transformers*—Approved devices employing isolation transformers, such as battery chargers, may be connected in the same manner as the boat system isolation transformer in accordance with Section 17 a. and b. directly to the shore conductors or to the secondary of the system isolation transformer.

APPENDIX

The information contained in this appendix is to provide supplementary data to aid in the installation of a shore power system.

1. *Receptacle*

The boat should be fitted with a fixed male shore-power inlet receptacle (*Fig. 405*) having a suitable watertight protective cover. Receptacles should conform to the standard configuration illustrated in *Fig. 406* for the maximum current carrying capacity of the boat's shore-power system.

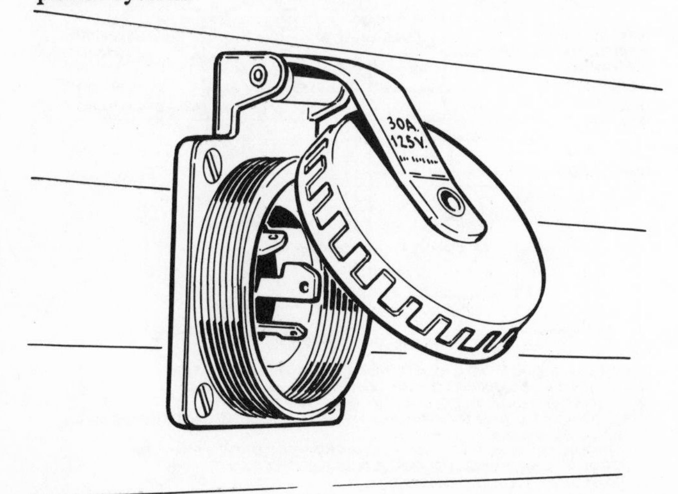

Fig. 405

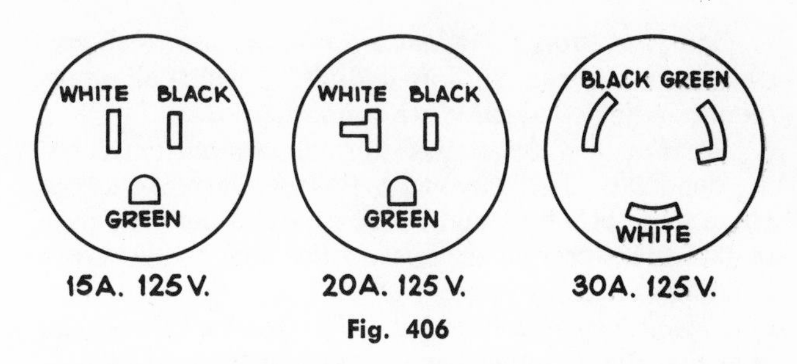

Fig. 406

2. *Cable*

A shore-power cable should be provided which will match the boat's shore-power inlet and extend at least 10 feet beyond the bow or stern. Type "ST" 3 conductor cable is recommended using slightly heavier gauge wire than the system otherwise demands to increase the cable strength and reduce voltage drop between shore and the boat (see *Fig. 407*).

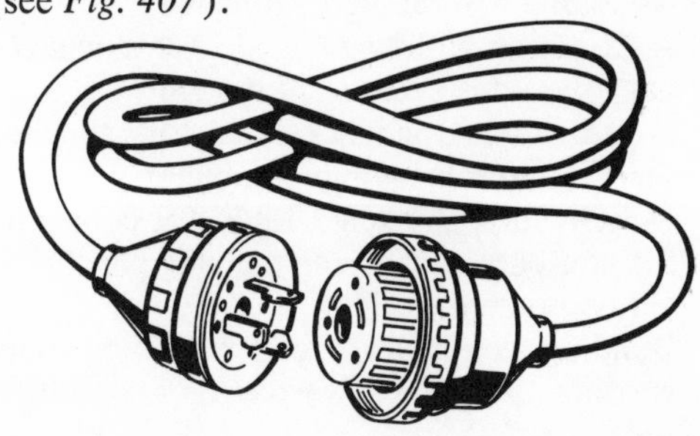

Fig. 407

Recommended practices and Standards Covering Bonding of Direct Current Systems
(ABYC Project E-1)

1. PURPOSE

This standard establishes requirements and recommended methods for bonding direct-current electrical systems:

—to provide a low-resistance electrical path, within the confines of the hull, between otherwise isolated metallic objects, particularly those in common contact with sea water and potentially subject to electrolytic corrosion due to stray currents;

—to prevent possible existence of an electrical potential on exposed metallic enclosures of electrical equipment;

—to provide a low resistance path to ground for voltages that may be considerably in excess of those for which the system is designed, as might occur when lightning strikes, and

—to minimize radio interference.

2. SCOPE

This standard applies to all boats equipped with direct-current electrical systems operating below 50 volts.

3. DEFINITIONS

a. *Ground*—A surface or mass at the potential of the earth's surface, established at this potential by a conducting connection (intentional or accidental) with the earth, including any metal area which forms part of the wetted surface of the hull.

b. *Bonding*—The electrical connection of the exposed, metallic, non-current carrying parts to the ground (negative) side of the direct current system.

c. *Common Bonding Conductor*—An electrical conductor, usually running fore-and-aft, to which all equipment bonding conductors are connected.

d. *Bonding Conductor*—A normal non-current-carrying conductor used to connect the non-current-carrying metal parts of a boat and the non-current-carrying parts of the direct current devices on the boat to the boat's bonding system.

e. *Engine Negative Terminal*—The point on the engine at which the negative battery cable is connected.

4. BONDING SYSTEM

a. *General*

(1) All boats equipped with a permanently installed electrical system shall be equipped with a bonding system.

(2) A bonding system shall consist of
—Common Bonding Conductor
—Common Bonding Conductor connection to negative side of electrical system
—Individual Bonding Conductors connected to the Common Bonding Conductor
—Individual Bonding Conductor connections to the non-current carrying metallic parts of electrical equipment.

(3) Bonding conductors shall be color-coded according to ABYC E-3 "Wiring Indentification on Boats."

(4) Bonding conductors shall be separate from the AC and DC electrical system grounding conductors. (See E-8, "Alternating Current Electrical Systems.")

(5) Bonding conductors shall be permanent, continuous, and at least of the same size as the conductors leading to the equipment to conduct safely any currents likely to be imposed on them due to stray-current leakage or short circuits; and in all instances shall be of sufficient size to permit operation of over-current devices in associated circuits. The engine bonding conductor shall have a current-carrying capacity at least as great as the largest bonding conductor in the bonding system.

(6) In multi-engine installations with cross-over starting systems, the engines shall be bonded together with a cable large enough to carry the starting current. The connections of this bonding cable shall be independent of any other electrical connections to the engines. This bonding cable shall be independent of current-carrying conductors as provided in ABYC E-9, "Direct Current Electrical Systems." *Note: the bonding wire (or cables) to the engine(s) must be large enough to carry cranking current, because a break in the cranking circuit could cause the cranking current to flow in an alternate path, (such as fuel lines).*

(7) The common bonding conductor shall be uninsulated copper or bronze strip, copper tubing, bare tinned-copper wire or insulated copper wire of the proper gauge. Copper braid shall not be used for this purpose.

(a) Common bonding conductors fabricated from copper or bronze strip shall have a minimum thickness of 1/32 inch and be no less than 1/2 inch in width.

(b) Wire, where used as the common bonding conductors, shall be at least no. 8 AWG. *Note: These requirements are based on both physical strength and the ability to make and maintain low-resistance connections, as well as current ratings.*

(8) Where the bonding system is used as a part of the lightning protective system, conductor sizes shall be as specified in ABYC E-4, "Lightning Protection."

b. *Items to be Bonded*—Exposed, metallic non-current-carrying parts of the following items shall have provision for, and be connected to, the bonding system.

(1) Propulsion and auxiliary engines. It is recommended that this bonding conductor be connect to the engine negative terminal.

(2) Metallic enclosures of all electrical apparatus including:

(a) Motor, generator and pump frames or enclosures.
Note: When the metallic frames of electrical accessories are directly attached to the frame of an engine, the engine bonding connection will serve to bond all such accessories.

(b) Cabinets and control boxes.

(c) Radio-equipment cabinets and enclosures of other electronic devices.

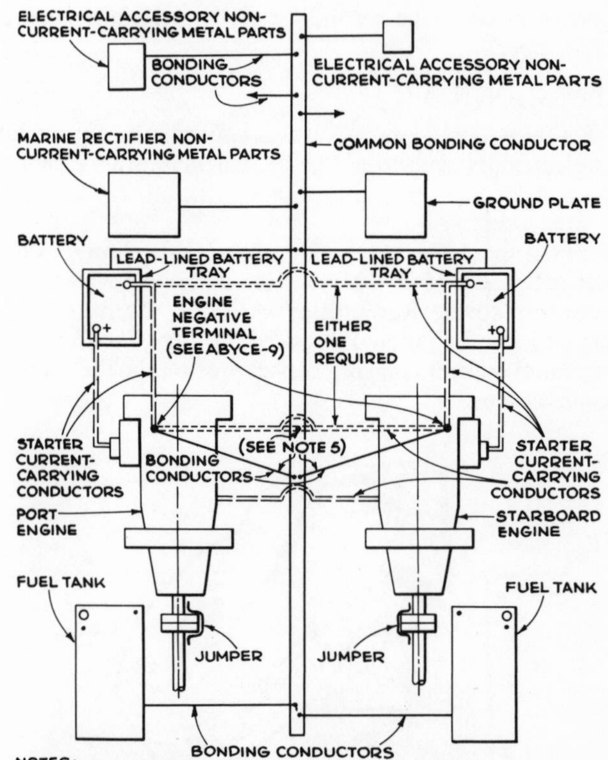

NOTES:
1. WIRES ADJACENT TO EACH OTHER THROUGHOUT SYSTEM
2. ELECTRICAL EQUIPMENT MAY BE INTERNALLY GROUNDED
3. SYSTEM SHOULD BE POLARIZED THROUGHOUT
4. SWITCHBOARD AND DISTRIBUTION PANELS, IF CONSTRUCTED OF METAL, SHALL BE BONDED
5. BONDING CONDUCTORS NOT REQUIRED HERE IF THIS STARTER CURRENT-CARRYING CONDUCTOR IS CONNECTED TO THE COMMON BONDING CONDUCTOR

Fig. 408

(d) Metallic conduit, cable sheaths, or armoring.

(3) Fuel tanks, fuel-fill deck fittings, and electrically operated fuel pumps and valves.

(4) Battery trays (lead-lined).

c. *Items Not Required to be Bonded*

(1) Electrically isolated thru-hull fittings need not be connected to the bonding system (See ABYC E-2, "Cathodic Protection.")

(2) Other electrically isolated metallic items except as recommended in ABYC E-4, "Lightning Protection."

5. INSTALLATION OF BONDING SYSTEM

a. *General*—The method of installation of the bonding system should be as illustrated in *Fig. 408*.

b. *Common Bonding Conductor*—The common bonding conductor shall be installed in a fore-and-aft direction such that it will not be totally or partially submerged in bilge water and in a manner that will permit bonding conductors to be as short and direct as possible.

(1) Splices in the common bonding conductor shall provide electrical continuity and mechanical strength equivalent to the original conductor.

(2) Metal fastenings, when used to secure the common bonding conductor to the hull, shall be equivalent to or more noble than the copper conductor.

(3) Connections shall be accessible for inspection and maintenance.

c. *Bonding Conductor*—Bonding conductors need not be insulated. Installation and connections shall be in accordance with ABYC E-9, "Direct Current Electrical Systems."

6. METAL-HULL VESSELS

a. *General*—The hull of a metal-hull vessel may serve as the common bonding conductor.

(1) Any item to be bonded (See paragraph 4 b) not in contact with the hull requires a bonding conductor to the hull.

(2) If the item to be bonded is connected to a thru-hull fitting galvanically incompatible with the hull, it shall be insulated from the thru-hull fitting and the thru-hull fitting shall be insulated from the hull.

MISCELLANEOUS ELECTRICAL PROJECTS

Poor Man's Radar Reflector

We have "borrowed" this item from Pete Smyth's old "TLC" column in the February, 1969 issue of *Motor Boating*. He gives credit to P/C Anson G. Hoyt, who in turn acknowledges borrowing it from the Coral Ridge Power Squadron Newsletter, who in turn borrowed it from something called "Twin Lights." It has been around.

Buy a 36″ square sheet of aluminum at your hard-

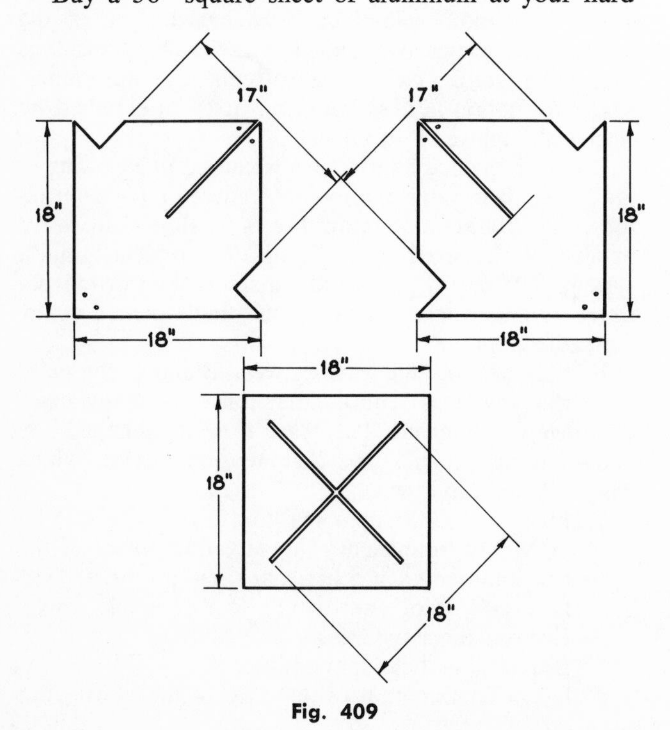

Fig. 409

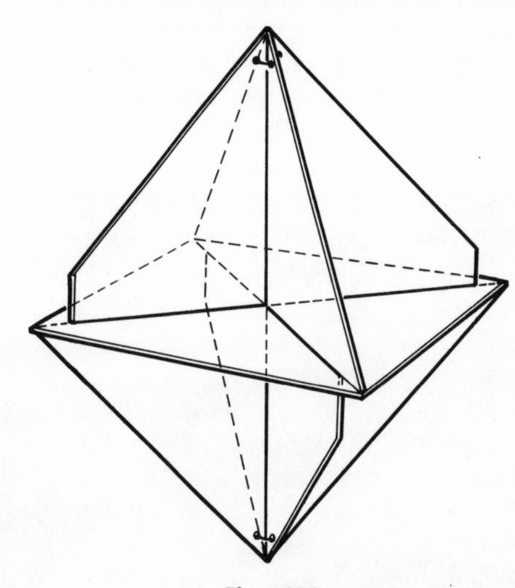

Fig. 410

ware store or building supply store. Cut the sheet into four 18″ squares. You need just three of these pieces to make the reflector, cutting them as indicated in *Fig. 409*. Drill the four holes as indicated on each of the two oddly-shaped pieces. Assemble, when needed, as shown in *Fig. 410* and suspend from any high location on your boat. It is said to make a little wooden boat show up like the *U.S.S. Missouri* on a radar screen.

When not needed, disassemble the screen and store it under a mattress, or in any other convenient flat spot.

Protection for Depth Finder

Here are two suggestions for housings that can be used to protect electronic gear that must be mounted in a relatively exposed location. While both are shown

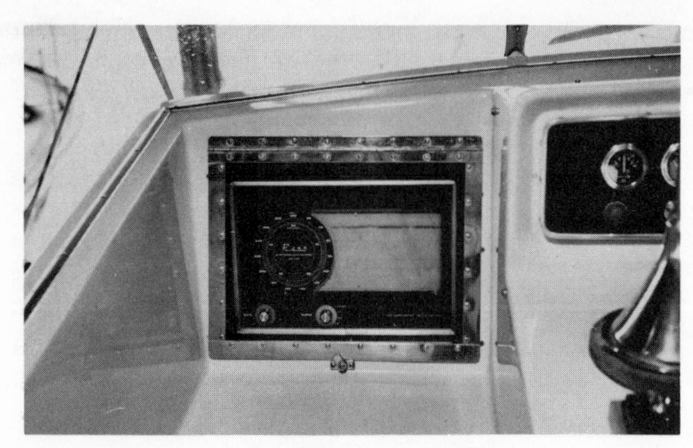

Fig. 411

with depth finders, similar units could be used to house radio receivers or direction finders (the DF would be removed from the housing during use, of course).

Fig. 411 shows a locker opening cut in a fiberglass bulkhead, and a hinged sheet of Plexiglas installed as a cover. Chrome plated brass trim finishes off the three edges of the Plexiglas not edged with the hinge, and a turn button opposite the hinge keeps the whole cover securely closed. With this arrangement, the depth finder can easily be operated and read, and yet it can be disconnected and removed from the boat for storage at home when not in use.

If there's no suitable bulkhead with space behind it for the above unit, consider the arrangement shown in *Fig. 412*. This is an attractive teak box built onto the side of a flying bridge. The Plexiglas door arrangement is similar to that for the built-in compartment. Again, "quick disconnect" in the power and transducer lines make it possible to remove the depth finder for storage at home. Both photos are by Gordon Manning.

Fig. 412

Fig. 413

Hinged Radio Antenna Clamp

In the normal mounting, an antenna clamp projects out from the side of the cabin in such a way that it easily snags your clothing—or your body—as you work past it along a narrow side deck. Gordon Manning's photo, *Fig. 413*, shows how one smart boatman minimized this particular hazard: he simply hinged the clamp to its mounting block. When it isn't holding the antenna down, it hangs down out of the way beneath the mounting block.

All it takes is a short length of piano hinge bolted to the clamp base, and to the underside of the mounting block. Be sure to drill a couple of shallow holes in the block to provide clearance for the bolt heads in the clamp base.

Suppress Radio Frequency Interference

The best marine radiotelephone can be almost useless if your boat's engine is creating so much static interference the radio signals can't be heard. One of the easiest, least expensive, and most rewarding projects is to remove ignition-caused radio frequency interference. The information here is based on material supplied by electrical engineer Lou Heiner.

Radio frequency interference is caused by sparking at the plugs, distributor cap, points, generator (or alternator), and voltage regulator. *Fig. 414* shows the wave pattern of the spark at the plug of a typical ignition system. The useful part of the spark is the portion between A and B; the rest is "hash" that's picked up by the radiotelephone.

By flattening out the wave between B and C, the noise from this source is reduced materially; in many cases completely eliminated. This wave train is "damped" by adding resistance into the high tension circuit, which can be done in four ways:

1. Place a 10,000 ohm resistor (Erie type L7VR-1OME or equivalent) in the center tower of the distributor, and a 5,000 ohm resistor (Erie type L7VR-5ME or equivalent) in each cable tower.
2. Use resistance type spark plug cable.
3. Use resistor type spark plugs.
4. Use a combination of any two of the above, but *not* all three.

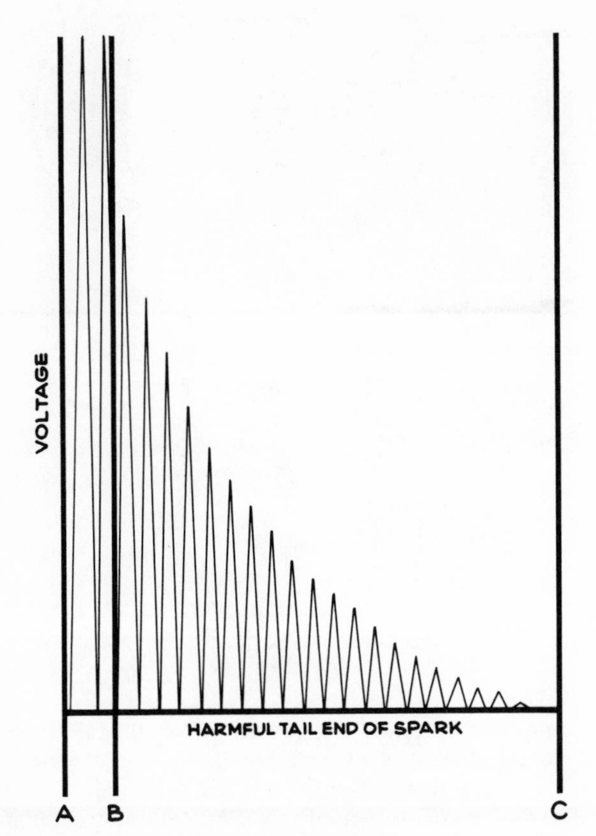

Fig. 414. Discharge across spark gap.

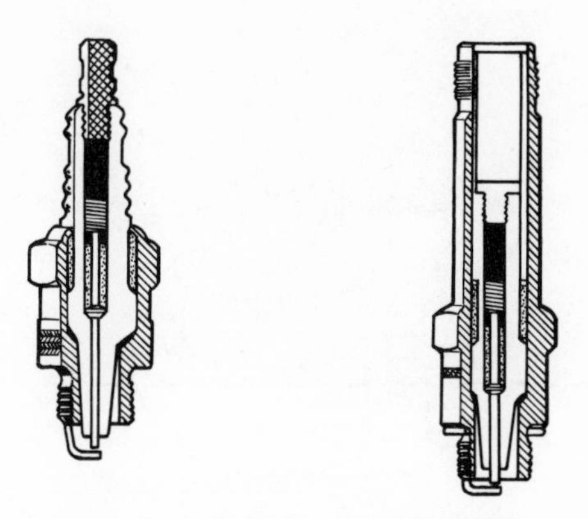
Fig. 416. Left: cross section of typical unshielded resistor spark plug. Right: typical shielded resistor plug.

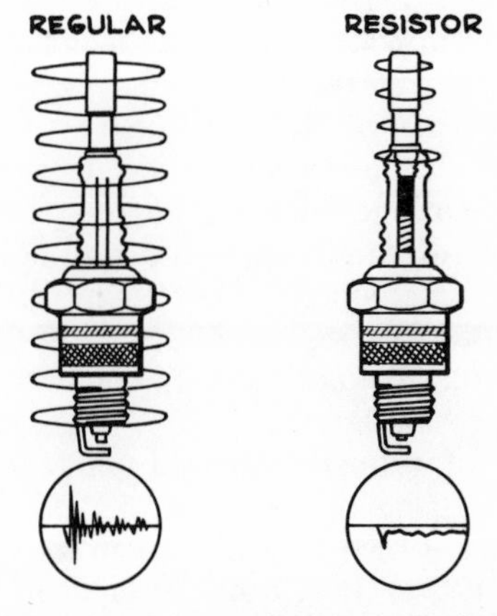

Fig. 417. Radio interference characteristics from plugs.

Fig. 415 illustrates the combination of resistor type plugs and resistor cables, and resistor plugs with resistors in the distributor cap towers. Note that some ignition systems incorporate a resistor in the distributor's rotor, which acts the same as an internal resistor-suppressor in the central tower.

The standard resistor type plug is shown in *Fig. 416A*; and it is this type that usually is used in marine applications. The shielded type, *Fig. 416B*, is more expensive, but it is waterproof and explosion proof. *Fig. 417* shows how the resistor plug flattens out the useless part of the spark discharge.

Resistor cables use a resistance center instead of a metallic conductor. They may be identified simply as "radio" or "radio resistance" cables, but present day standards specify two types: HTLR (High Tension Low Resistance—3,000 to 7,000 ohms per foot); and HTHR (High Tension High Resistance—6,000 to 12,000 ohms per foot). Normally, these cables are purchased in sets with cables pre-cut to proper lengths for the particular engine, and with the proper terminals at each end.

Note that care must be used in handling these cables. Never pull on the cable itself when removing it from a plug or the distributor cap! Pull on the boot or the terminal. Never cut resistor cable to attach a screw-on suppressor, and never try to repair an end terminal. Replace the entire cable—and preferably the entire set.

If you have no marine telephone, but you're picking up engine static on your broadcast band receiver, resistor type plugs, or resistor cable, will generally be all that's needed to eliminate the interference. For radiotelephones, however, use of the resistors in the dis-

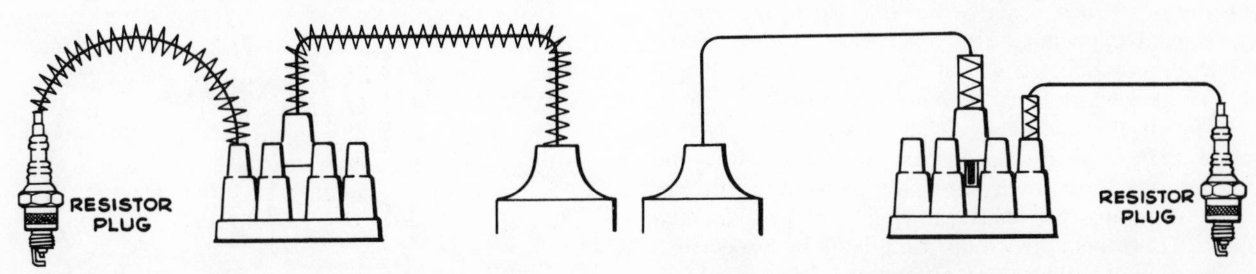

Fig. 415. You can generally choose either (A) resistor plugs with suppression cable, or (B) resistor plugs with a 10,000 ohm resistor suppressor in the center of the distributor, and a 5,000 ohm suppressor in each of the towers. Many operators of heavy duty boats prefer (B). It is not recommended that these two alternatives be combined.

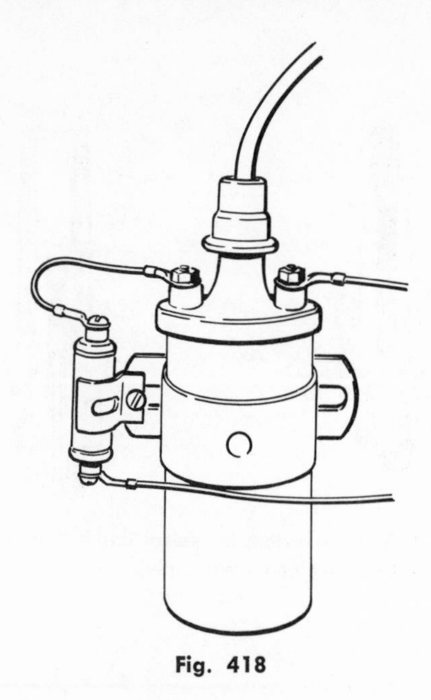

Fig. 418

tributor towers in conjunction with standard cable and resistor type plugs is recommended.

As a high-tension spark is generated between the rotor tip and the cable inserts within the distributor cap, it is also a source of interference. The best prevention here is a clean, new rotor and cap, as the most noise is caused by dirty, worn components. Don't try to file away corrosion on a rotor tip; replace it!

Breaker point "bounce" at high engine speed creates high frequency interference over the entire radio spectrum. Clean, properly-adjusted points reduce this—and improve engine performance.

Next install a 0.1 MFD feed-through coaxial capacitor (Sprague 48-P-9 or JN-17-907 or equivalent) as close to the coil primary terminal as possible, between the primary terminal and the ignition switch. This is shown in *Fig. 418*. At the time you do this, remove the coil mounting bracket, clean any paint away from it and the engine block where they make contact, and reinstall it.

If your engine has a generator, a worn commutator can generate interference that's heard as a high-pitched whine. If the commutator appears to be rough and uneven, or if the brushes are worn to half or more of their original length, the generator is due for an overhaul.

When the generator is in good condition, remove the factory-installed by-pass capacitor and install a 0.5 MFD coaxial capacitor (Sprague 48-P-18, rated at 40 amperes, or JN-17-965, or equivalent). *Fig. 419* shows how this is to be grounded to the generator frame under the screw provided for the original by-pass capacitor. The wire that goes to the Armature terminal on the generator is removed and is reconnected to one end of the coaxial capacitor. The other side of the coaxial capacitor is connected with a short (3″ or less) length of #10 gauge wire to the Armature terminal, as shown.

Most, if not all, new engines have an alternator, rather than a generator. It has no commutator, and brushes ride on smooth slip rings. However, worn or rough slip rings can cause a whine on the radiotelephone. Have them "trued up" on a lathe by a specialist.

The diode rectifier of an alternator system should be completely noiseless, but a defective diode can cause noise. In this case a 0.5 MFD capacitor (JN-17-965

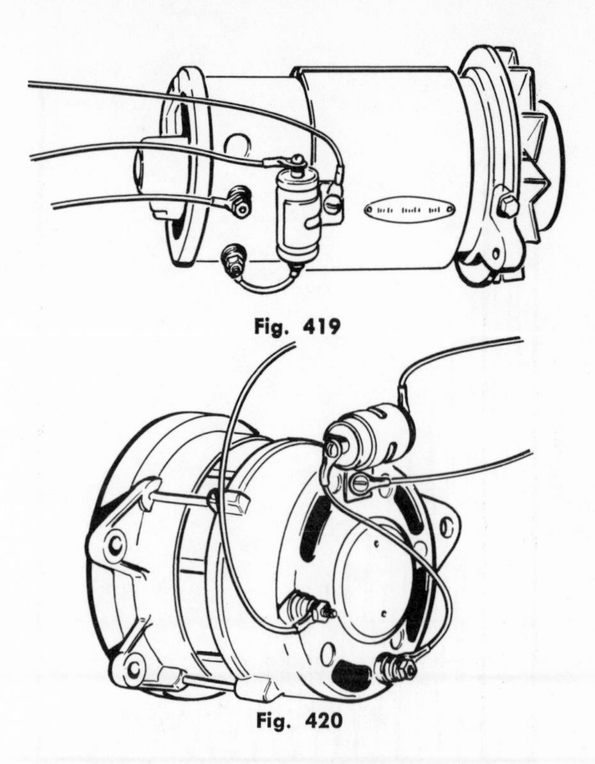

Fig. 419

Fig. 420

or equivalent) should be connected to the alternator output terminal as shown in *Fig. 420*. Do not connect any capacitor to the alternator Field terminal!

In some cases, to completely eliminate alternator interference, it may be necessary to use shielded wire between the alternator and regular terminals. Be sure to ground both ends of the metallic shield.

If your voltage regulator is causing interference, it's heard as an erratic popping that changes only slightly with engine speed. If your engine has a generator, mount two coaxial 0.5 MFD capacitors (Sprague 48-P-18, or JN-17-965 or equivalent) rated at 40 amperes, in series with the battery lead and the regular BAT terminal, and the generator armature lead and the regulator ARM terminal. This is shown in *Fig. 421*. Shielded wire from the generator armature and field terminals to the corresponding terminals on the regulator also helps.

An alternator regulator is similar to that used with a generator, except that it may be a single control or a double control system. Install a 0.5 MFD coaxial capacitor (Sprague 48-P-18, or JN-17-965, or equivalent) at the Ignition (I) terminal of a single unit regulator. On a double unit regulator, install the same type of capacitor on the battery terminal. Be sure the case of the capacitor is grounded.

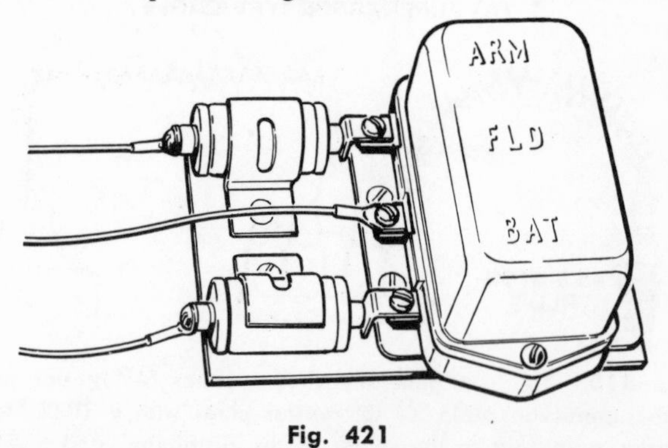

Fig. 421

5. MECHANICAL SYSTEMS

Power Steering for a Houseboat

This power steering rig was designed by A. T. Stretch to counteract the torque of a pair of left-hand stern drives on his 43′ houseboat when use of counter-rotating propellers was not a feasible solution to the problem.

In this case, Bendix automotive parts were used, including a hydraulic pump, a piston and cylinder assembly, and a valve assembly. These were purchased from a wrecker; a heat exchanger for the hydraulic fluid was purchased new. Total cost for parts was less than $50.

The piston had an 8″ travel in the cylinder, which just matched the travel of the tiller connecting bar. The ball joint was removed from the tiller connecting bar, and the hole in the bar was enlarged as necessary. Then the cylinder was bolted in place, through the pivot end, using the rubber-mounted joint on the cylinder. See "F" in *Fig. 501*.

In a machine shop, a bracket was made up to take the piston's thrust. It is a "Y"-shaped fitting made of 1/8″ x 2″ steel, with mounting holes in the legs, and a hole in the bottom of the "Y" for the end of the piston. Stainless 3/8″ bolts were used to secure the bracket to the transom.

A right angle adapter bracket was needed to connect the boat's steering gear Bowden rod to the hydraulic valve trigger. The original steering rod universal joint was cut off short, and an adapter plate was welded to the cut-off end. This right angle adapter plate had a tapered hole drilled in it to match the taper of the valve trigger, and the opposite end of the plate was drilled and tapped to match the threads at the end of boat's steering system Bowden rod. The Bowden rod socket then was removed, and the adapter plate screwed on in its place. Then the plate was placed over the valve trigger, and the securing nut was tightened.

To mount the valve assembly, it was necessary to cut the valve mounting rod to a length that would fit within the length of the tiller connecting bar, with the valve located at the mid point of the tiller connecting bar. The rod end was bent as shown at "C" in *Fig. 501*, and the section that faces the tiller bar was ground flat. Two 9/32″ holes were drilled through the mounting bar, and matching holes were drilled through the tiller connecting bar. A spacer, also with matching holes was inserted between the two bars, and the mounting bar was fastened in place with 1/4″ x 2½″ bolts. The space provides ample clearance for the valve's hydraulic fittings and lines.

At this point, travel was checked, so that the steering wheel would be in the amidships position when the stern drive tiller bars were parallel to the keel. Adjustment was made by loosening the clamp around the

Fig. 501. Bowden rod "A" engages valve assembly "B" which is bolted to the steering arm bar "C." Y-bracket on transom "D" takes thrust of hydraulic piston "E." Cylinder pivots on center of steering arm bar, "F."

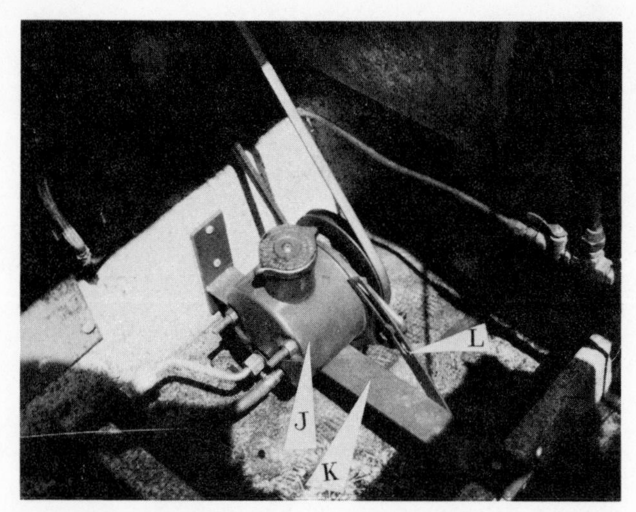

Fig. 502. Hydraulic pump "J" pivots on angle iron "K" mounted between stringers in bilge. Slotted bar "L" affords adjustment of belt tension.

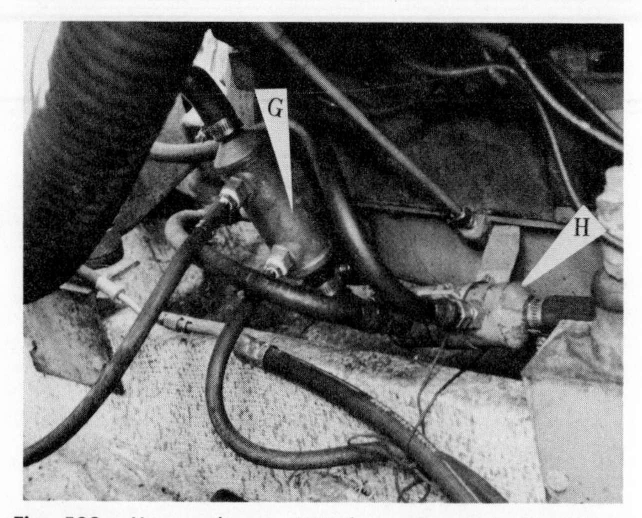

Fig. 503. Heat exchanger "G" for cooling hydraulic fluid is connected in series to output of engine transmission heat exchanger "H."

Bowden cable housing, and sliding the housing in the desired direction. Travel should be equal on both sides of dead center.

It also is possible to adjust travel by loosening the clamp on the valve mounting shaft, and screwing the mounting bar in or out.

The hydraulic pump was mounted on an angle iron bracket bolted between stringers in the bilge, as shown in *Fig. 502*. It pivots on its mounting, and the slotted bar "L" permits adjustment of belt tension. The power takeoff is a pulley that was welded to the face of the engine's water pump pulley. A straight stick laid across this drive pulley was used to determine the correct alignment of the hydraulic pump pulley. Note that in this installation, the hydraulic pump was located on the side opposite the engine's other belts to minimize bearing wear on the water pump, and the hydraulic pump mounting bracket was tilted to correspond to engine tilt, to minimize belt wear.

A Chrysler 260 hydraulic transmission heat exchanger was used to keep the hydraulic fluid in the power steering system cooled. Without it, in a marine installation, the fluid could accumulate enough heat to smoke, according to Stretch.

The outlet hose between the boat engine's heat exchanger and the exhaust manifold was cut, the new heat exchanger was installed "in series" with the first.

Hydraulic lines were made up to length at an auto parts store. The old fittings had been left on the Bendix units when purchased, so it was possible to show the exact terminals that were neeled. High pressure flexible hose assemblies were chosen, rather than copper, to compensate for steering bar movement and vibration problems.

One hose leads from the return side of the valve unit to the heat exchanger, and another runs from the exchanger to the low-pressure inlet on the pump. A high pressure line runs from the pump outlet back to the valve inlet, and two short high pressure lines connect the valve to the cylinder unit.

With the installation complete, the system was filled with Type A, Suffix A hydraulic fluid, and tested for faults. First the Bowden rod was disconnected, and the engine was started. After a check at all fittings for leaks, pliers were used to grasp the trigger and push on it. If the tiller moves in the direction pushed in this test, all is well. If it moves in the opposite direction, reverse the lines to the cylinder.

Next the Bowden rod was re-connected, and the steering wheel was turned back and forth, with the engine idling, to purge the system of air. Hydraulic fluid was added as necessary. After a brief test ride, the fluid level was rechecked.

Stretch notes that although the hydraulic pump has a built-in overload relief system, it is not advisable to force the steering wheel against the stops when making a turn. He did find that steering was much easier, and that his boat held a straight course with "hands off" unless a good sea was running.

Solid Walnut Ship's Wheel

Here's a traditional ship's wheel suitable for most sailboats with wheel steering, and for power boats as well. Of course size of the wheel should be compatable with size of your boat; most power boats need a wheel of no more than 24″ in diameter. The 33″ diameter wheel illustrated here (*Fig. 504*) is suitable for sailboats in the 30′ to 40′ range; larger yachts might use wheels from 36″ to 48″ in diameter—but these should have eight spokes, spaced at 45 degree angles around the rim.

Nick A. Milin, Jr., designed this wheel, and he notes that its construction is "not a project for the jacknife carpenter; precision is essential. The woodwork is intricate in spots, the angular measurements are critical, and power tools are essential for the repetitive cuts." Here is how Milin describes the project:

"Accuracy can be guaranteed by the use of the triangular jig shown (*Fig. 505, Detail A*). Take time to make an accurate jig, and you may rest assured that each piece will be precise and correct.

"Any small wood lathe will do for turning the spokes.

Fig. 504

The rim sections are not turned on a lathe; they are bandsawed from planed lumber, edged with a shaper or hand router, and fastened between the spokes. After assembly and shaping, the outer rim is sliced into two equal parts on the table saw and glued to the completed wheel. Let me assure the reader that this is the easiest and *best* way to make the rim. Turning a section such as this on the lathe requires caution and considerable experience.

"Begin construction by cutting six spoke blanks from 2″ walnut reduced to 1⅝″ dressed planks. Finish the blanks exactly to size, since the square center portion of each will become the mating surface for the rim sections. You may prefer to cut a template from sheet metal, or attempt the duplicate spokes from direct measurements. I'm convinced that templates are a wise investment unless you are a master at duplicate turnings. When your spokes are sanded smooth, trim and finish the rounded ends by hand. Remember that the square sections should have the corners sanded smooth on the lathe before you remove them.

"The hub may be turned from a bandsawed disc of 2″ walnut. Round the edges to a ⅛″ radius and bore the proper center hole for your steering shaft on the lathe. Sand the hub smooth and mark the centers for the spoke holes. This operation is critical, so lay the lines accurately, and use care to insure a perfect 60 degree interval between the spokes. If your lathe has an index head, use it to mark the centers. Then mount the hub on a snug-fitting 1″ pivot dowel clamped to a drill press table. Tilt the table to a vertical position, and bore the holes with a 1″ power type boring bit. Bore the first hole, then rotate the hub 60 degrees on its pivot, clamp, and bore the other holes in succession.

"Outline the six inner rim sections of the wheel on a 1¼″ planed walnut plank. If you draw as shown in *Fig. 505, Detail B*, waste will be minimized, and the grain will run properly on each piece. Cut the sections on a band saw, and sand them to a perfect arc on both inner and outer edges. Then, using a ½″ radius molding cutter, round all curved surfaces evenly.

"You are now ready to joint the ends of each inner rim section. Construct the triangular jig as shown in *Fig. 505, Detail A*. Strike off index marks as shown, and slip the rim sections between them, sanding the edges of the rim sections until each one seats snugly against the jig surfaces. This will insure perfect joints when you assemble the wheel.

"The mortised keys between the spokes and rim sections must be fitted carefully since they will determine alignment during the gluing process. If you have a mortising attachment for your drill press, the process is simple. If not, mark and cut the recesses with a ⅜″ chisel. Notice that the key is tapered to allow room for the rim sections to slide over the key. Seat the keys and make a trial assembly before attempting the final gluing.

"The wheel must be assembled in three distinct operations. The flat spokes are first glued into the hub and clamped to a flat surface to insure alignment. Make sure that the mortised sides of the spokes face each other, and that the 60 degree angles are maintained. Use *waterproof* resin glue and follow the maker's instructions to the letter in mixing the glue. Allow ample time for the glue to set, then clamp the hub to a flat circular disc of heavy plywood about 36″ in diameter. Fit the inner rim sections and the mortise keys into position. Study *Detail C, Fig. 505* carefully, then nail wooden blocks around the edges of the disc between the spokes and insert sliding wedges against them to exert equal pressure on the individual rim sections, forcing them into position between the spokes. When your trial assembly is complete, and you are sure that each section mates accurately, slip the rim sections apart, one at a time, and glue. Don't waste time when gluing; join all six sections quickly and make the final adjustments with your sliding wedges and clamps. If

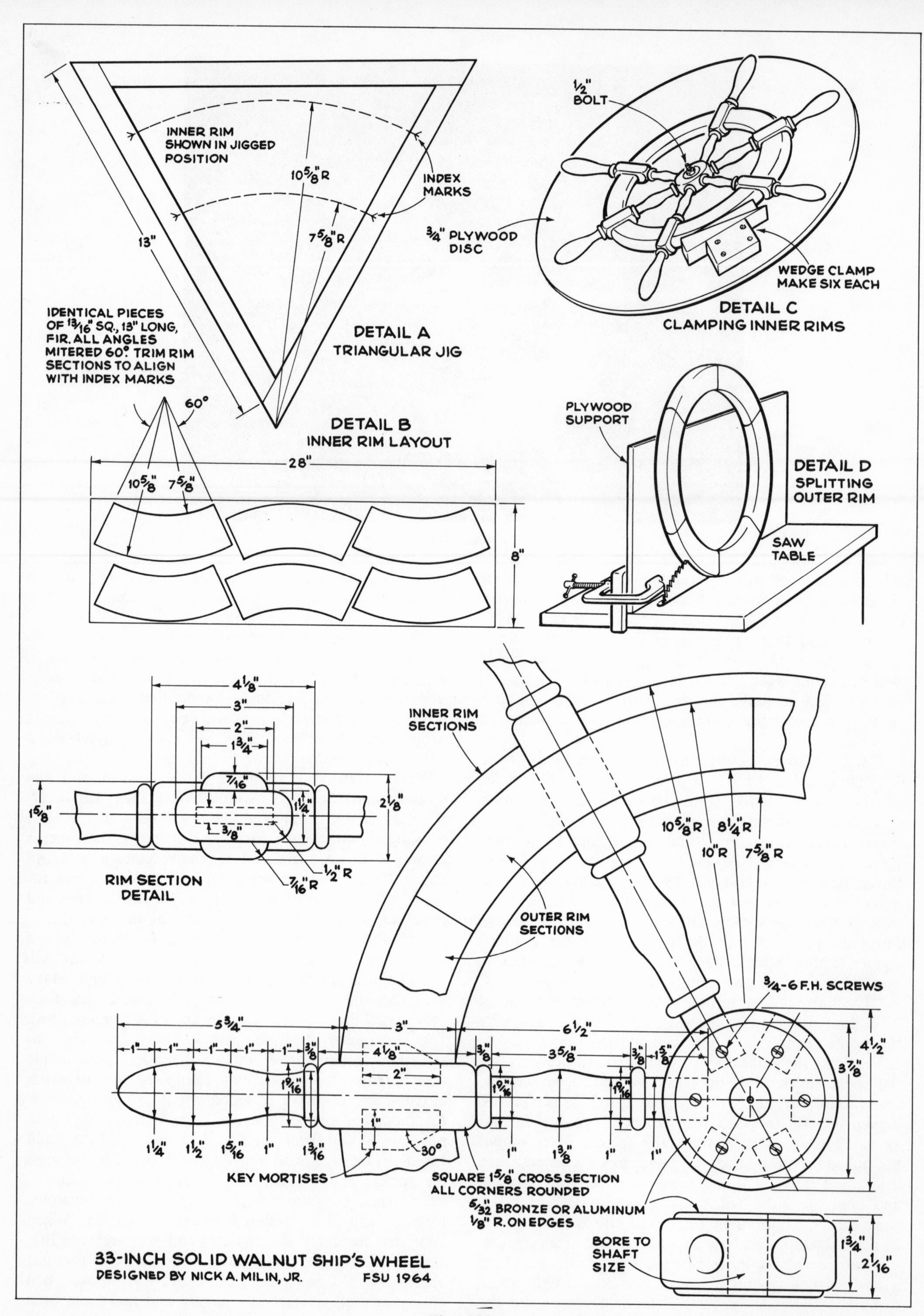

INNER RIM
SHOWN IN JIGGED
POSITION
10 5/8" R
INDEX
MARKS
7 5/8" R
13"
IDENTICAL PIECES
OF 13/16" SQ., 13" LONG,
FIR. ALL ANGLES
MITERED 60°. TRIM RIM
SECTIONS TO ALIGN
WITH INDEX MARKS
DETAIL A
TRIANGULAR JIG
1/2"
BOLT
3/4" PLYWOOD
DISC
WEDGE CLAMP
MAKE SIX EACH
DETAIL C
CLAMPING INNER RIMS
60°
DETAIL B
INNER RIM LAYOUT
28"
10 5/8
7 5/8
8"
PLYWOOD
SUPPORT
DETAIL D
SPLITTING
OUTER RIM
SAW
TABLE
4 1/8"
3"
2"
1 3/4"
7/16"
1 5/8"
1 1/4"
2 1/8"
3/8"
1/2" R
7/16" R
RIM SECTION
DETAIL
INNER RIM
SECTIONS
10 5/8" R
8 1/4" R
10" R
7 5/8" R
OUTER RIM
SECTIONS
3/4-6 F.H. SCREWS
5 3/4"
3"
6 1/2"
1"
3/8"
4 1/8"
2"
3 5/8"
1 5/8"
1 9/16"
4 1/2"
3 7/8"
1 1/4"
1 1/2"
1 5/16"
1 3/16"
30°
1 3/8"
KEY MORTISES
SQUARE 1 5/8" CROSS SECTION
ALL CORNERS ROUNDED
6/32" BRONZE OR ALUMINUM
1/8" R. ON EDGES
BORE TO
SHAFT
SIZE
1 3/4"
2 1/16"
33-INCH SOLID WALNUT SHIP'S WHEEL
DESIGNED BY NICK A. MILIN, JR.
FSU 1964

Fig. 505

your keys are fitted properly, your wheel will slip together easily and quickly.

"Now begin the outer rim sections. These are cut in the same way as the others, but assembled in one unit. Cut six sections from 1″ planed walnut, and glue them in a circle, paying close attention to the joints. The pieces may be cut slightly oversize, allowing you to sand them into a perfect circle. All four edges should now be rounded with a 3⁄8″ or 7⁄16″ radius shaper cutter. Then clamp an upright 24″ square of plywood to the fence of your table saw to guide the rim accurately, and carefully slit the circular section into two equal parts as shown in *Detail D, Fig. 505.* Removal of the 1⁄8″ saw kerf will leave two rim sections, cut to their 7⁄16″ final dimension. Remember to plan your moves and check your work constantly.

"The outer rim sections may now be laid on the wheel and inletted, making sure that the joints are spaced halfway between spokes. Mark the recesses carefully, and make all your measurements with the rim in the same position. Carefully recess the outer rim to allow each spoke a snug fit. When the sections mate properly, glue the rims to the wheel using at least one clamp between each spoke.

"Do not be overly generous with the glue! Brush a *thin* layer on the mating surfaces, and wipe the excess from every joint before it stains the adjoining wood. If you have sanded all parts before assembly, your wheel is almost done. A final sanding with 6/0 paper will give you the satin finish that characterizes walnut.

"Finishing should begin with a good paste wood filler. Don't use the filler in its original light color. It will mark the wood with beige streaks that are almost impossible to remove. Depending on your own preference, you may add various stains to the filler to match or darken the wood. Make sample runs on scrap pieces until you are sure of your ground. Follow instructions for wiping off the excess.

"Final finish is a matter of personal taste. There are any number of excellent finishing techniques, and the author can vouch for only one basic premise—*keep it simple!*

"The final step consists of fastening a bronze or aluminum plate on each side of the hub to take the strain of the mounting nut. The plates should be edged on a lathe with a 1⁄8″ radius curve. Drill and countersink the plates for matching flathead 3⁄4″ screws. If your steering shaft has a keyway, file a matching slot in the hub and insert a brass key before mounting your wheel."

FLYING BRIDGE CONTROLS

Add a Flying Bridge

Many add-on flying bridge installations turn out to be a disappointment at the best, or downright dangerous at the worst, because fundamentals of hull design, and the requirements of control and steering systems, are misunderstood. Harold C. Rickborn, a naval architect and marine engineer, tells exactly what must be known before such an installation is attempted.

His information regarding controls and steering is so good it is recommended reading for all boatmen who want to know more about these often neglected systems.—Ed.

By Harold C. Rickborn

Flying bridge comfort and convenience can be added to most express and sedan cruisers, and houseboats, if proper consideration is given to the size of the boat, the strength of its cabin structure, and the types of engine and steering control systems that are installed.

The technical problems involved have been simplified by a decade of concentration by one small company, Rickborn Industries, Inc., of Bayville, N.J. The firm offers a variety of one-piece "self-fitting" flying bridges styled to blend with the architecture of boats ranging from the smallest day cruiser that safely can take such an installation to the largest houseboats. In addition to units sold for custom add-on jobs, they are used today as original equipment by more than a dozen prominent boat builders, including some of the biggest boat producers in America. Based on Rickborn Industries' experience, here is what you should know about a flying bridge installation.

Let us start by describing a good flying bridge. It should be large enough to contain the necessary equipment to operate the boat, be comfortable and accommodate the operator and a guest or two within the command area and of a size that will look well and still be small enough to keep the sail area to a minimum. Sail area is any fixed vertical portion of a vessel, and as the term implies, such vertical surfaces exert pressure against the hull in direct proportion to the force of wind blowing against them, the same as a sail on a sailboat transmits the wind pressure from the sail through the mast to move the vessel through the water.

The size of the bridge should not only be governed by sail area, but also by weight factors. One must consider the weight of the bridge, its equipment and the passengers, particularly when all seating accommodations are occupied. It takes a pretty good size boat to accommodate close to a half ton of weight, ten feet above the water line. Still this is a fair example of the weight we are dealing with above the windshield of many 32-footers. A light weight bridge (65 pounds), can very easily total 250 pounds or more, including windshield, railings, ladder, seats, controls, steering gear, bridge cover, anchor light, interior trim panels, etc., and may hold three or four adult passengers as well.

Two factors are of prime concern when contemplating such a project. First is the stability of the boat. If the center of gravity is raised too high, the boat will become top heavy. Second is the strength of the cabin on which the bridge will be located. It must be capable of bearing the vertical load pressures and also be strong

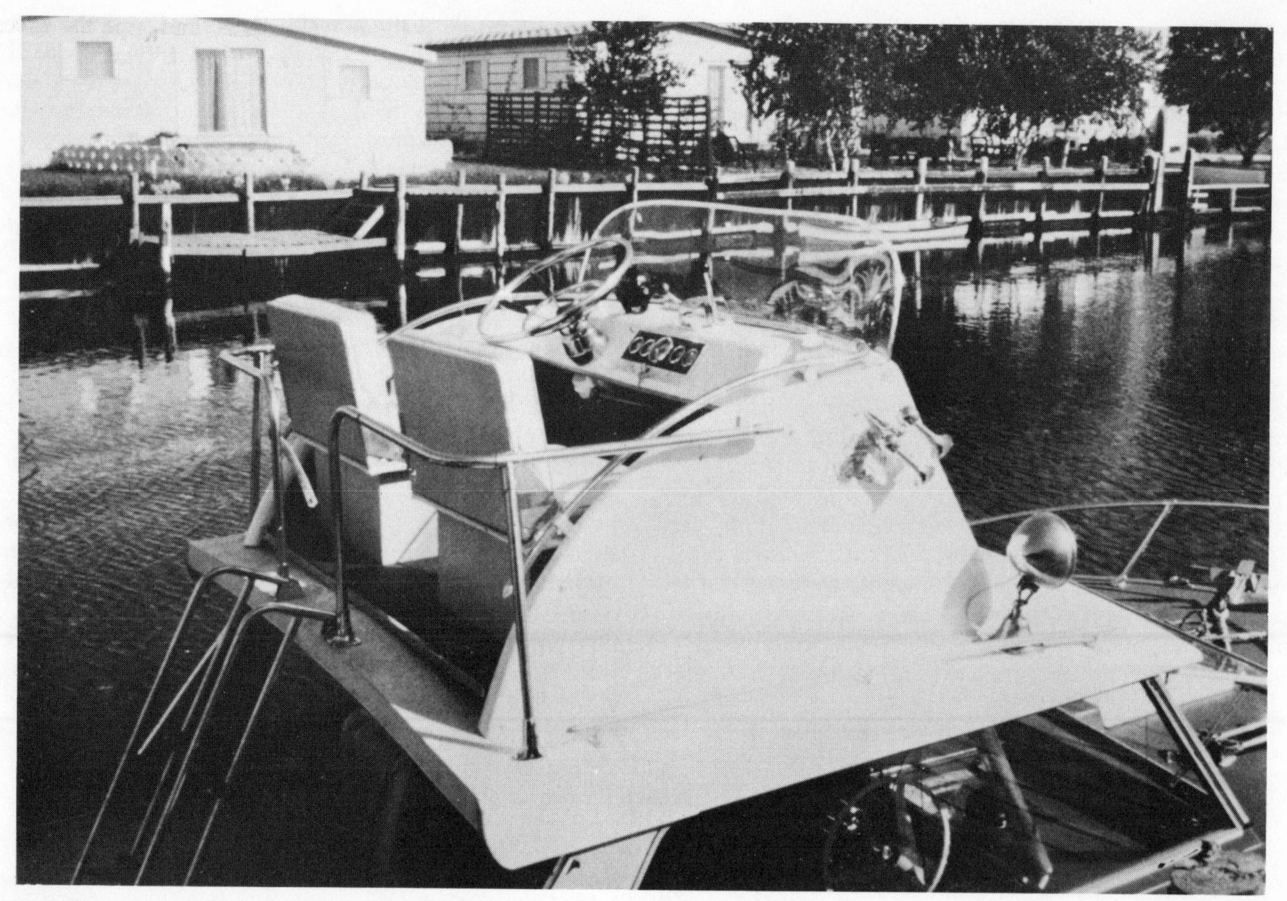

Fig. 506. Flying bridge is installed here on a 21′ Penn Yan, about the smallest boat that can take such a unit.

enough to withstand the transverse thrust produced by the load. Because of these two factors, it is often necessary to say "No" to some potential customers.

Many requests for information come into the Rickborn office from owners of small cruisers in the 20-foot class. Some of these boats are light weight, outboard powered over-nighters with a sedan trunk cabin, and a windshield on the aft end. Originally a Navy top extended aft from the windshield about 4½ feet. The owner, having replaced the canvas top with a hard top, now inquires about the possibility of adding a flying bridge. This may sound humorous to a seasoned boatman, but, to the neophyte who never heard about a center of gravity, it's an entirely different story. Many such people are disappointed to learn that their boat is too small to accommodate a flying bridge. There are no inflexible rules to govern what boat is suited. But 21-ft. day cruisers with inboard power and husky beams would usually represent the smallest boat, and 30-ft. cabin cruisers would usually represent the smallest boat with two levels of cabin. It is best to make certain that your particular boat is suited for a flying bridge before proceeding with such a job.

Steering Gears

The most difficult decision in a flying bridge installation involves the steering gear. This is because there are many types of steering gears in use and there is a variety of systems for dual station steering. To decide which is the best method for adding second station steering, a number of factors should be considered:

1. Which addition will operate best?
2. Which is the least complicated system?
3. Which will be the quickest to install?
4. Which one will require the least attention for trouble free operation for years to come?
5. Which will be the least expensive to purchase?
6. If one system costs considerably more than another system, is it worth the added cost?

The most popular boats in use today employ single cable push-pull steering gears in all sizes up to 32 or 34 footers. Many boats contain gear and shaft type steering systems. Some of these employ a gear box in the control console connected to a tower shaft which holds a pitman arm and operates a longitudinal rudder bar connected to the rudder arm. As the steering wheel is turned the longitudinal bar moves fore and aft. This type of steering gear usually operates with about four turns of the steering wheel from hard aport to hard astarboard. For the larger size boats or larger rudder loads, the same type of system is used, but the steering wheel takes about six turns from hard-to-hard.

Most of these gear and shaft systems are locking gears, some of them are non-locking. The difference is that the boat with a locking gear will stay on course when you let go of the steering wheel, while the boat with the non-locking gear will not. The fastest way to determine which type is in the boat is to take the boat for a ride, put it into a turn and let go of the wheel. With the locking gear the boat will continue to turn,

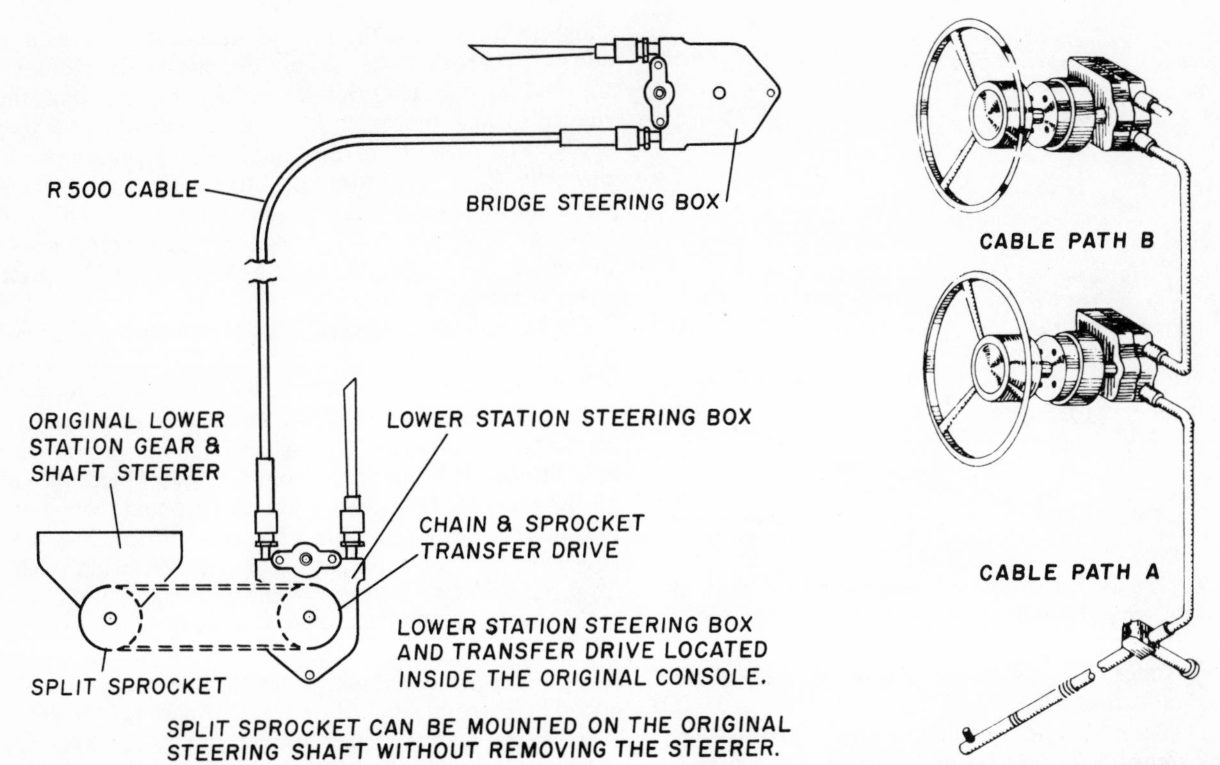

Fig. 507. Chain and sprocket transfer drive can be used to connect flying bridge steerer with gear, push-pull cable, or hydraulic systems.

Fig. 508. Teleflex dual steering system uses single cable that runs from flying bridge, through cabin steering head, to rudder.

with a non-locking gear the wheel will spin and the boat will straighten its course from the pressure on the rudder blades.

There is another type of steering gear which employs the gear box back at the rudders. With this type the longitudinal rudder bar revolves in the bilge and is usually connected to the steering wheel by a chain and sprocket drive. These systems employ a locking gear exclusively.

There are also hydraulic steering units wherein the steering wheel is mounted to a shaft which, through one arrangement or another, operates a master cylinder. This is connected by copper tubing to a slave cylinder which moves the rudder arm as the wheel is turned. There are a variety of hydraulic steerers, and most modern day systems are reliable. They are installed by most large boat builders on a custom order basis only. Because of the higher costs of these units, they are not exactly common.

Another arrangement is available from a number of manufacturers which operates on the "pull-pull" cable principle rather than on the "push-pull" principle. Sometimes referred to as "tension systems," these units vary, depending upon the brand involved. Some have a single cable attached to both ends of the pinion driven rack, in which case the rudder is pulled by the cable core on either side of the rack. As the rack moves to the left, it would pull the rudder bar to the right and the boat would turn to the left. Reversing the direction would cause a pull on the opposite side which would work in like manner, but in the opposite direction.

One popular steering unit employed very widely, particularly in the houseboat industry, is manufactured by Teleflex Incorporated. This system employs a pinion gear driving a larger gear. The cable core is trapped between the two. When the wheel is turned hard over, the excess core protrudes from the opposite side of this gear box for a little over nine inches. It is covered by a plastic sheath called a "spent cable tube." Because of the unique design of this gear box, it is possible to put a longer core through it and instead of having nine inches on the spent cable side of the gear box, you could have, for example, twelve feet. This could be run through a 10-ft. casing (commonly referred to as a conduit), where it would then enter a second gear box identical to the first, would run through that gear box and come out with its 9¼ inches of excess core, into a spent cable tube attached to that box.

This is an excellent system but it, too, has its limitations. For this reason the manufacturer recommends that the second station be located so that there is no more than a 10-ft. casing between the two gear boxes. Under some circumstances, it is not necessary to be restricted to this 10-ft. recommendation, but this recommendation most assuredly must be followed when the lower station employs a long cable to the rudders such as in a houseboat.

Experience shows that twin engine houseboats, for example, in the 40-ft. class, employing this system, should also be equipped with power steering. Even with a power steering unit added to this system it is easier to turn in one direction than it is another. This is because of the back-lash within the conduit when the cable core is pushing the rudder bar, not pulling it.

It might be noted here that there are other factors which contribute to the pressure put on the steering system. For example, with I/0s, the trim tabs on the outdrive units play an important part. These are small

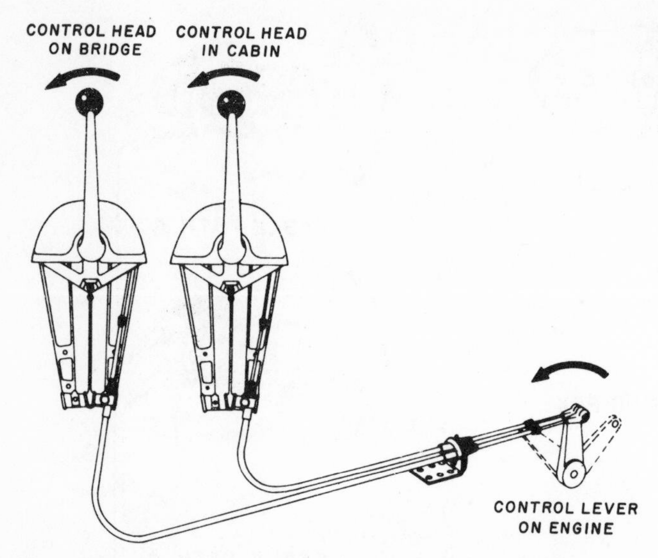

Fig. 509. Parallel engine control system for throttle or clutch has separate cables leading to appropriate lever at the engine.

adjusting vanes attached to the bottom aft end of the outdrive cavitation plate.

The Owner's Manual for Chrysler Drive 90° explains their recommended method for adjusting the I/0 trim tabs. The trim tabs are designed to compensate for propeller side thrust which moves the bow of the boat in the opposite direction to the rotation of the propeller. To adjust these trim tabs, loosen the Allen set screw which locks it, rotate the trim tab slightly in the direction in which the bow is turning, retighten the set screw, and take the boat on a test run. Adjusting this trim tab should provide "hands off" steering in the speed range for which you have adjusted it. For example, let's assume that the adjustments were made to provide "hands off" steering at 3200 rpm, the "hands off" range is approximately 800 rpm, which will provide the same ease of steering at 2800 rpm, through 3600 rpm.

Generally speaking, the "hands-off" adjustments may be arrived at on twin engines with the trim tabs straight in line with the unit. On a single engine boat, a 5° or 6° rotation in the direction in which the bow is turning will usually prove satisfactory.

Lining up the outdrives, it will be found that in most cases, setting the I/0's steering arm adjustments so that each unit points outboard about ½″ off center, will provide better steering, make it easier to come out of a turn at high speed, and may even increase the boat's maximum speed a half mile an hour or so.

Propeller rotation direction plays a major role in steering. When you are lucky enough to have twin engines with opposite rotation props, your boat can be handled quite easily, even on a windy day. The same boat with dual left hand propellers cannot back to port against a light breeze in most cases. If you own a twin engine houseboat turning left hand wheels, remember that when docking you will always bring her stern broadside to the dock on the *starboard* side only.

When adding a bridge on an inboard cruiser which has been in service even a short time, it is wise to check for bent rudder shafts. It is amazing how many boats are in service with these shafts bent. A bent rudder can show up the instant the second station steering gear is added. To check these, simply disconnect the clevis on the end of the longitudinal rudder bar so that the rudder(s) may be turned by hand. It should move very easily. The pressure of one finger should be ample to move it from hard-to-hard. Sometimes the packing gland on the rudder shaft is set up too tight. This can cause wear to the shaft as well as added pressure to the system. They should be set tight enough to keep the water out, but no tighter.

On boats with gear and shaft type steering systems, it is advisable to lubricate all connections. Most boatmen doing this for the first time will be shocked to learn that there is no lubricating system in their steering gear. The majority of these systems contain no zirk or alemite fittings. It is simply a "squirt oil can operation" at all the clevises. It is wise to place cardboard or waste rags underneath these parts when oiling them. It is also advisable to have someone turning the steering wheel from hard-to-hard during the entire oiling operation.

Our concern is to find the best method for making any one of these units work from two stations, even though they were originally designed to work at only one. There are a number of ways to accomplish this.

Let's start with the single cable steerers. The majority of these can be paralleled; that is to say, we simply run another single cable push-pull steering system from the bridge back to the rudders. The anchor blocks of both cables are located as close together as possible, and a ball joint joins the original and the bridge steerers at the rudder connection.

When the original steering gear uses an exceptionally long cable, such as in a houseboat, parallel installation is not recommended. It results in an over-abundance of backlash. Likewise, some straight rack and pinion steerers do not lend themselves to parallel use in conventional cruisers. Morse Controls offer a steering station exchanger which can help out in such a situation. The exchanger disconnects the steering cable not in use. It is available for inboards, not for outdrives!

When gear and shaft steering is encountered, a number of approaches are available. First, consideration should be given to the age of the boat. If the boat has eight or more years of service behind it, the gear box may be considerably worn. It may seem perfect in every way until the second station is added, then the wear shows up in increased pressure. To check such a system, disconnect the longitudinal rudder bar from the pitman arm. (This is the first arm encountered in the steering system on the steering wheel end.) Turn the wheel hard over. Look for drag; they hang up at the extreme ends of the pinion travel, if at all. The pressure of one finger on the steering wheel should permit moving the wheel in the opposite direction with no noticeable starting pressure against the finger. Any detectable hang-up indicates worn bearings in the gear box.

It is simple to remove this worn box, and replace it with a short single cable steering gear connected to the forward end of the longitudinal rudder bar. A matching single cable steerer is then run from the bridge and connected at the same location on the longitudinal rudder bar. This arrangement is common today in many stock cruisers.

When the lower station gear and shaft steerer are going to be retained, a transfer drive system may be used. The Rickborn R-500 System for this arrangement consists of a split sprocket which attaches to the steering wheel shaft. A short chain is run to a Teleflex gear box containing a matching sprocket. That gear box is connected to a matching gear box on the bridge by a push-pull cable. The one to one ratio into the input shaft keeps the second station pressure to a minimum.

The single cable system enjoys the advantage of complete leg room under the bridge dashboard.

The Tower Tube

The "tower tube" is the pipe which carries all the control cables and wires between the bridge and the lower station. This tower tube should always be included when a bridge is being added to a boat. It is the key to a successful flying bridge installation since by its location, all control cable paths are determined. The shorter the cables are, the easier the controls will work. This applies to steering gear, shift and throttle controls alike. Never attempt to run control cables, steering gear and wiring down the sides of the wheel house in order to avoid using a tower tube. This method is reserved strictly for the boat builder who incorporates it into the design of the boat and uses specific components and systems which lend themselves to such an arrangement.

Shift and Throttle Controls

While shorter cables are more desirable than long ones, it is well to remember that they do require sufficient length to permit graceful bends without placing strain on any of the connecting points. It is usually better to have a cable a foot longer rather than three or four inches too short. While both cables may reach, the shorter one will be constantly pulling against either the control head or the control end, depending upon how it is installed.

There are a variety of shift and throttle controls available; some of them lend themselves to dual station use more than others. Consideration must always be given to the amount of room available for mounting control heads. One does not have the latitude for arranging the controls on the bridge that the boat designer enjoyed when he laid out the lower stations.

In selecting control heads for the bridge, one should check the maximum dimensions of the control head to see that it will fit within the space allowed on the bridge. Practically all present day control heads made in the United States are built of durable material which can withstand weather. Care should be taken to avoid selecting bridge control heads constructed from some of the cheaper alloys.

The question often arises as to the best installation method for shift and throttle controls—whether they should be run in "tandem" or in "parallel." By connecting the control heads in tandem, the cables are run from the bridge control head to the lower station control head which is, in turn, connected to the engine. In a parallel installation, the cables are run from the bridge control head directly to the engine.

Parallel installations are generally more desirable

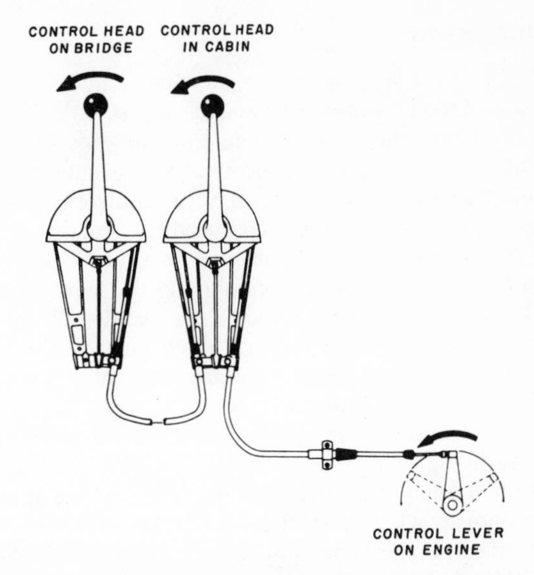

Fig. 510. Series system has cable from flying bridge that operates cabin control head and single cable leading to the engine.

when the cable lengths involved are relatively short and the cable paths contain a minimum amount of bend.

Tandem installations are a must when the lower station cables are exceptionally long, such as those found in houseboats.

Cable bends can make a big difference in how well a system operates. It must be remembered that a bend to the right or left of the tower tube creates just as much pressure as a bend in the fore and aft direction. For this reason it is better to avoid cable paths which resemble neatly installed plumbing. Every sharp bend is an "elbow." It is a wise man who gives his engine room space to control cables as a first consideration, rather than attempting to tuck them neatly out of sight where they will develop unbelievable resistance resulting in stiff controls and short life expectancy for the cables.

In deciding between parallel and tandem installations, realize that a control cable would require approximately a 90° bend to reach the carburetor. If that same cable were connected in tandem, it would require a 180° bend to reach the lower station control head. Realizing the difference, it is well to plan ahead and select cable paths with the fewest possible bends.

Location of Shift and Throttle Controls

Shift and throttle controls should preferably be located so that they are easy to use and equally easy to identify. Color coding should be employed whenever control head locations are not completely obvious. Throttle levers should be kept to the left of shift levers on single engine boats and throttles should be colored red, while shifts are colored black. On twin engine vessels the preferred arrangement would have the throttles in the middle for single handed operation of both engines and with a shift on either side. Twin engine, two lever type controls having the throttles in one control assembly, and the shifts in another identical control assembly, should be mounted with the throttles on the left side and color coded red. Shifts should be mounted on the right side and color coded black.

Transmissions

While throttle systems on gasoline engines of the inboard, I/0, or outboard varieties are practically universally alike, the transmissions are not. For example, on inboards one usually encounters hydraulically operated transmissions. These may be controlled by the same size levers, cables and control heads as the throttle. These may be controlled in exactly the same manner as the carburetors employing the same control head, same size lever and same cable. Manually operated transmissions require much greater operating pressure. They can usually be identified at the control station by large handles one foot or more long necessary to operate them. They do not lend themselves well to flying bridge installations.

With manual transmissions our choices are limited. First choice, when possible, is to locate a pair of used hydraulic transmissions and replace the manuals. Some manual transmissions can be converted to hydraulic; others cannot. It is best to contact the manufacturer of the transmission for the answer to that question. There is also an alternate choice. It is to employ the Morse MJ Control—not generally recommended for flying bridge work. There are some places where the MJ can fill the need. When using this control, it is best to mount it vertically, employ a short MC cable straight down to where it can connect directly to a rod and bell crank improvisation. It should be pointed out that the operating limit of this control is 80 ft. pounds. With an 80 pound load on the working end of the cable, the control handle will require about 55 pounds to operate. This unit should never be connected from the flying bridge by cable all the way to the transmission.

There are some inboards still in service which employ electric shifting transmissions. These are relatively simple to control from the bridge. They use a standard type control head with an electric switch mounted inside instead of the usual control cable.

I/0 Transmissions

I/0 transmissions come in a variety of arrangements. It is questionable whether one could pick on a particular type and say that it is the most common. The "shifter dog" type of transmission probably leads all others. Then there is the "shifter dog" combined with an hydraulic clutch. Also, there is the completely electric shifting I/0, and last but not least, the I/0 which employs the standard hydraulic marine transmission used on the inboards.

The straight shifter dog I/0 can be controlled in the same fashion and with the same equipment as is used to control the throttle. This also applies to the I/0 equipped with the standard marine hydraulic transmission. The electric shifting I/0, like the electric shifting inboard, uses the same control head, but with an electric switch inside. Then there is the highly popular Chrysler 210 and 225 horsepower I/0s which employ the 90° Dana Drive. These are designated Models 80 and 81. These units use a shifter dog in conjunction with a standard automotive type clutch; the clutch being operated by an hydraulic cylinder. Normally, this two-stage operating transmission is controlled by a single lever control. The single lever control has two cables. One engages the shifter dog while the second engages the clutch. To dual station this unit the single lever control is removed. It is replaced by a dual lever control containing an electric switch. Back in the engine room the manually operated hydraulic valve is replaced by an electric solenoid valve controlled by the switch inside the two-lever control head.

Instrumentation

Flying bridge instrumentation is best kept to a minimum, particularly if ferrous metals are employed in the instruments on the bridge. Instruments on a bridge, even though covered with a good canvas cover, are still exposed to more moisture than is customary at the lower station, which is usually better protected from dampness.

Good instruments are not cheap. The standard gauges usually consist of tachometer, engine temperature gauge, engine oil pressure gauge and ammeter, or preferably, a battery condition gauge, a starter ignition switch and a panel light switch. Panels for boats with twin engines would naturally have double the number of gauges and an extra starter ignition switch.

Modern instrument panels are pre-wired with all the wires terminating in a plug. A wiring harness with a matching plug runs from the panel down to the engine room. It is wise to omit ammeters on the bridge and substitute battery condition gauges in their stead. This permits parallel wiring and eliminates the possibility of burning out gauges during the bridge installation. One of the benefits to be gained is that by employing battery condition gauges on the bridge and leaving out the ammeters, you have eliminated "serious" wiring. With "serious" wiring a break in the line between the ammeters can stop the boat dead in the water. With parallel wiring the same break in the wire could prove a mere inconvenience.

The battery condition gauge offers other advantages too. For example, if your boat has not been used for a period of time and on going aboard you discover a dead battery, or one that is considerably lower than the other, your battery condition gauge informs you immediately when you turn on the bridge ignition. A low battery on one engine may indicate that your bilge pump has been running even though there has been no rain and this, of course, would indicate a leak. The battery condition gauge also lets you know when your voltage regulator is defective.

Wiring a parallel instrument panel is very simple. It involves only eight wires per engine. All the wires are B.I.A. color coded. There are three 10-gauge wires; one is black and goes to ground; one is red and is attached to positive battery at any convenient location; the third is orange and is only used in series wiring; it makes a very handy "space" wire for the parallel type panel. The remaining wires are usually No. 16 gauge. The white wire attaches to the starter terminal of the lower station starter switch, or it may be run directly to the starter solenoid. The purple wire is connected to the ignition terminal of the lower station ignition switch or it may be run to the positive side of the ignition coil. The tan wire is connected to the temperature sending unit; the blue wire connects to the oil pressure sending unit, and the gray wire connects to the point side of the ignition coil.

Compatibility of Instrument Panels

Not all instrument panels are compatible with each other. For example, two compatible temperature gauges may be operated by a single dual station sending unit. When you are adding a second station, it is necessary to determine whether the old and the new are compatible or not. There are instruments in existence on boats today which were built most recently, which cannot employ dual station senders even though the gauges are of the same brand. With such gauges it is necessary to employ a sending unit for each gauge. This is equally true when using incompatible instruments. Without getting technical, the difference in compatibility is a difference in the resistance in OHMS in the various units.

When it is necessary to employ a second temperature sender, and there is no threaded opening to receive it, it is wiser to cut into one of the engine cooling hoses, using a pipe T and close nipples held in place with hose clamps. Make certain to run a wire from that fitting to a good solid ground on the engine. Without it, the sender will be eaten by galvanic corrosion (electrolysis) and will fail in a short space of time.

Temperature alarm senders should be placed where their sensing areas are directly in the main stream of the engine water cooling system; otherwise they may not operate even though the engine is actually overheated.

Alarm Systems

There are also alarm systems available which are economically priced, which may be used in conjunction with, or in place of, an instrument panel. These alarms consist of buzzers operated by oil pressure sending units and temperature sending units on the engines. When the oil pressure drops, the buzzer will buzz; if the engine overheats, the buzzer will buzz. The alarm system is tested automatically every time you start an engine. Since the engine has no oil pressure when you turn your ignition switch on, the buzzer buzzes until the engine starts.

A note of caution on the use of alarm systems: The alarm will sound regardless of the reason, if the engine stops. For example, it will also sound the alarm if your engine stopped because you ran out of gas, or your fuel line plugged up. In short, don't assume that you have lost oil pressure or have an overheated engine the instant it stops—simply shut off the ignition and look for the trouble in the usual fashion.

While tachometers are not absolutely essential on single engine boats, they are desirable. On twin engine boats tachometers have considerable value. They permit proper synchronization of the engine speeds. In fact, some skippers prefer good quality electric tachometers in preference to an engine synchronizer. Usually an engine synchronizer is accurate within 20 or 25 revolutions per minute, while the electric tachometers would usually be accurate within about 50 revolutions per minute. The difference between the two is negligible and the cause for each has been argued pro and con many times.

Tachometers should always be employed on a flying bridge installation on a houseboat. This is especially true if it is a twin engine boat. The reason is that the operator is so far away from the exhaust outlets that he could fail to detect an increase in the rpm of an engine due, for example, to a slipping propeller, a lost propeller, or any of a number of reasons, and this would be especially true at high speed while running into the wind, which would also carry the sound away from the operator. An engine running free at full throttle could suffer very serious damage.

Deck Rails and Ladders

Deck rail sets are handy and it is wise to arrange them with safety in mind. Location of engine hatches in the cockpit, or doors in cabin bulkheads, will dictate whether the bridge ladder shall be mounted for port, center, or starboard entrance. In any case it should be at the after end of the cabin structure, not on a side. On some commercial sport fishing boats, the ladder is side-mounted in order to keep the cockpit clear for fighting chairs, and the skipper is usually the only one allowed on the flying bridge.

Side-mounted ladders are dangerous in use on a boat when it is underway, particularly in rough weather and a beam sea. It is much wiser to keep your flying bridge ladder within the confines of the cockpit.

Using a Flying Bridge

It may come as a surprise even to some veteran boatmen, but there is a correct way to use a flying bridge which the prudent skipper will add to his list of good boating habits. The boat should be started from the lower station, after the blowers have been operated for five minutes. Make a check of all control systems, with the possible exception of shifting into gear.

Check the steering by turning the wheel from hard-to-hard, and return it to the mid point so you'll know your rudders or stern drives are aimed straight ahead. Any change in feel of the steering since the last time you operated the boat will indicate potential trouble. Should this be the case, seek out and solve the problem before leaving your slip or mooring.

A visual check of all instruments should be made to see that all pressures are correct, and that the generators or alternators are charging (and immediately after starting the engines, they should be). Allow the engines to run until normal temperature is shown on the temperature gauges. At this point the engines and blower switch should be shut off at the lower station. Re-start the engines immediately from the flying bridge. When this procedure is an unbroken habit, you will have the advantage of being able to shut off your engines from the flying bridge under emergency conditions.

Most dual station ignition systems are wired in parallel; if you start the engines from the lower station, then go to the flying bridge without first shutting them off, turning the ignition key there would have no effect on the engines. Both lower station and flying bridge switches must be in the "off" position in order to stop the engines.

There's another way to wire the ignition so that you will have "emergency shut-off switches" at both stations. At the flying bridge station install an "on-off" switch in series in the hot wire leading to the *lower* ignition switch. The "on-off" switch at the upper station normally would be left in the "on" position, but it could be flipped "off" in an emergency to kill the engine. Similar switches can be installed at the lower station so that engines can be shut off from either place in an emergency.

With all the foregoing information in hand, your flying bridge installation should be completely successful, comfortable, safe, and easy to use. You'll find it's a different world of boating up there. It is cleaner, pleasantly quieter, delightfully airy, and it's a surprisingly comfortable ride. It's quite a shock to come down from the bridge and find every loose article in the boat rolling around in the cockpit, when you had thought conditions weren't that rough!

And the cost of adding a flying bridge is usually less than the value it adds to your boat.

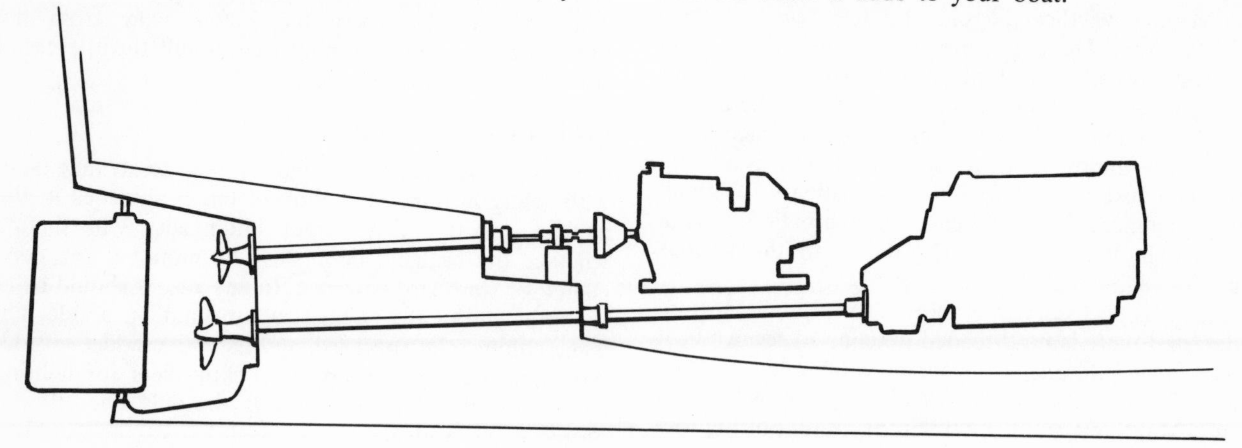

Fig. 511

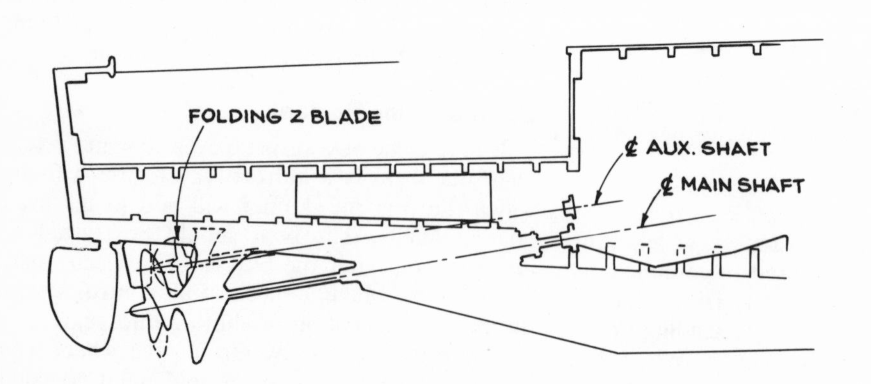

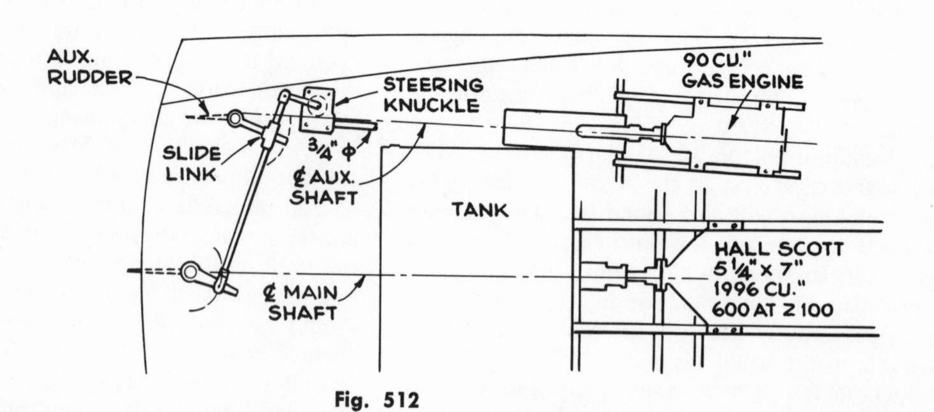

Fig. 512

Rig for Standby Power

What do you do on a single screw boat when the engine *really* quits, and no shipboard facilities are available for making the necessary repairs? You just switch to your standby emergency power source, and you're on your way! Here are some systems of this type used by naval architect William Garden on boats of his design, as well as some he suggests as feasible.

Fig. 511 illustrates a piggy-back arrangement, with the auxiliary generator sitting above the main shaft. The generator is coupled via a clutch to its own shaft, and drives a two-blade propeller that can be aligned behind the deadwood to minimize drag.

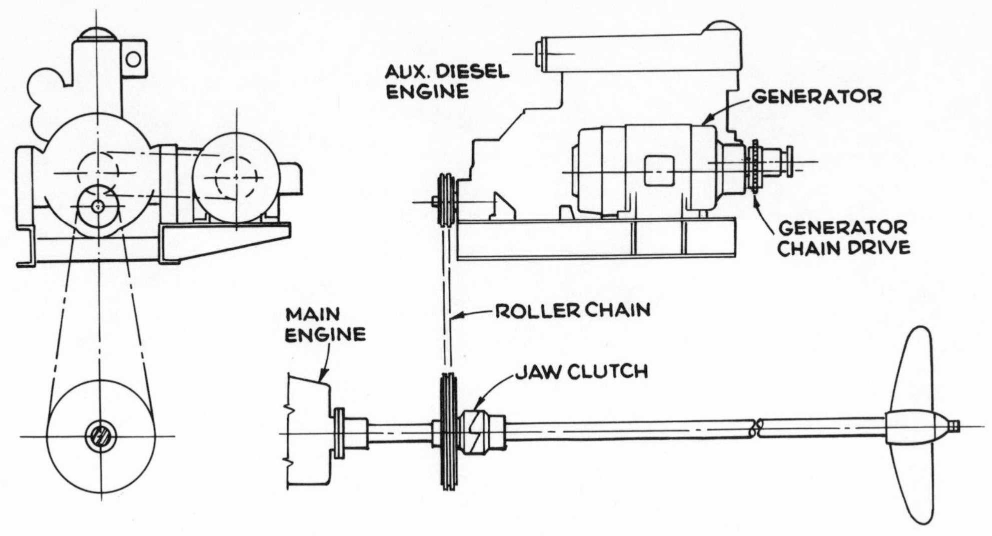

Fig. 513

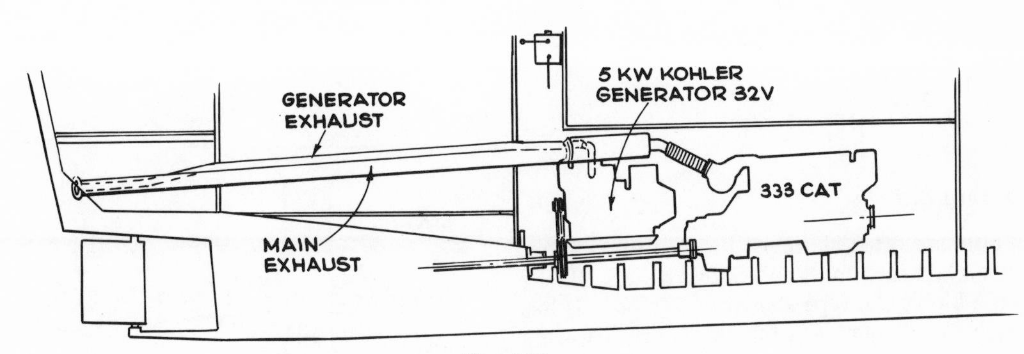

Fig. 514

In *Fig. 512* the main engine is centered in the normal manner, and a small auxiliary is off to port, splayed out slightly to help counteract the torque that results from its off-centerline location. Here a secondary rudder is used behind a folding two-blade propeller, and the rudder is actuated by linkage from the main rudder. This rig could be used to advantage as a trolling motor, according to Mr. Garden.

The drawing in *Fig. 513* shows how a generator could be connected by chain or belt drive directly to the main shaft. The generator must be located directly above the shaft, and the drive connected to the shaft with a jaw clutch.

In *Fig. 514*, a 5-kw Kohler generator is used to drive the main shaft with vee-belts. This arrangement was fitted on one of Garden's heavy-duty diesel cruisers and has worked out well. During normal generator operation, an idler pulley arrangement is backed off to remove the belts from the main shaft.

Another way to couple a generator to the main shaft is through use of the Denison Hydraulic Marine Drive unit sold by Deri Ltd., Burgess Hill, Sussex, England. It is illustrated in *Fig. 515*. Another hydraulic drive is that produced by Fairey Hydraulics Ltd., also of England. This has its own propulsion unit, as shown in *Fig. 516*. Both these are said to operate it with engines of about 10 horsepower, and direction of rotation is controlled by three position control valves that provide forward, neutral, and reverse.

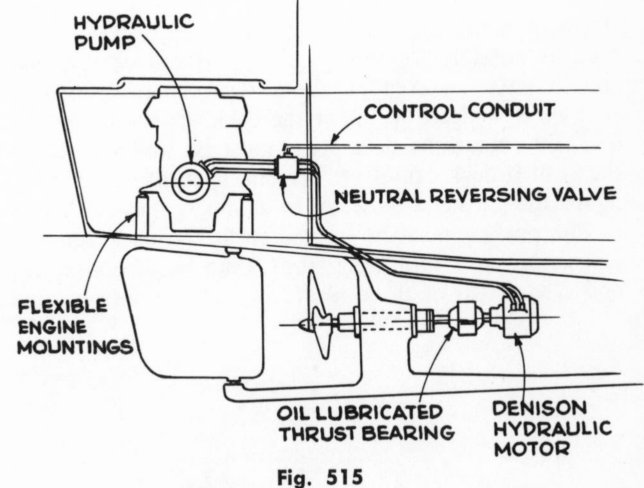

Fig. 515

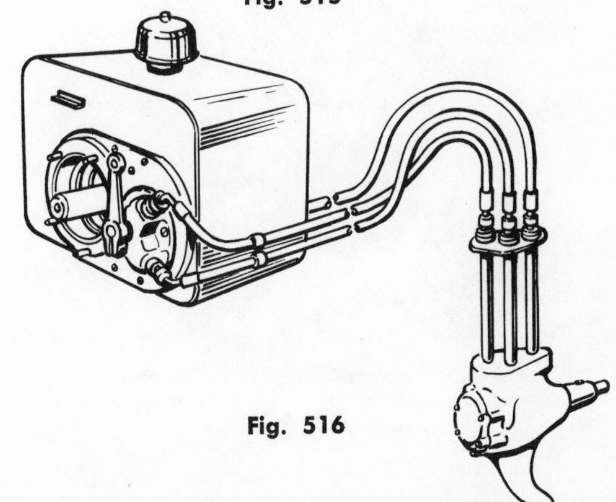

Fig. 516

6. MOORING & ANCHORING GEAR

BITTS

Simple Mooring Bitt

Mooring bitts are often skimpy—or even missing entirely—on fiberglass runabouts and small cruisers. Here's a way to add a bitt of the type shown in *Fig. 601*. It has ample strength for all purposes but the heaviest towing jobs.

With this bitt, as with any deck fitting subject to any strain, it is necessary to spread the load over as much area as possible. In this case a "partner" of plywood should have an area of about two square feet. This partner is wedged up under the deck, as shown in *Fig. 602*. Of course the deck itself must be well-secured to the hull! If deck beams are present, spaced from 1′ to 2′ apart, the partner can be cut to fit snugly between them.

The partner must be curved to fit the deck camber; just make up a simple jig from scrap hardwood stock, and clamp two or three layers of ¼″ marine plywood in place, with a good marine glue between the layers. When the glue has cured, the lamination will retain its curvature.

Fig. 601

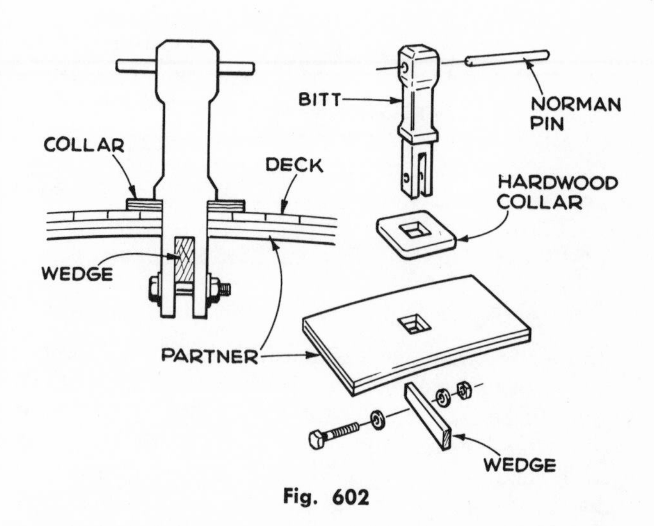

Fig. 602

Make up the bitt itself from white oak, or a similar straight-grained hardwood. Use 2″ x 2″ stock for boats up to 25′ in length; 3″ x 3″ stock for larger ones up to 32′ or so in length. This type of bitt would not be suitable, unless tied into the hull structure, on anything larger.

Round off the corners below the norman pin to minimize rope chafe. The pin itself can be of bronze (chrome-plated if you desire), marine aluminum, stainless steel, or a straight-grained hardwood of suitable diameter and length.

The hole through the above-deck collar, and through the deck itself, should provide a snug fit for the bitt. Bed the bitt and collar in a good synthetic sealant such as the polysulfide (Thiokol) type. Use epoxy adhesive on the upper face of the partner, between it and the deck. When everything is in position, drive a wedge in between the bolt through the bottom of the bitt, and the bottom face of the partner.

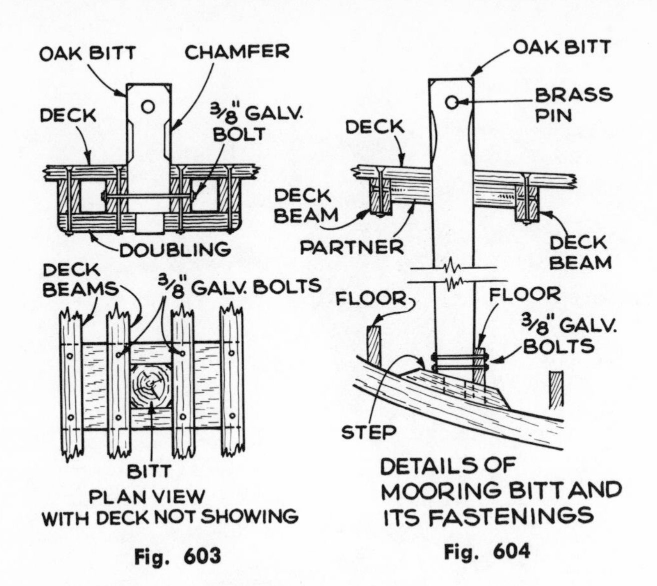

Fig. 603

Fig. 604

Bitts for Wood Boats

Here are two extremely sturdy mooring bitt arrangements for wooden boats, or at least those with wood decks and closely-spaced deck beams as shown in *Fig. 603*. These bitts are particularly suitable for large boats, those of 35′ to 50′ in length. They should be of 3″ x 3″ or 4″ x 4″ white oak stock; the pin should be about 1″ in diameter, and its length about three times the dimension of the bitt (a 9″ pin for a 3″ thick bitt).

Fig. 603 shows the mooring bitt framed into the deck members, with two extra deck beams installed, and the bottom of the bitt stepped into a doubling piece. The size of the doubling piece may be proportioned as shown.

Fig. 604 shows the mooring bitt extending through the deck and seated into a step securely fastened to the stem or keel, depending on exact location of the bitt on deck. The deck is reinforced where the bitt passes through it by framing a partner into the deck beams.

The bottom of the bitt should be framed or set into the keel or stem step, and an extra floor should be set and fastened to the frames. The bottom of the bitt is bolted to the floor member.

In all cases, the wood for the bitt should be well-seasoned, as otherwise the exposed end is likely to check badly. This not only spoils the appearance, but allows moisture to enter the wood and start decay.

For the bitt shown in *Fig. 604*, select a location between two deck beams, and make a filler block to fit between the beams under the deck. This usually can be of 2″ stock, unless the boat is very large or very small; the top must be planed to fit the curve of the deck camber. Give the top surface a good coat of marine adhesive, or even a liberal coat of marine paint, and push the block up into place between the beams. Fasten with wood screws set in through the deck, and also through the beams if there's room under the deck to do this work. Avoid putting fastenings where the opening is to be cut.

Note: If the deck is of light construction, add a second block to fill the space between the beams ahead of the first block. The pull on bitts is usually ahead.

Cut the opening through the deck and filler block as close as possible to the exact size of the bitt to eliminate the need for wedging, and bevel the edge of the deck slightly around the opening to provide a good seam for caulking compound.

Stowing the Anchor

When it comes to stowing an anchor, you want to make sure you can get to it quickly, release it easily, handle it with your available crew (by yourself, if necessary), and retrieve it with a minimum of fuss when its job is done. When in place, there should be no chance of its flukes snagging or injuring anyone on board. Illustrated in *Figs. 605–613* are some well-thought out arrangements spotted and photographed by Janet and Gordon Groene.

Fig. 605. Rubber rollers hold this lunch-hook-size CQR anchor neatly above wave action on a Bristol Trawler. However, care must be taken that the rode doesn't chafe on rollers, and that tidal current action doesn't pop the rode out of its guides when at anchor.

Fig. 606. Here is an uncluttered and convenient rig which allows a Danforth anchor to be slipped out for immediate use. Note the wood holder that keeps chain from rattling or sliding around on deck.

Fig. 607. This small bowsprit allows the anchor to be secured safely and easily, or dropped clear of the hull quickly when it's needed.

Fig. 608. This is a secure, safe, self-stowing CQR holder. Note that the anchor can be readied for use rapidly, and that chain clears the hull.

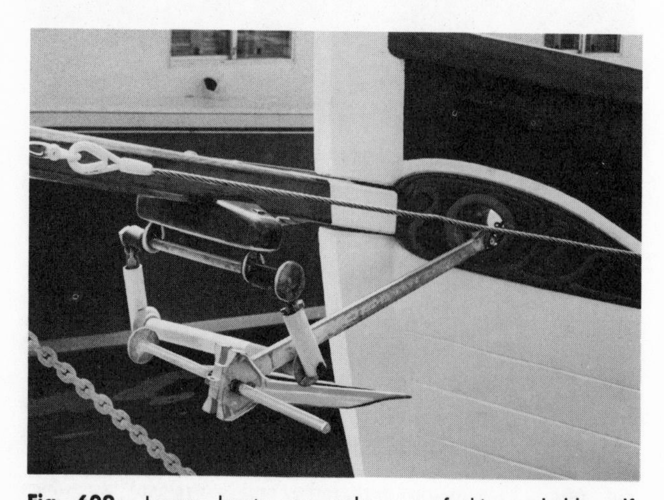

Fig. 609. Larger boats can make use of this workable self-tending method of carrying an anchor, although in this case the rig might be modified slightly to make sure the anchor won't foul in the bobstay.

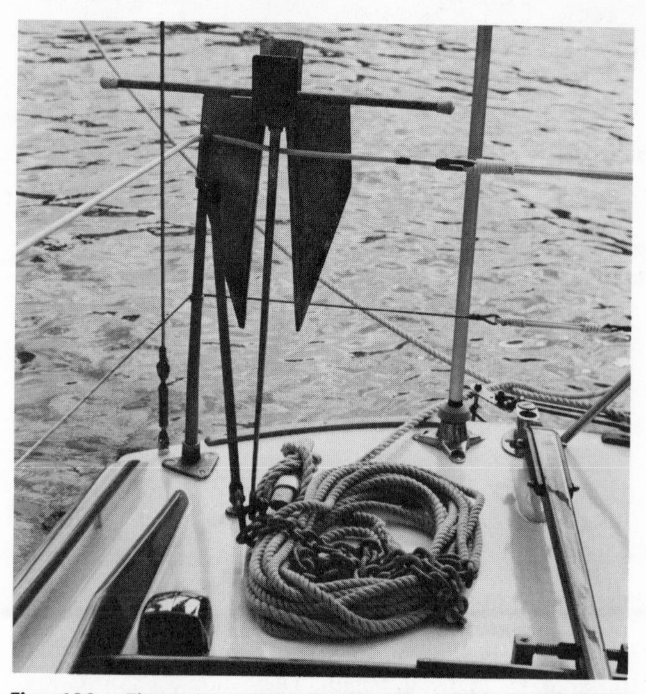

Fig. 610. This stern anchor is set for emergency use in a shallow or restricted waterway where depth is fairly constant. With a secured rode of proper length, it can be tossed over to act as a brake if the boat is drifting down on any sort of obstruction.

Fig. 611. This anchor is released by sliding the heavy U-bolts outboard along the wooden cross piece. As the Groenes suggest, the chain should be secured better than this if the boat is to operate in heavy seas.

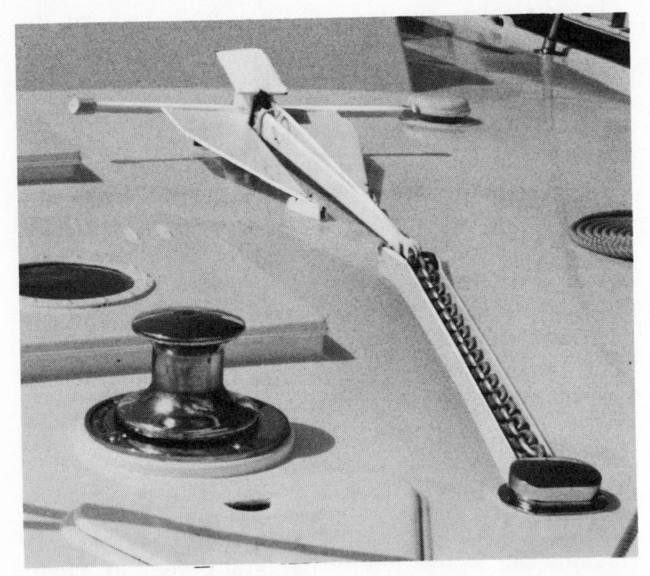

Fig. 612. Here's a practical way to provide for the anchor chain if the anchor itself can't be stowed near the hawse pipe. It's just a channel that's fastened to the deck, and it keeps the chain in place, and ready for tangle-free deployment.

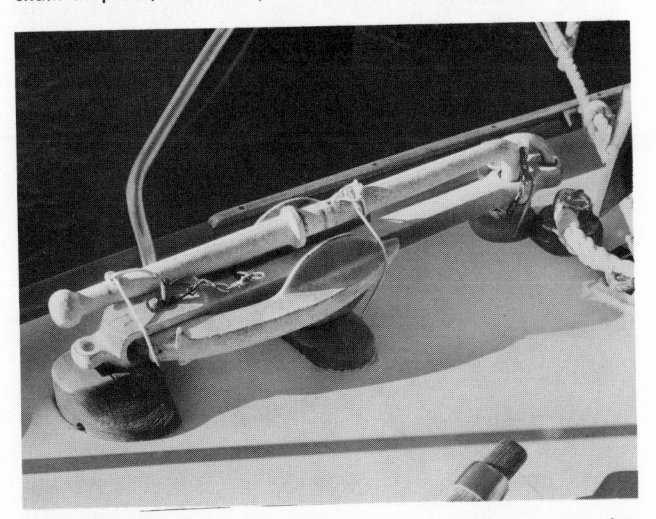

Fig. 613. This heavy, folding Yachtsman anchor is mounted in three teak chocks, and tied so it can't come adrift accidentally. This should not be considered an emergency anchor as it takes time to unfold it and pin it in the operating configuration. Be sure to grease all sliding pins and folding parts so they won't bind with rust.

Bow Pulpit Anchor System

This is a particularly beautiful assembly, as well as providing an extremely efficient system for handling a Danforth anchor at the bow. As Gordon Manning's photograph (*Fig. 614*) shows, the pulpit is of 2″ thick teak stock, edged with a chrome-plated brass rub strip.

The winch in this case is an electric one for added convenience. Brass "angle iron" lines the inside of the slot to prevent chafing there, and flat brass strap protects the teak underside from the anchor flukes.

When the anchor is brought up with the stock through the slot, tension on the rode holds the flukes snug against the bottom of the pulpit. When it's time to drop the anchor, there's nothing to unsnap, unshackle, or untie.

Fig. 614

Anchor Rode Reel

Another anchoring convenience for small boats is a reel on which your anchor line can be wound to keep it out of the way under the foredeck, and to allow it to run out freely when it's needed.

You can make such a reel that will take up to 200′ of ½″ anchor line for only a few cents' worth of material, using this method developed by Gordon Manning.

You'll need:

2 ¼″ plywood discs, 11″ diameter.
1 pc. aluminum strap, $\frac{3}{16}$″ x 1¼″ x 25″.
2 1¼″ aluminum deck flanges (Reynolds).
1 pc. 1¼″ o.d. aluminum tubing, 10″ long.
1 pc. ¼″ brass rod, 20″ long.

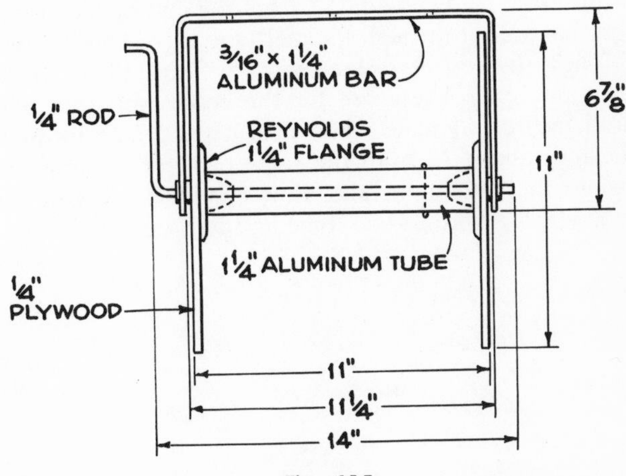

Fig. 615

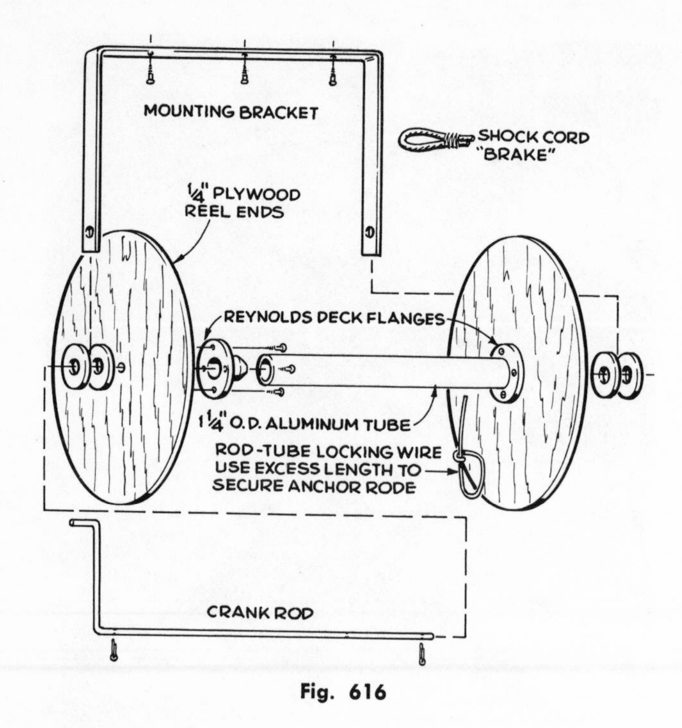

Fig. 616

8 ¾" #6 aluminum metal screws.
4 ¼" brass or aluminum washers.
2 1/16" cotter pins.

Cut the two 11" discs from ¼" plywood stock, and sand them to smooth up the edges. Drill a ¼" hole for the crank rod in the center of each.

Next lay off a bending line 6⅞" in from each end of the 25" length of aluminum bar. If you form a right angle at each of these lines, you'll have exactly 11¼" between the two arms of what is now your support bar, and this takes the reel nicely. A good-sized vise and a monkey wrench will simplify the bending operation.

To assemble the reel, use the two 1¼" Reynolds flanges, plus the 10" length of aluminum tube. Remove the locking bolt and spring clip from each flange, and drill out the center of each with a ¼" drill to take the crank rod. You will actually need only a press fit for the tube over the flange hub, so the locking device can be discarded. Attach each flange to the inside face of the plywood end panels, as shown in *Fig. 615*, with four wood screws.

Make two right angle bends, both in the same plane, at distances of 14" and 19" from the end of the crank rod that will fit through the reel (*Fig. 616*). Drill holes through the rod at distances of ¾" and 12⅞" from the same end. These are for the cotter pins that will hold the rod in place. Also drill a third hole through the rod, about 3" from the same end, for pinning the rod to the aluminum tube. Corresponding holes in the tube allow a wire to lock tube and rod together.

In assembling the unit, use a washer between the reel ends and the frame as well as between frame and cotter pins. The wire used to lock the tube to the rod should be about 6" in length; the excess length can be twisted around your anchor line to hold it.

The anchor reel should be hung athwartships from a deck beam, or a stout block of wood attached under the deck. *Choose a location you can reach easily.* See that the line feeds up smoothly to the deck pipe opening, and have the reel handle on the end nearest the center of the boat. A loop of shock cord placed around the frame outside one of the reel ends will act as a slight brake to keep the reel from running too fast on any sharp pull.

Anchoring Made Easy

T. W. Cowthorne of Detroit, Mich., got tired of climbing out to the bow of his little cruiser to handle the anchor. He came up with the scheme shown in *Fig. 617*. Basically, his idea consists of reeving the anchor rode through a block which is shackled to a messenger line that runs through another block at the bow. This messenger line is led aft to a cleat near the transom.

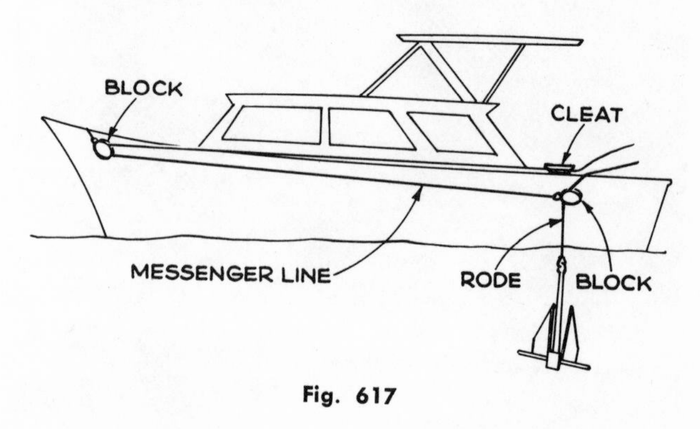

Fig. 617

The anchor is stored in the cockpit. To drop it, Mr. Cawthorne slacks off on the rode and heaves in on the messenger line until the block attached to it is at the bow. Then he carefully drops the anchor overboard, and pays out the rode in the normal manner until he has the scope necessary for the circumstances.

To raise the anchor, two different systems can be employed. One is to haul in on the rode in the normal manner until the anchor is two-blocked at the bow; then ease off on the messenger, and pull the anchor aft by its rode. The other method, which avoids anchor digs in the hull, is to slack off on the messenger line until its block is aft at the cockpit, and then heave in on the anchor rode.

7. RIGGING

RIGGING GIMMICKS

While the British have no monopoly on ideas of this type, their magazine *Practical Boat Owner* has provided its readers with the selection illustrated here (*Figs. 701–706*).

Halyard Holder

This handy idea was submitted by Ed Demere of Newport, R. I. It's a bar on which halyards can be clipped when not in use with their sails.

The holder (*Fig. 701*) can be made up of ⅜″ stock, with the support welded to the center of the "U". Ends of the rods are flattened and drilled for the blind rivets used to attach them to a metal mast, or for screws used to attach the ends to a wooden mast. If the mast is metal, the holder should be fabricated of a metal that's galvanically compatible to the mast, or it should be insulated from the mast by use of suitable insulators and fasteners.

Fig. 701

Jib Sheet Tweeker

At least that's what Roger Tuck calls this arrangement (*Fig. 702*) he devised to provide a downward pull to headsail sheets. He notes that it is to be used where a smaller boat has only one fixed sheeting point for a variety of headsails.

A nylon thimble has a length of line eye-spliced to it. The sheet is run through the thimble and back to its winch. The line with the thimble is led down through a chainplate shackle, or other suitable fitting forward,

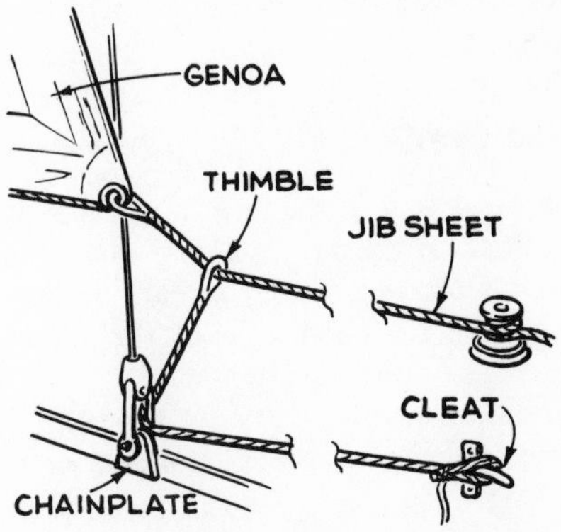

GENOA
THIMBLE
JIB SHEET
CLEAT
CHAINPLATE

Fig. 702

and back to a cleat. By adjusting the downward pull, a sail such as a genoa will set better, and reduce or eliminate leach flutter. Mr. Tuck notes that a thimble arrangement should be provided for each side of the boat.

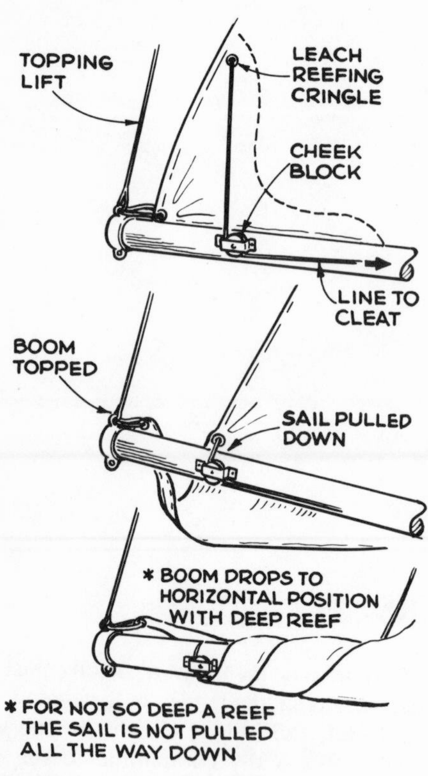

Fig. 703

Leach Cringle for Roller Reefing

By installing a reefing cringle (*Fig. 703*) on the leach of the mainsail, and a cheek block on the boom below the cringle, it is possible to eliminate the boom-droop that's a common problem when roller reefing is used.

When it's time to reef, the boom is topped, and the reefing cringle is pulled down as near to the boom as necessary, and the reefing line is cleated. The sail then will reef very neatly, and the boom will not sag when the topping lift is slacked off. If the line from the reefing cringle is led forward to a tube cleat near the gooseneck, reefing can be a single-handed operation.

This idea was submitted by P. J. Van Rooyen of South Africa.

Tabernacle Eye Bolts

When a mast is stepped in a tabernacle atop a cabin, L. P. Thomas suggests replacing the standard bolts with similar-sized eye bolts in an arrangement that provides an eye on each side of the tabernacle (*Fig. 704*).

The eyes then form a very strong point for a safety harness line for crew members working on the foredeck or at the mast. Also, the eyes can be used to secure the ends of halyards, he notes.

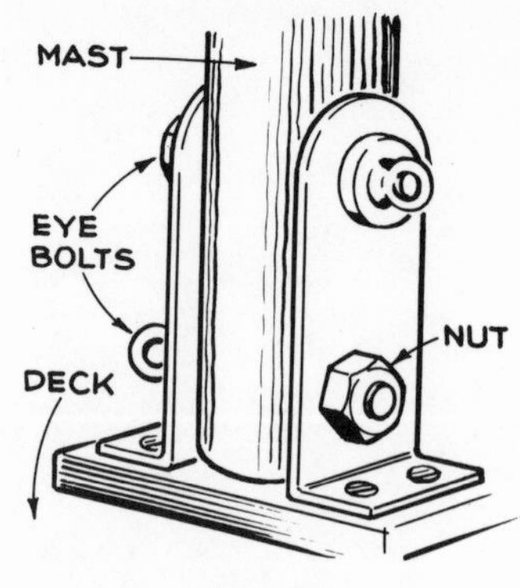

Fig. 704

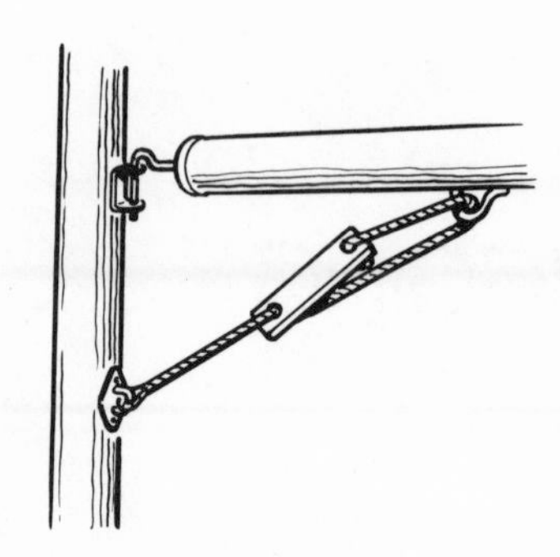

Fig. 705

Dinghy Boom Vang

D. R. Howard saw this arrangement on a Mirror class dinghy in England. It's simply a length of line between the mast and boom, doubled back from the boom to a wooden slide, arranged in the manner of tent guy rope (*Fig. 705*). Cost is minimal, adjustment is simple, and it should be very effective on small dinghies.

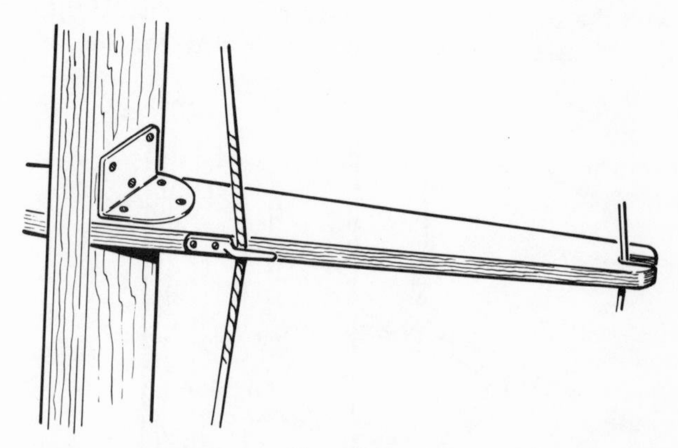

Fig. 706

Spreader Thumb Cleats

Here's a simple arrangement that will end the rap of halyards against a mast. A pair of thumb cleats (*Fig. 706*) are positioned on the spreaders, about 18″ out from the mast. The halyards are pulled out along the spreaders until they slip into the thumb cleats, and then they are tensioned. Peter Mere noted this rig in Eric Hiscock's book, *Voyaging Under Sail*. An alternative, with wooden spreaders of sufficient strength, is to provide notches in the after edges.

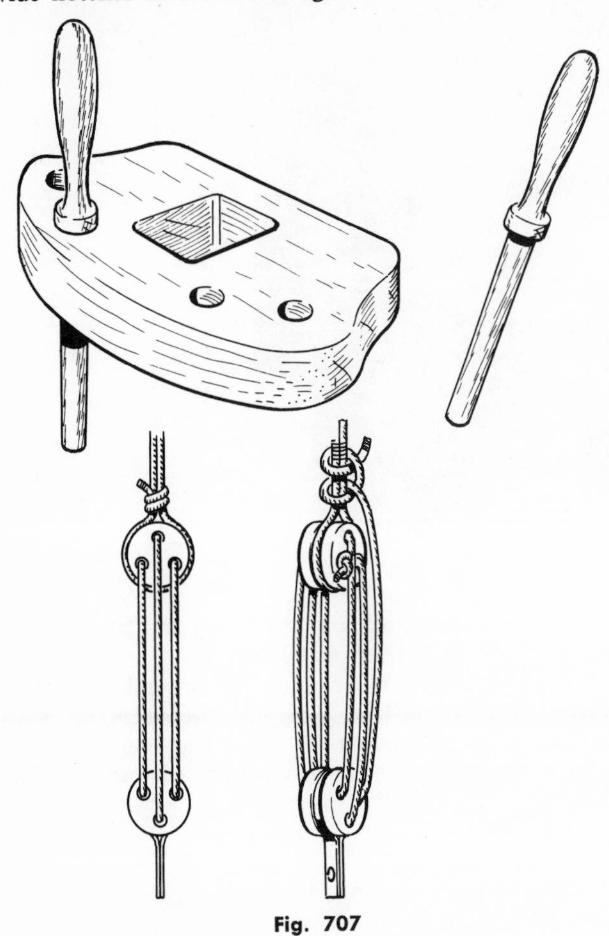

Fig. 707

The Character Boat Touch

Everyone can't have, nor does everyone want, a character boat, but every boat can have character, according to *Motor Boating & Sailing* editor Pete Smyth. Here's what he wrote in the *Motor Boating* "TLC" department, back in 1968:

"You can add the character touch to your boat with some simple, practical, old-fashioned fittings which, while they might be incongruous on many modern synthetic hulls, might be appropriate for you.

"Replacing turnbuckles on shrouds with deadeyes and lanyards, and belaying pins for cleats, are two examples of character-lending fittings that are useful as well as decorative, and can be made at home with the tools usually found in the boat-owner's household.

"Both deadeyes and belaying pins, being round, are most easily turned out on a lathe, but both can be made, too, by hand work on round stock which you can get from your lumber yard in the form of curtain rod or pole.

"If home projects aren't your cup of tea, you can buy belaying pins, but they are usually made of metal. Bronze or iron pins are effective for repelling boarders, but wooden ones have the advantage of being floatable.

"Round stock, about 1¼″ in diameter, is best for belaying pins. If you haven't a lathe available, handwork with a rasp and sandpaper will shape them up to look like the accompanying illustration (*Fig. 707*).

"For deadeyes, stock three or four inches in diameter, depending on the size of the boat and the lanyard to be rove through them, can be bought. Saw the stock in slices, the thickness depending on the need; drill them as indicated; and finish them by hand. Hardwood is best. The strength of the wood is not too vital, because, when in use, the deadeyes are compressed by the opposing stresses against them, which will prevent splitting.

"Belaying pins require a fife, or pin rail, or some reasonable substitute. The accompanying drawing shows how to make a type which fits over the mast of a small sloop."

Fig. 708

Bridge for a Sailboat

It's not a bridge in the traditional sense, but it has the shape of a bridge, and it's the name given to it by Stan Miller of the Long Beach, Calif. Marina. He developed the rig for the popular Cal 20, but it would work as well on any similar sailboat.

As the photo by Lois Kennedy shows (*Fig. 708*), it is made of heavy teak members. These are through-bolted right from the cross member down through the uprights, and backing blocks under the cabin top. It has to be very strong, and it is suggested that the backing blocks be longer than the width of the uprights, in order to spread strains more along the fore-and-aft plane of the cabin top.

The jib halyard winch and its cleat are mounted on top of the bridge. Two cam cleats on top, and three on the bottom side of the bridge, are used for spinnaker lines, boom vang, and the Cunningham—the rig used to tighten the luff of the mainsail.

Four-to-One Outhaul

Lois Kennedy photographed this outhaul rig (*Fig. 709*) designed by Stan Miller for a Cal-20. The use of two pad eyes on the boom, the leach cringle, and

Fig. 709

two blocks provides a four-to-one mechanical advantage when adjusting tension of the main, and the cleat is positioned on the boom where it can be reached easily, even with the boom swung out in running.

The outhaul is spliced to a pad eye on the starboard side of the end of the boom, then is run forward through the leach cringle, aft to a block on the port side of the boom, and forward along the boom. The end is spliced to the second block.

A second line is spliced to the second pad eye, which is secured on the port side of the boom well forward of the second block. This line then runs aft through the second block, and then forward to the cleat.

8. MISCELLANEOUS BOAT PROJECTS

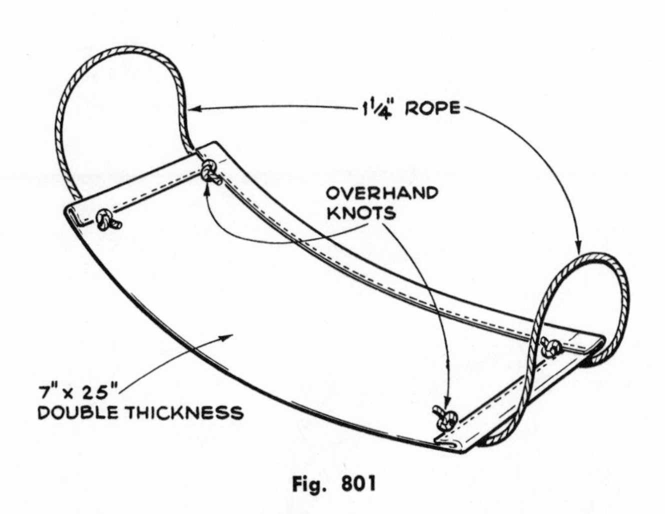

Fig. 801

Seagull Carrier

This sling (*Fig. 801*) was devised by A. R. Harper of Scotland to carry his little Seagull outboard motor from his car to his boat, and back. The idea, presented in Britain's *Practical Boat Owner* magazine, is certainly suitable for any small outboard. Even though they may be light in weight, their projecting parts often make them awkward to handle.

The sling is a double thickness of heavy canvas that measures 7″ x 25″ after stout hems have been sewn in the three open edges. Rope handles are passed through grommets at each end. Harper notes that the larger the diameter of the rope (within reason), the more comfortable it will be to the hands.

Naturally, the sling has to be positioned so the motor is cradled at its center of balance.

Keel Positioning Guides

This idea was developed by Glenn Hensley as an aid to those owners of trailerable sailboats with partially retractable keels. Often it is difficult to get the keel to slide correctly into its trailer support when the boat is to be hauled.

Fig. 802. Bolt antenna feeler on each fender so there's clearance of about 1″ between feeler and hull on each side of boat.

The two guides are made from spring-base replacement type auto radio antennas. Mounted on the trailer fenders, they provide "feelers" which can be used by

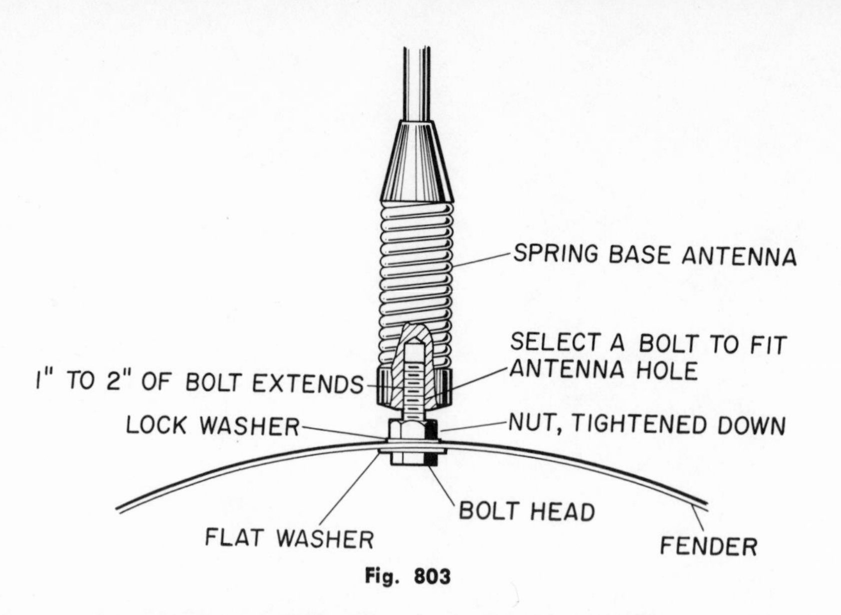

Fig. 803

you or your crew to visually guide the boat into its proper position on the trailer. Position the guides on the fenders so there's about 1″ clearance between them and the hull.

Just drill a hole through each fender at the proper point, and fasten a bolt through the hole from the bottom, as shown in *Fig. 803*. Follow the instructions for attaching the antenna to the bolt (which in this case acts as the stub of a broken auto antenna).

When the boat is being hauled, just make sure it is centered between the feelers as the keel comes up onto the trailer. The spring-base antennas will bend in any direction, then snap back up to the vertical, if they are pushed out of line by a momentarily drifting boat.

Fig. 804

Davit Lifts for a Small Cruiser

One way to protect a small boat from weather, worms, and barnacles is to keep it out of the water when not in use. *Fig. 804* illustrates a pair of davits capable of supporting a 1,500 lb. outboard cruising rig well above water level. George Byrnes, who worked this one out, advises that it would not be practical where a normal tidal rise or seasonal water level variation is in excess of 6′.

The davits themselves are bolted through stout pilings, which in turn must be well-sunk and braced to

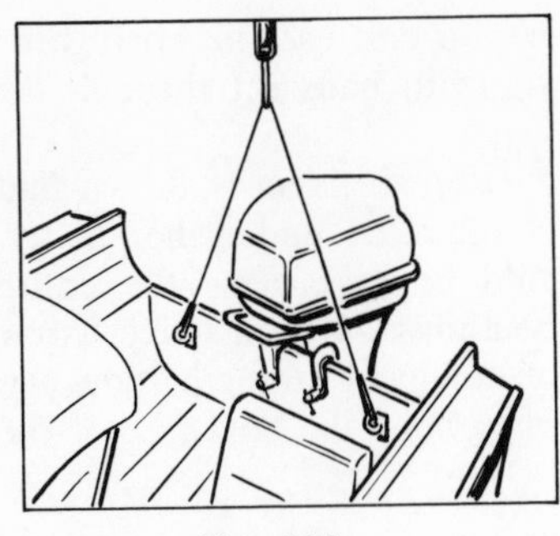

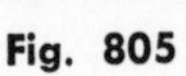

Fig. 805

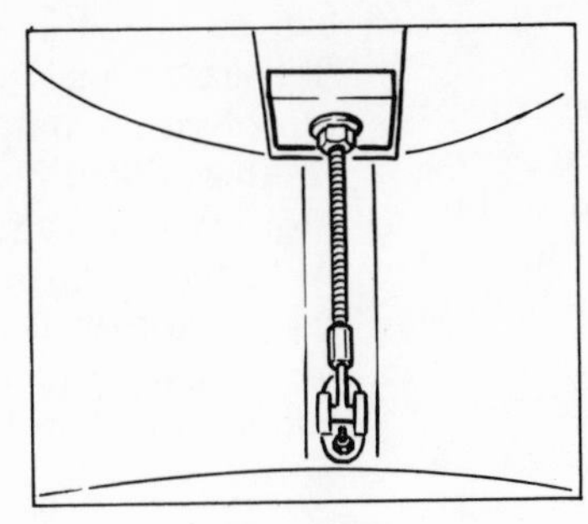

Fig. 806

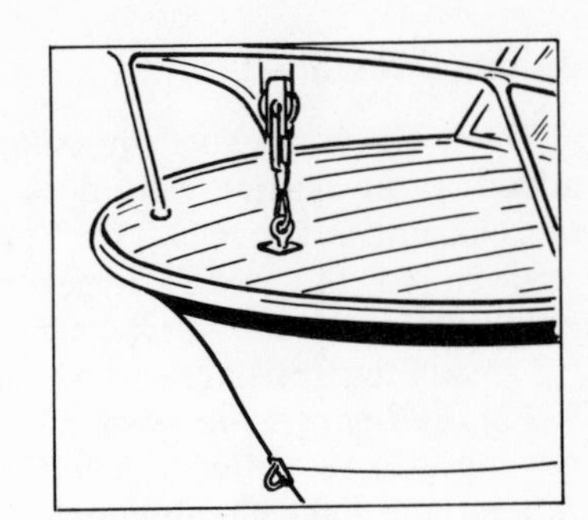

Fig. 807

take the load. Each of the davits is rated to take more than the total load of the boat and its gear.

Attaching points must be added to the boat, and since they will be taking considerable strain, a great deal of attention must be given to their installation.

Two eyes are installed on the inside face of the transom, as shown in *Fig. 805*. They are through-bolted, of course; use stainless steel or marine bronze. In effect you will be lifting a very strong transom, with the motor hanging on it. The relatively light hull just follows along.

If your boat is an inboard, it may be possible to lead the davit line right to the lift ring on the engine. In any case, it is advisable to lead the strain straight down to the engine, and let the engine mounts carry the weight of the hull. If your engine is mounted amidships, the rig is best left supported by the water.

The eye at the stem should pass through the relatively weak foredeck, and connect directly to the keel or stem member directly beneath it. On a fiberglass boat it may be necessary to glass in a suitable wood block, carrying the fiberglass well out to the surrounding hull in order to distribute the stress as much as possible.

Note in *Figs. 806* and *807* that the eye on deck is positioned directly above the bow eye on the stem. A fitting is bolted to the bow eye, inside the stem, to take the threaded rod that passes down from the deck eye. The rod is adjusted to provide just a touch of upward pressure on the deck. In this case, a wooden stem member is imbedded in the fiberglass, and the bow eye bolts through this member.

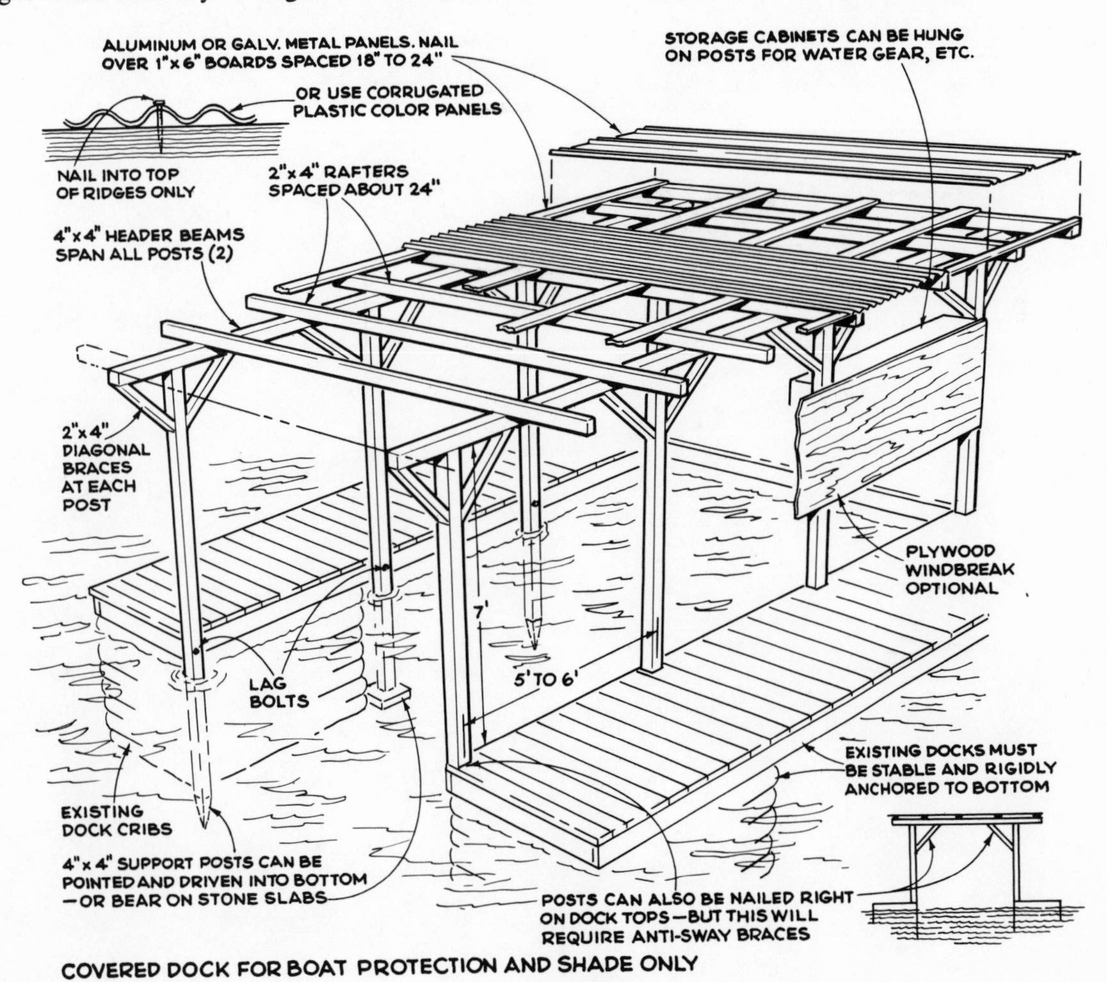

COVERED DOCK FOR BOAT PROTECTION AND SHADE ONLY

Fig. 808

Add a Dock Shelter

Hank Clark designed this simple shelter that can be added to an existing rigid dock that's on sunk pilings or rock cribs. Tough 5″ x 5″ posts are bolted or lag-screwed to the dock framework—It's best first to point the ends and drive them well into the bottom for maximum resistance to winds.

Fig. 808 shows the posts with 4″ x 4″ headers supporting 2″ x 4″ rafters. Nail 1″ x 6″ planks across the rafters, and light aluminum or galvanized metal panels can be nailed in place, or you can use the corrugated fiberglass panels as shown, with nails set through the top of ridges only.

An optional plywood windbreak panel is shown that protects a storage cabinet mounted under the shelter. A further refinement would be to enclose the entire shelter to turn it into a boathouse. If you make a few of the overhead beams of sufficient strength, you can add a block and tackle rig to hoist the boat free of the water.

9. THE FINISHING TOUCH

PAINTS AND PAINTING

Almost every boat project involves a finish coat of paint or varnish, where poor application can spoil a lot of excellent work. Because "Your Guide to the Perfect Paint Job," by Fred Clark, is the most comprehensive report on marine paints and paint application available, we are including it here. It first appeared in the February 1971 issue of *Motor Boating & Sailing*.

YOUR GUIDE TO THE PERFECT PAINT JOB

By Fred C. Clark, Jr.

Polyurethane, epoxy, vinyl, alkyd: all spell confusion on the marine paint scene, these days. Boat owners ask: Why does paint peel? How do you paint aluminum or fiberglass? Why does marine paint cost so much more than good housepaint? And finally, the $64 question: Which paint should I use on my boat?

Ask around the waterfront, and you can rack up a variety of answers. One boatman says: "After three years, Brand X still looks like new." In the adjoining slip, the owner of a sister ship grouses, "That lousy Brand X is murder. It peeled off my boat in less than three months. Brand Y is the only one I'll ever use, from now on!"

Let's see if we can investigate modern boat paints and come up with some answers that will help the intelligent boatman keep his vessel neat and sharp with a minimum of expense and labor. Note, though, that we said *minimum*. In these days of automation, it is natural to seek products that take the work out of work. Although modern surface coatings are much more attractive and last far longer than old style paints, it still takes a good bit of careful work if you want a good looking vessel.

There are four major parts to good boat painting. Like a chain, the finished job is no stronger than the weakest link.

1. Selection of the right paint for the job, the hull, and the operating conditions.
2. Choice of good painting tools and their proper care.
3. Proper surface preparation; it comprises half of the work.
4. Finally, the proper application of the paint or varnish.

Selecting Paints

Most of us never have to face more difficult paint problems than those on our boats. The marine environment is as rough and tough as it comes. A paint film, thinner than a page of this book, must adhere to various hull surfaces with the grip of modern adhesives. On the water, the boat twists, flexes, swells, and shrinks. We expose it to hurricane winds, ultraviolet sun rays, rain, salt, waves, and sprays. We hit pilings, bang other boats, then walk on it with sand and gravel in our shoes. To withstand this treatment, good boat paints must have far better ingredients than those which serve adequately around the house. Top-notch marine coatings contain the best of everything, and the quality is almost always reflected in the price.

Science has made great strides in the space-atomic age, and modern marine paints reflect the advances in chemistry. Greatly improved anti-foulants serve both fast and slow speed vessels. Special products do a fine job on aluminum, fiberglass, and ferro-cement hulls, as well as on the traditional wood and steel. These sophisticated chemical products require somewhat different techniques than the shoreside paints we are accustomed to, though they aren't necessarily more difficult to use. Just different. It really isn't necessary to understand all the complexities of paint chemistry, though a few basics will aid you in selecting the best product for the job. Let's list a few salient features of the principal ingredients of modern boat paints.

Alkyds. These are a whole family of useful synthetic resins, and are the mainstay of the industry. Most auto paints are alkyds, in this case designed to dry hard to withstand the road hazards and punishment of gravel and rocks. Great for their purpose, auto paints are too brittle to withstand the wracks and twists which a boat goes through. So the manufacturers add more oil to marine alkyds for proper flexibility. Alkyds have excellent sun resistance, and anti-chalking, or ambering characteristics. They cover and flow out smoothly, are easy to use, and relatively inexpensive as good marine paints go. In normal service, alkyds can last three years or more. One disadvantage of alkyds is that they don't withstand well long periods of immersion. But this characteristic can be overcome neatly, as we'll discuss in the section on paint blends.

Epoxy. This is the muscleman among paints, noted for its adhesion, hardness, water resistance, and ability to handle water- and air-borne pollution. True, two part epoxies are a bit more difficult to use, requiring careful mixing of the parts, and precise attention to the induction (waiting) time between mixing and application. Epoxies do not hold their color quite as well as other paints, and have a tendency to oxidize (chalk). To keep them looking sharp, they must occasionally be buffed or rubbed down.

Polyurethane. Elastic toughness, color retention, and chalk resistance are big points here. Urethanes are very hard, and can be burnished out to a magnificent polish, sometimes seen on the more expensive show boats. But so far, chemically cured two-part urethanes are so tricky to use that they are practical only for carefully controlled factory application. In normal boat yard use, shelf life is sometimes a problem and the hardness is so great that it is difficult to rough up prior coats, so that later ones can get a grip. I once tried to abrade a cured urethane, and could cut it only with dry "wet-or-dry" paper, and a lot of elbow grease.

Vinyls. These are uniquely suited for underwater use. They withstand immersion well, and make excellent vehicles for hard anti-fouling bottom paints.

Acrylics. These resins dry quickly and resist weathering very well. They are often an important part of spray touch-up "varnishes," and, of course, show up in many blends.

Blended Paints. Compounding a boat paint, like so many marine things, is very much a compromise. Long life, ease of application, quick drying, flexibility, hardness, appearance, and price are all desirable characteristics, but often at opposite ends of the formulation see-saw. Each of the marine paint manufacturers, like gourmet cooks, does it a little differently, but ends up with a fine product. Such companies as Z-Spar, Woolsey, Pettit, International, or Baltimore Copper, to name a few, have big research labs, working year round to improve the product. They also have test panels on and in the water, all over the country. Before a single can reaches your dealer's shelf, it has served a tough test period on different boats, in different waters. If you take a fine alkyd, high in sun resistance, low in water resistance, blend it with a phenolic, low in sun resistance, high in water resistance . . . *Voila*, a brand new ball game. Modified epoxies will retain some of the hardness, adhesion, and chemical resistance, and pick up the anti-chalking qualities and easy application of the alkyd partner. Polyurethanes add toughness to their blends, pick up resistance to yellowing from the other ingredients. Acrylics add speed drying, plus weather resistance—and so on down the line. Though these gross simplifications may cause paint chemists to blanch a little, we aren't writing this for their edification. Boat owners need to know what they are reading, when they pick up the ads for these excellent paints.

Often the ads will claim that the modern paint will far outlast *"ordinary"* or *"conventional"* marine paint. I dug around to find what was called "ordinary" boat paint. I concluded that it was the old type paint marketed up to World War II, before the present day synthetics were fully developed. You can still buy "ordinary" marine paint from the bargain outlets, because it is a lot cheaper to make. But considering the clear cut superiority and longevity of today's surface coatings, using the old stuff would probably rate in the penny-wise-pound-foolish category.

With some general idea of the strengths and weaknesses of the major components, let's get down to some recommendations. With the tremendous variety of weather, operating conditions, and other variables, it is not possible to be too specific about paints for boats located over an entire continent. We'll give you the principles. You do the detective work in your area, with dealers and with owners whose boats you admire.

For especially polluted areas, where chemical contamination, grime adhesion, or severe abrasion represent big problems, the two part epoxies would give a little longer life. Boatmen facing these problems shouldn't mind the slightly involved application, cost, or the need for an occasional polish, or slight loss of color retention.

For the in-between situations, the blends of one-part epoxy or polyurethane would give a long life, with excellent adhesion and hardness. One point to consider is whether the blend would yield a full extra season. In many instances we bang and abrade our boats, and cosmetic damage occurs far sooner than would result from the ravages of the elements.

Finally, for normal use, consider the alkyds. Under average conditions any of the good alkyd enamels should last three seasons, or even longer, on topsides or deck. Fine too, for trailer boat bottoms, or those which are dry sailed. Unless specifically compounded for underwater use (these are usually sold as "Hard Racing Bottom paints") regular alkyds are not recommended for immersion periods of more than 10 days or two weeks. Easy to use, relatively inexpensive, with most of the good qualities we need and want, today's alkyds are beautiful finishes which last a long time in normal boating waters. With the proper primer, they may be used on hulls of any material.

But *note well:* Each of the major manufacturers combines, cooks, and blends his brew a little differently. You simply *must* stick religiously to the *system or method* outlined in the pamphlets or on the can. Use only the recommended solvent, cleaner, brush rinse, etc. The chemists *know* what their paint needs, so don't try to outguess them, take short cuts, or mix brands. Not all paint types are friendly or compatible. With sophisticated paints, reading the directions "after all else fails" is a mighty expensive folly. Listening to waterfront wise-guys is equally perilous.

We've used several of the leading brands on different boats, recently, and had satisfaction from all. Sometimes we prefer one system over another, and so will you. But if one isn't available, we go with another, follow directions, and achieve excellent results. Our secret opinion is that there is far greater difference between World War II type paints and today's, than there is between products of the top marine specialists.

Chemists and technicians employed by paint manufacturers follow through on every complaint, such as the owner who claimed the product peeled in three months. Invariably failures result from not following the directions, either in the preparatory or application stages. We'll outline some of the common problems, a bit later on.

Preparatory Coatings

Sealers are used on wooden hulls. One type is a preservative which penetrates the wood fibers carrying toxins in deeply, to inhibit rot. Another sealer sinks in, to even up the blotting power of the wood. Planks have hard and soft growths alternating, and if not sealed the softer areas will soak up more paint and possibly interfere with adhesion. You may end up with a paint job that has a wavy, uneven appearance. It is a simple quick step, so be sure to seal bare wood.

Undercoats are paints that are loaded with talc. They are made in various vehicles, such as alkyd, epoxy, and so on. The purpose of the undercoater is to fill minute voids and irregularities in the surface, so that the final coat will be the smoothest. Since the undercoater is put on to achieve an even surface, most of it should be sanded off, which will leave only the low spots filled.

Primers are preliminary coats designed for adhesion. They bite into relatively hard, nonporous surfaces such as plastic and metal, giving a tight bond for final coats. Metal primers usually contain acid, which etches into the surface. Which do you need, and how much? The manufacturer of the system you choose will carefully spell out the answers. Follow the "book" for a finished job.

One seemingly small item which was always important, but is even more so now, is stirring. Even if the paint store has vibrated the stuff for you, mix again just before you use. The proper way to do it is to pour off ⅓ or ½ of the liquid from the supply can into your paint pail. Then take the paddle and dig the heavy material out of the bottom, with a lifting motion. When the bottom seems free, gradually pour back the liquid from the pail and continue stirring. This is a simple task, but many paint failures can be laid to lazy, inadequate mixing.

If you are working on a previously opened can of paint, always strain it before you start. You get a smoother job when you strain out the lumps and hardened particles. Anti-fouling paints need far more stirring than topside finishes. The metals are heavy and have a great tendency to sink to the bottom. You want each brushful to have its share of poison, and vinyls dry fast, sometimes in 15 minutes. A helper who will constantly stir the antifoulant, as you brush, is a real help.

The one exception to constant stirring, of course, is varnish. Stirring introduces air into the varnish and causes bubbles which spoil the appearance of brightwork.

Since moisture inhibits paint adhesion, it goes without saying that any paint must be applied only to dry surface, and the paint must achieve hardness before it is exposed to moisture. So, sleep in a little longer on those dewy mornings, work on something else on foggy, rainy, humid days. And quit early, so the finish has at least four hours to dry before the condensation hits the hull at sundown.

Varnish

Varnished brightwork is beautiful, but still requires much work. The ultraviolet rays of the sun bounce off paint, but with clear finishes, they go through to the wood and bounce back out, to give the finish a double whammy, resulting in a far shorter life. Ultraviolet filters help some and slow down yellowing. The single part urethane blends have a longer life, though operating conditions and care determine the life expectancy of a "clear." With correct application and care, any of the top brand clears should go a full season, and the recoat drill is always two coats, the next year. One fresh-up coat just won't do, on varnish. Paid hands, on saltwater based yachts, frequently chamois down the brightwork. Salt is hydroscopic, attracts moisture droplets which act as tiny magnifying glasses to intensify the ultraviolet attack. If you can chamois off, after a hard thrash outside, you'll improve varnish life and appearance. In short, the drier you can keep your brightwork, in sunny weather, the longer it will last.

Tools of the Trade

It is often said that the tools and their care separate the craftsmen from the kids. Some boat owners' paint kits would make a decent finish impossible, even for the most skilled and patient professional. Brushes, of course, top the tool list. Since spraying, and to a lesser degree rollers, require practice and skill, we'll limit our discussion here to brush painting, which *can* be handled ably by almost any careful owner.

Nylon brushes, which work so well with latex paints around the home, are less useful around the boat. Some marine finishes such as vinyl or epoxy will actually attack nylon, so the standard recommendation is for natural bristle brushes. These aren't cheap, and there is simply no way to get around it. Put even the finest, most expensive marine finish on with a bad brush and it may look as though it had been applied with a whisk broom. Don't try to save on short bristle brushes. Get long ones that will carry and spread the paint evenly.

To add insult to injurious cost, you'll need more than one brush size for paint, and entirely separate brushes for varnish. Small boats will need a 1″ paint brush for working around the rub rail and boot top, along with at least a 3″ brush for topsides. Larger boats will probably need something in the 1″ -2½″ -4″ sizes. Older or poorer quality brushes can be used for the bottom paint, or for paint remover. Varnish needs the best brush, preferably ox hair, or even better if you can afford it, badger bristles. The 1″ size works well for narrow toe rails, with larger sizes needed for big areas of cabin or bulkhead. You can easily spend $50 to buy a good set of brushes from scratch. Console yourself, though, that they will last for years, be a joy to work with, and yield results that can be achieved in no other way.

To keep brushes in shape, you will need two holding cans, one for paint brushes, the other for varnish brushes, while the job is in progress. If the cans are fairly shallow, drill a 3/16ths inch hole in each brush handle just above the metal ferrule so that they can be suspended by a piece of coat hanger wire. Brushes should rest with the tips a couple of inches above the bottom of the can, with the level of the keeping liquid a little below the level of the ferrule.

After use, rinse the brush two or three times in the solvent recommended, then turn the bristles up and pour solvent down into the heel. Work and knead this back and forth and rinse the residue out of the heel. A brush comb is also helpful to clear small particles from the bristles and straighten them out. Kerosene is one of a number of good keeper solutions, and if you cover the brush and can with a plastic bag or wrap, fastening with a rubber band, you'll eliminate a lot of evaporation, as well as bar dirt from the solution.

When the painting is finished, take all the time needed for a thorough brush cleaning, ending with a detergent wash and water rinse. Use a metal brush comb to shape the bristles, then wrap in a waxed paper guard, or kitchen aluminum foil.

Other Tools. Remember that paint must be stirred, even during use. If you don't have a supply of lathe, pick up stirring paddles from your supplier. A mask or respirator is a *must* for sanding, particularly poisonous anti-fouling bottom paint. Don't take chances. A head covering helps keep the splatters out of your toupee or wiglet. You may need to strain the paint, so get a couple of paper funnels with gauze netting for this. A flexible b'ade putty knife is a most useful painting adjunct, along with either a cheap, stiff bristle brush, or a painters dust brush, to clean the corners and indentations.

At least two cheap plastic paint pails will be needed. Pros almost never paint from their original supply cans, amateurs frequently do. The pail is easier to handle, helps with thorough mixing (insufficient mixing is a frequent cause of failures), and keeps air away from the closed supply. If the original paint or varnish can is left open for any length of time, the liquid starts to harden, and small lumps form that detract from the finished appearance. If you use the pails to clean brushes at the day's end, they'll be ready to go again. And don't forget the all important varnish cup. This is simply a tin drinking cup, with holes drilled near the rim to take a section of coat hanger wire. We'll explain its use in the section on varnish application.

Tack rags are vital to good varnish work, and may be bought for around 35¢ each, or you can make your own. To do this, take a couple square feet of double ply cheesecloth, dunk in water or turpentine, and wring out. Spread cloth on clean flat surface, and bead varnish over surface. Then knead and spread the varnish through the entire rag. Add more to make the rag as sticky as flypaper. Fold to a handsize pad, and store in tightly-closed mason jar.

Abrasive Papers and Sanding Machines. A great deal of sanding goes along with boat painting, so here are a few tips to ease this chore as much as possible. Forget the cheap, light-colored flint (sand) paper often used around the house. Its short life and inefficiency make it expensive in terms of both money and energy. Red garnet paper is considerably better, but the aluminum oxides, sold as open coat or production paper, are the ones to use. Get plenty, for it won't spoil or go stale, and you always seem to need more just when the marine store is closed. It is graded by the number of grits per square inch, so the higher the number, the finer the paper. No. 50 is very coarse, 80 is medium, 120 is finer, and 220 or 320 are very fine. The silicone carbide wet papers are also very useful on metal or plastic boats.

Ordinary steel wool is no good around a boat, since the slivers imbed themselves in hulls or old paint, and before long they oxidize and make dirty rust streaks. Stainless steel or bronze wool can be used, though even these should be used with care, since the wools tend to burnish and polish more than they cut and rough. Synthetic abrasive pads such as Scotch Brite or Supreme are fine for dirt removal, and don't shed like the ordinary steel wools. They are great for getting into hollows and corners. Unfortunately the range of "grits" isn't nearly as wide as for papers, but they are useful supplements.

There are three common types of sanding machines: circular, or attachments for electric drills; belt sanders; and vibrating or orbital pad sanders. The circular type is fine for removing great gobs of material, but has a tendency to cut and leave swirl marks, so is of somewhat limited use. The belt sander is a fine cutting tool, but like the circular type, can cut too deeply if one is not accustomed to its action. They are great in the hands of skilled men who use them every day.

Pad type, orbital sanders are slower, but almost anyone can use them successfully, with relatively little risk. If you are buying a tool, remember that sanding a boat may take considerable time, and the tool tends to get hot. It isn't hard to burn up a light, inexpensive, home workshop tool on big surfaces like a boat hull. Buy or rent medium or heavy duty tools.

Handling the Brush

Keep about 3″ of paint in the bottom of your paint pail, and dip the bristles about half way up. You don't want to fill the brush to the heel. Since the brush is supposed to carry paint from pail to surface, don't scrape it nearly dry on the rim, after dipping. Instead, just tap the excess off in the pail.

Easy 12″ to 18″ strokes seem best for most painters. After painting the first section, move ahead 12″ to 18″ and paint back into the wet surface to eliminate laps. Many pros take their first strokes up and down to get a cover, but always finish with horizontal strokes. Vertical finish laps (except on a varnished transom) tend to promote runs and sags. Trying to put on a coat that is too thick, also causes runs. It just isn't possible to try to cover with one thick coat what should be done with two medium ones.

Use your smaller brushes to cut in the areas along sheer and boot top, and the larger sizes for the big areas in between. If you use masking tape, lift it before the paint dries. Hard, painted tape is tough stuff to remove and usually lifts adjacent areas.

Dust is the bane of all paint and varnish jobs. Many times it is extremely difficult to control, but whatever you can do to keep it down will add to the final appearance. That beautiful finish which auto painters regularly achieve is in part due to the dust-free environment in which they work. They even chase visitors out, since lint from cotton and wool clothing is no help. Nylon coveralls are good here. Some top yards do their finish work in a covered floating shed, which is about as dust-free as one can get around the waterfront.

If blustery days bunch together, like a string of freight cars, consider putting on the preliminary coats, and the first of the finals, and then launching. It is harder to paint from a float or dinghy than from a staging ashore, but the appearance may be far better than a job loaded with dust, if that is the alternative. Try always to avoid painting surfaces that are in direct sunlight, for this speeds drying and tends toward lap and brush marks. The ideal temperature range is 50 to 90 degrees, in case you have a choice.

Anti-Fouling Paint

In saltwater, and many freshwater areas, as well, boats are immersed in a soup of living organisms. All sorts of growths, both plant and animal, want to take up a homestead in or on our hulls. The obvious trick, of course, is to apply a bottom paint which will gradually exude poison over an entire season, and thus drive the foulants away. In general, there are two types of antifoulant, semi-soft (or semi-plastic) and hard. The semisoft plastic resins become porous, and allow the poisons to work to the surface, as time goes by. Harder types are often compounded with vinyls, or include epoxy, which resist high speeds and abrasion better. These too become porous and allow the suspended poisons to leach out, at a graduated rate. One big difference is that the binder of the hard types is very much stronger. Vinyls are the more popular for most boating uses. Since vinyl, like lacquer, requires a harsh solvent to keep the particles in suspension, it will lift most of the nonvinyl paints already on the hull. Vinyl over vinyl presents no problems, but if you are not sure, try a test patch and see if the old stuff puckers up. If it does, take it off. All off. Otherwise peeling is almost sure to occur.

One trap which fools many owners is the appearance of old bottom paint, especially a vinyl that has been in the water a season. Since the binder is very strong, the paint may appear in very excellent condition, and in need of only a little freshening. But beware! That fine-appearing bottom has had all the reservoir of poisons leached out of it, and is useless for repelling the boarders. Give it the full treatment as prescribed by the maker. Its function is different from the coating used on topsides or deck, remember? Keep your poisons up.

As most everyone knows, different geographic locations have different degrees of fouling. Worst are the warm tropical areas. Another factor is the time of exposure. Obviously a northern-based craft in the water only three months a year, needs less protection than a Gulf of Mexico sister, afloat twelve months each year.

Though copper compounds have been the main antifoulant poison for years, and work very well, they do have one particular drawback. They galvanically attack exposed ferrous metal fastenings of wooden hulls, scraped steel or aluminum ones, or the outboard or outdrive on boats of any material, if there is the slightest break in the barrier coats you have erected. The tin compounds are friendlier to other metals and have a clear cut advantage in this important regard. TBTO was the first and is still widely used. For tougher fouling situations, the TBFT can be made in greater concentrations, and is more powerful.

Pricewise, the poisons are expensive, and the more a paint contains, the higher the price. You should select one which will keep your bottom clean for the season, yet not pay more than necessary for a mix that is overly potent. Prices will vary between $19 and $63 a gallon, depending principally on the amount of poison involved and the type of base. Look carefully around the label. Somewhere, you'll find a little box which will divulge the percentage of poison, and tell what kind it is. That $63-per-gallon super soup is 75 percent copper, and if you pick up a can you'll believe it.

Painting Principles

No matter whether your hull is aluminum, fiberglass, wood, steel, or ferro-cement, there are certain principles which apply to all boats. We'll run through these basics first, then discuss each hull type separately, to cover special requirements.

A new coat of paint can adhere only to the surface to which it is applied. If that surface is an old coat of paint, as is frequently the case, adhesion of the new coat will be no better than that of the old. With hull twist, wrack, swell, and shrink, plus the punishment of sun, wind, rain, salt, and spray, marine coatings face a mighty tough environment. If you don't follow instructions, paint in damp weather, or skimp on the important surface preparation steps, you'll have some vivid personal answers to the question "Why do paints peel?" Let's try for an understanding of surface preparation.

Moisture, wax, oil, dirt, and grease prevent paint from getting a good grip. Everyone knows that the surface must be clean, but what is clean? Many clean looking surfaces, such as brand new fiberglass or aluminum hulls are, for paint purposes, contaminated no matter how shiny they look. Mills use oil to ease aluminum sheets through the rolling mill, and fiberglass manufacturers use a wax-like release agent to keep the boats from sticking to the molds. Remember that auto body and fender men merely grease chrome before spraying a bumped out fender. When the paint has hardened, the greasy paint on the chrome is simply wiped off. Boats used in the sea also have a good coating of salt, which attracts moisture, and can thus lift new paint. All of these things have to come off. All off.

The first step is to go over the entire boat with soap, water, and stiff brush to remove salt and dirt accumulations. If the boat has been painted before, check to see if the old coat is hard, and adhering well. If much of it is checked or cracking, take it off down to the bare hull with paint remover and scrapers. If the old paint is sound and sands off to a dry powder, chances are you can clean it up and repaint with alkyd type enamels. If you have chosen one of the top rated vinyls for the bottom, you will have to remove the old coating unless you *know for sure* that the former paint was also a vinyl. The only way to be sure with one of the epoxy-urethanes or blends, is to try a test panel in accordance with the manufacturer's instructions. All your work and expense will be wasted if you build the new finish on a poor foundation.

Over the years, many different cleaners have been suggested for boats. Lacquer thinner and acetone are two that are frequently recommended. These dry so quickly that they really can't do the job well. Instead, use the solvent cleaner recommended by the maker whose system you choose. These are designed for the job and you know that they will be compatible with subsequent coats.

Always clean before sanding. Sanding creates heat, and if you start abrading a dirty surface you will drive salts, wax, etc. right into the pores of the hull where it will hide until later. Eventually it will sneak out and give you a low blow on your paint job. Since waxes and oils aren't too easy to see, take it slow and steady, when cleaning. No more than three or four square feet should be cleaned at a time. Give the hull a good dose of cleaner, then wipe thoroughly with clean rags. As soon as a rag gets dirty, discard it, otherwise you will just be smearing the glop around. When the solvent and clean rags indicate no further dirt, it is the time to start sanding. Some instructions suggest sanding first, then wiping the surface with solvent. But consider that the heat of sanding can drive some things into the pores of the hull; others are in loose particles lying on the surface. A wet rag will wipe some of the loose matter right back into the pores you have just opened. Clean first, then sand. And when sanding is finished, use vacuum air pressure or a tack rag to remove debris.

Tricks for Different Hulls

Fiberglass. Plastic hulls don't need paint for protection, as do wood and steel. Good gel coats usually last several years, under normal conditions, before the wax and polish routine fails to bring back their original beauty. During this time, the gel coat continues to cure and harden, as does the mold release wax, and any other polishes you have added. All of these *must* be removed, if paint is to adhere. Not even the tight gripping epoxies can get a hold on plastic surfaces that aren't totally *clean.* Take the time and elbow grease to remove all of the waxes, using the recommended solvent and plenty of clean rags. Don't continue to wipe with dirty rags, which just smear. It is exactly the same amount of work to do the job right.

Because of their splendid adhesion, epoxies are often chosen for primers and finish coats. Epoxy paste compounds are the choice for filling scrapes and gouges, and again, the *indentation* must be clean, if the paste is to get its grip.

Is sanding necessary on a fiberglass hull that is receiving its first coat of paint? Some systems say yes, others, no. We'd certainly sand if the system called for it. And it would be safer, and give a stronger grip, even for those which don't, for sanding provides a tooth to improve adhesion. With a power sander and fairly coarse grit, roughening the surface shouldn't take too long, and can be done under almost any reasonable weather conditions. Do you need a talc loaded undercoat on a fiberglass hull? That depends on how rough the surface is, and how fine a finish you want. Epoxy based undercoaters stick well, and are sanded almost all off, the same as others performing the smoothing function. Bottoms rarely get undercoating.

Vinyls are usually chosen for fiberglass bottoms that need anti-fouling, and since they adhere well directly to fiberglass, no primer is needed. Trailer boats and those that are dry sailed can use epoxies on the bottom or epoxy primer and alkyd enamels, the same as the topsides.

Previously painted fiberglass may or may not need scraping down, depending on the condition and the type of old paint. Chipping, flaking old finishes obviously must come off. Most paint removers contain Methylene Chloride as a base, and these will attack the fiberglass gel coat in time. *Always* take the paint remover off fiberglass as quickly as it will lift the paint, and immediately rinse with fresh water. Do a small section at a time. Since paint remover also contains wax to keep it on the surface, this too must be cleaned away with a solvent compatible with the new paint. The strength of the volatiles (solvents) gives you an idea as to whether the new paint will lift the old. The final test is to try a bit of the new paint on a sample test patch. Usually, if incompatible, it will lift in half an hour. Stripping is not fun, but the advantages of modern, longer lasting finishes and anti-foulants thoroughly justifies the labor.

Making your decks rough with some abrasive is extremely important from the safety standpoint. Smooth, shiny decks really aren't safe, as any sailor with a little experience knows, and they kick back the sun's rays and make it mighty hard on the eyes, as well. At one time, ground walnut shells were used for abrasive, but since these contained oil, they interfered with adhesion. Ground pumice, volcanic ash, or one of the man-made grits are all good. You can mix them into the final coats, provided you keep them well stirred during application, or make up a salt shaker type box and sprinkle the rough material into the wet coat.

Don't be afraid that rough decks will be hard to keep clean. A stiff, long handle scrub brush and kitchen cleanser work well, and tough finishes like epoxy or urethane will stand this punishment nicely. Sharp decks aren't so pleasant on bare feet, particularly at the start of the season when one's soles are soft. But it's better to have feet that need toughening than a crew member overboard on some dark, rainy night.

Aluminum. Like fiberglass, aluminum doesn't really need paint for protection. The natural oxidation coating which normally forms to protect the metal, of its own accord, isn't the prettiest finish, however, and is a fine surface for attracting and holding oil, grease, and dirt. Unpainted hulls will probably have traces of the mill oil on them, even if you can't see it, along with the so called "white rust" products of corrosion, which must also come off to insure paint adhesion. A mild alkaline cleaner will probably be suggested for the system you choose. As with plastic, take it thoroughly and slowly, limiting your effort to three or four square feet of surface at a time, changing rags frequently. Indentations and depressions can be filled and smoothed with fairing compounds suggested for aluminum. Sanding is usually recommended as a prep step for aluminum. The same precautions for putting new paint over old apply with these hulls, as with others.

As you are working closely with your hull, check carefully for any evidences of galvanic corrosion (electrolysis). All non-aluminum fittings and attachments must be electrically insulated from the hull with neoprene, micarta, or similar nonconductors. If these are not installed, or are breaking down, the aluminum can be destroyed. Replace any insulators that are the least bit questionable.

Since aluminum is nonporous and smooth, it needs a metal etching primer. These usually contain an acid, which you mix in, just before the primer is applied. Once primed, the finish coats may be alkyd, epoxy, vinyl, or any of the blends. If you want to use copper anti-fouling, four to six barrier coats are recommended, to prevent galvanic action between the copper and the aluminum hull. The nongalvanic tin compounds are the best bet for aluminum, since they eliminate this possibility. The Aluminum Association recommends only vinyl paint systems, with TBTO vinyl anti-fouling paint for bottoms.

Steel. Modern finishes really show their superiority on steel boats, and the extra long paint life does much to help with the rust problem. The rule of thumb is to keep at least four coats between the metal and the elements. New surfaces must be sand-blasted, a professional job, to clear off any rust or mill scale. Smaller jobs can be handled with a wire brush in a power tool, but it is a long hard job with any sizeable surface at all.

This cleaning is followed with an etch primer, usually containing red lead to help inhibit the rust. As with aluminum, barrier coats are needed for copper bottom paints, if used, with the tins a better choice. Steel hulls, like aluminum, should also be closely inspected for good insulation between hull and nonferrous fittings. Many metal hulls are equipped with impressed current cathodic protection, which does a fine job. But if out of adjustment, the system can cause paint to peel even if everything else is in first class order.

Wood. The porosity of wood and the fact that it can provide food for borers and rot spores, among other things, makes wood somewhat different from metal and plastics. Sealers are used to combat both of these situations. Very thin sealers containing poison penetrate the wood to inhibit the parasitic invaders. Since there are alternating hard and soft growths in woods, these must be sealed so that the softer parts won't blot up more of the undercoater, and spoil adhesion, or cause a wavy-looking final finish. Always seal bare wood.

Undercoats are more important to smooth up a wooden hull, since there are normally more irregularities. With adhesion less of a problem with wood than with harder materials, primers are not normally needed. One difference with wood is that the material tends to hold moisture in its pores more than the harder hull materials, and thus requires a longer spring drying time, if the boat has been stored in a foggy, moist area throughout the winter. Exactly the same precautions apply to refinishing over old coats, as those we have already outlined. Since adhesion is not a problem, you can use any of the top quality marine finishes with satisfaction. If you don't abuse the boat to the point that retouching will not restore the appearance, you can expect two to three years, or even more, from today's finishes.

Ferro-Cement. These hulls contain a relatively strong alkali, which can tend to cause problems with some primers. Epoxy blends withstand this well, and have tested out satisfactorily. With a good foundation, further coats of epoxy can yield a finish as smooth as the final plastering job allows. When well done, the entire boat can be as beautiful as any other.

All-Important Tips

Varnish. Due to the passage of ultraviolet rays through the surface, varnishes inherently have a tougher life than paint afloat. Usually twice as many coats of varnish are needed, with four a minimum on new work, or old that has been wooded down. Preparation must be carefully handled, since there is no pigment to cover any imperfections, and varnished brightwork is used as the accent and highlight on boats of every hull material. Figure on taking twice as long to varnish any given area as you would to paint it.

If the old finish needs removing there is a good chance you will have dark spots to be bleached. Just mix ½ cup of oxalic acid crystals in a quart of hot water, and label it POISON. A cup of borax in another quart jar

TIPS ON BRUSH CARE

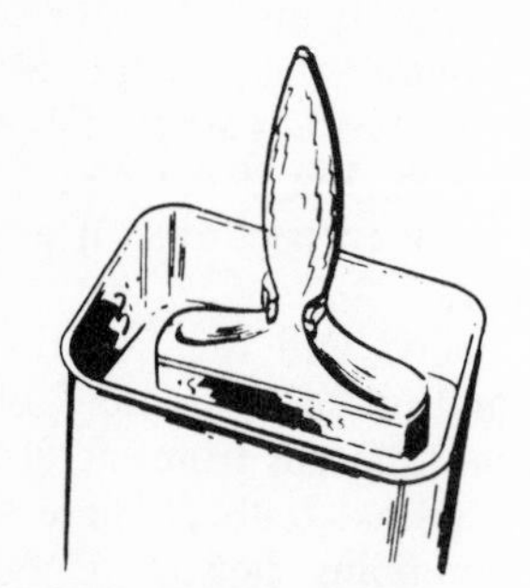

IF BRUSH IS NEWLY USED, CLEAN IT IN THINNER TO REMOVE THE PAINT.

IF THE BRUSH IS NOT TO BE USED AGAIN FOR SOME TIME, WASH IT THOROUGHLY IN MILD SOAP AND WARM WATER TO REMOVE ALL LOOSE PAINT AND SOLVENT.

COMB THE BRUSH CAREFULLY TO REMOVE ALL TWISTS AND CURLS AND TO MAKE SURE THE BRISTLES ARE STRAIGHT. THIS IS A VERY IMPORTANT STEP.

AFTER THE BRUSH IS COMPLETELY DRY, AND NOT TO BE USED AGAIN FOR SOME TIME, SOAK BRUSH AND WRAPPER IN RAW LINSEED OIL AND KEEP WRAPPED UNTIL NEXT JOB.

Fig. 901

of hot water will neutralize the acid. Put the oxalic acid on the dark spot until it is light enough, then stop the bleach with the borax, and allow it to dry at least overnight before proceeding. On new and old cleared wood, it is usually recommended that a paste wood filler (sometimes containing a stain) be used to seal, and "lay" the grain of open wood. Do a relatively small area with sealer, and when it is dull, rub it off with a rough cloth, such as burlap. And this time, don't worry about the rub rag being loaded with filler. The more filler the rag contains, the better it works at evening things out. Save the very nicest painting day for varnishing, as warm, dry, and windless as possible. Your best brush, of course, is reserved for the brightwork, kept in a separate keeper can and solution from those used for paint.

In addition to all the other things you fight with a finish, bubbles plague varnish people. Here is how the pros beat those bubbly craters which spoil appearance. Before using a varnish brush, they lay it flat in the pail and pour varnish over it, working out all the air trapped in the bristles. They carefully pour varnish from the supply into the pail, and immediately cover the supply can. Dipping gently into the pail, they then take the brush to the little varnish drip cup, knock the drips off, and flow the work on, with as little rebrushing as possible. Every six or eight feet they take a nearly dry brush and go back over any bubbles that have appeared. By then the bubble has mostly drained, and is easily smoothed.

Insufficient sanding, before recoating, is a common cause of varnish peeling. And since dust of any sort is more obvious than on paint, the careful use of the tack rag to remove dust on and around the work is a most essential technique. The best workmen don't try to save the varnish that is left in the pail or drip cup, partially hardened and bubbly. Make some more tack rags if you want to save it. Work carefully, and your brightwork can be the envy of the marina.

Fading. This is an extremely difficult thing to discuss except in generalities due to differences in the intensity of the sun in various boating areas. Whites and greys, are excellent for fade resistance, and the new greens and blues are far superior to older type pigments. Yellows and reds are more fade prone, though again, much improved in modern finishes. Since pastels are mixtures of color and white, and thus weaker, they may not hold color as well as stronger pigmentations. But a little fading won't hurt a well-pigmented color, and today's top products will give a long glossy life and resist fading.

Scheduling. Following the directions, particularly in regard to time, is important in attaining the big gains now possible with marine finishes. So make up a schedule card, indicating how long to wait after cleaning before sanding, when to overcoat a preliminary, etc. Don't paint yourself into a corner with a prep coat that must be allowed to dry for four hours and be recoated within six, by applying that preliminary at 3:30 in the afternoon! Think ahead, so that things work out. It takes a little doing, of course, but then most worthwhile things require a bit of noodling, along with the mechanics involved. Marine finishes are no harder—no different. There are plenty of other chores around a boat, and these may be done while the waiting or curing time passes. And it does allow a bit of time for gamming with friends you might not have seen since last boating season.

At the start we mentioned the four parts to boat painting: Selection, tools, preparation, and application. There is a very important fifth part, which we almost forgot. A great many beautiful boats include this last ingredient, so if you can, arrange to have a wife who loves to paint.

Dripless Paint Pot

For a dripless paint pot, use a plastic pail, and drill two 1⁄16″ holes just below the top edge, parallel to the bail, as shown in *Fig. 902*. A length of wire cut from a coat hanger is passed through the holes, and bent at the ends to keep it in place. Length of the wire should be about 1½ times the width of the largest brush you plan to use.

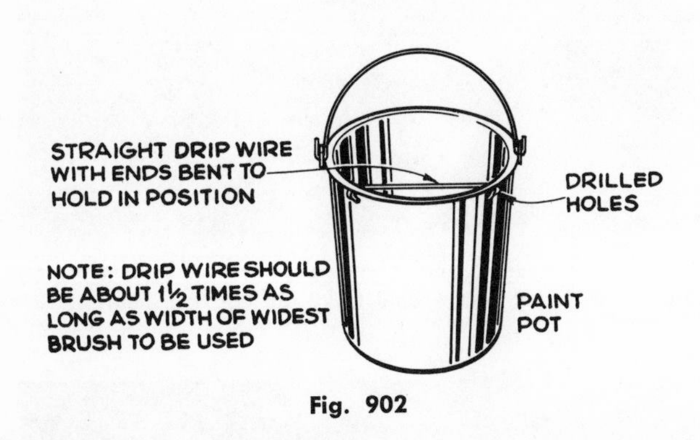

Fig. 902

Dip the brush in the paint—about ¾″ is deep enough—and press the brush lightly against the wire as you withdraw it from the pot. You don't want to take too much paint off the brush.

If paint is to be poured into the pot from a can of previously-used paint, use a nylon stocking as a strainer. And when unused paint is poured back into the can, seal the can tightly, wipe excess paint from the top, and store the can upside down. This will help prevent the paint from skinning over in the can.

Simple Way to Clean Brushes

Often it seems the hardest part of a paint job is cleaning the brushes properly. Dallas Tinling worked out this method that involves no muss, no fuss, and very little solvent.

Two cans are used; one is an old quart oil can or vegetable can, the other is a two-pound coffee can. Brushes are washed in the coffee can, and the used solvent is poured into the oil can for disposal in a suitable facility. Tinling claims a 2½″ brush used for almost any type of marine coating can be cleaned with only six ounces of solvent. Here's how to do it:

Pour about one ounce of solvent into the coffee can. That's just enough to cover the hump in the bottom of the can. Put the tip of the brush in the solvent and press the brush down, bending all the bristles in the same direction so that they are bent flat to the bottom, and the solvent wets the entire brush. Work the brush up and down a few times to pump the solvent through the bristles and out around the ferrule. Turn the brush over and repeat.

You now have about an ounce of thin paint in the bottom of the can. Pour it out into the second can, and pour an ounce of clean solvent into the wash can. Repeat the washing process; this time you will have very dirty solvent to pour into the waste can. Add a third ounce of clean solvent to wash can, and proceed as before. Continue in the same manner until the six ounces of solvent have been used. You probably will get only a slight trace of color in the fifth solvent rinse.

Next you need a source of running water, and some hand soap. It does not matter if the water is warm or cold,Tinling reports. With the last solvent still in the brush, work it across the wet soap, and then work it around in your hand. The water miscible oil of the soap and the solvent and the water all will combine somewhat. Work this mixture around with the brush just a little, then hold the brush under the running water and wash some of it out of the bristles.

Run the brush over the soap again, and repeat the lathering process. You repeat this six times. About the fourth time you'll get thin suds; the fifth time you'll get thick suds, and the sixth time is just to make sure. Set the brush aside to dry, and it will be clean and soft the next time you need it.

If you get paint on the ferrule or handle of the brush, just use a little solvent to clean it off. If you have paint on your hands, wet them, soap them, and pour a bit of solvent into one palm. Rub the mixture in thoroughly, then, without rinsing, and a little more water and soap. Keep adding a little soap and water until you get a good lather, then rinse.

Wood-Grained Fiberglass

Here's a finish that provides the beauty of natural wood with the durability of fiberglass. With it you can have a teak deck surface, or a mahogany transom, on an all-fiberglass cruiser (or runabout, or whatever), and it's no more work than papering the wall of a room.

Basis of the finish is a product called Pacolon, a tough, tissue-like material developed by the Paper Corporation of United States. It is imprinted with a wood grain, and when applied with a colored resin and protected by a layer of fiberglass cloth, it gives the appearance of well-varnished wood.

The Pacolon is available in a kit from Pettit Paint Co., along with base and top coat resins, two jars of base coat resins (teak and mahogany), a length of fiberglass cloth, and a can of minute glass beads that can be mixed with the top coat resin if a skid-resistant surface is desired. The kit contains enough material to cover about 25 square feet; retail cost is about $35. A typical installation job is shown in the Gary Miller photographs, *Figs. 903* to *908*.

Fig. 903. In this sequence, Pacolon installation is on a new boat; on old boats, scrape surface to be covered down to bare wood, or remove paint and wax from a fiberglass surface.

Fig. 904. Pigmented coat of polyester resin is brushed evenly onto the deck. Let it cure until tacky—at least two hours.

Fig. 905. Pacolon strips are unrolled and pressed onto the resin. If appearance of seams is desired, overlap ¼".

Fig. 906. If no seam is wanted, butt joint can be achieved by slicing through the overlap, peeling away each excess layer.

Fig. 907. Fiberglass cloth is positioned, and cut to fit area. It can be taped in place on vertical surfaces, but not to Pacolon.

Fig. 908. Final coat of resin is applied. Weave of cloth "disappears," allowing pattern of Pacolon to show through.

10. BOATKEEPER TOOLS

Tool Selection

What are the basic tools that the boatkeeper should have in his workshop, and how should they be selected? These questions are well-answered in the following Pete Smyth article, which appeared in a 1969 issue of *Motor Boating*:

"The boatkeeper is a craftsman in the true sense of the word. Due to the nature of the beast he is taking care of, virtually all his projects require one or more hand crafts. Some people choose to call them arts, and perhaps they are. We won't debate the point for either definition, boatkeeping still depends on hand skills and therefore hand tools.

"More correctly, since some power tools are very useful indeed, boatkeeping depends on hand-held tools. Floor or bench mounted tools, while they may occasionally be handy, are by no means essential to the care and feeding of any boat, be she a dink or a 75-foot yacht. Among the power tools in the nice-to-have, but easily-lived-without category, are such homeowner's favorites as circle or radial saws, planers, jointers, and jig saws. Less popular around the house but more useful for boats is a band saw, but this tool can be replaced nine times out of 10 by the modern saber saws. In fact, the newer variable speed saber saws can handle many jobs in many different materials, that a band saw couldn't touch.

"A power saber saw is a real asset to boatkeeping, as is a good pad sander, preferably one with both orbital and straight-line action. The orbital movement is good for rough work, while the straight-line does a fine finish job, minus the tiny swirls that mark the trail of the orbital sanders. Belt and disc sanders have their place, particularly in repairing fiberglass. However, they can easily be rented in most parts of the country.

"In selecting a sander, indeed any power tool, don't be fooled by nomenclature like 'heavy duty' and so forth. Read the label that is attached to every power tool. The label will indicate the amperage the tool will draw. This is a direct measure to the oomph built into the tool: twice the amperage, twice the power.

"Buying power tools is pretty much like buying any piece of mechanical gear. You get what you pay for, and vice versa. Two identical-appearing drills may carry widely divergent prices. On the surface they look the same, with the same chuck sizes and so forth. Reading the two labels may indicate two different power plants, but more likely the real difference will be buried inside the machine. Cheap tools have cheap bronze bearings, better tools have ball bearings, good tools will have either ball or roller bearings. A cheap tool must be used sparingly, two holes here and four holes there, but a really good tool can be run continuously without fear of damage.

"The grade of tools most useful to boatkeeping, which implies rather intensive but somewhat sporadic working habits, is in the middle between the best and the worst. The cheapest is a waste of money. Tools in this category lack the power and the stamina to accomplish anything. Yet the best power tools are a waste of money, too, because the average boatowner simply doesn't have enough work to require the capability built into the best tools.

"This refers to power tools, but it applies to some hand tools, too. Hammers, for example, range wildly in price, once again causing the novice tool buyer to scratch his head and wonder why two pieces of metal that look so much alike can vary in price. Banging nails for an hour with each of them soon shows the difference. A really good, balanced hammer can be used all day without wearing out the wielder. The cheap hammer will demolish the best carpenter in no time, and bend over a lot of nails in the process. Obviously, a hammer around a boat will only be used now and again, indicating a tool of better quality than the worst but short of the best.

"However, there is one area where *not* buying the best is a total waste of time and money: cutting tools, including chisels, saws, drills, planes, and so forth. When you buy a cutting tool you are buying steel. Low price indicates cheap, soft steel. High price indicates hard, expensive steel. Let's take a for instance. Let's say that you have to do a lot of fitting to install some lockers, most of which requires chiseling. You arrive at the yard and go to work with your discount store special chisels. Five minutes later, you find that the wood you're working is getting much harder and tougher as you go. Ten minutes after that, you're convinced the wood has petrified into solid granite and, really, you'd be better off chewing your way through it. If you have a whetstone, you can sharpen the chisels up a bit, but as soon as you go back to work they'll be dull. The result of all this is a hard day of sheer frustration, frustration that could have been completely avoided by the purchase of the best chisels you could find. The few dollars mean nothing next to the waste of time and effort.

"Actually, the dollar difference between buying good cutting tools, in the right sizes, is not much, if any, higher than buying a lot of cheap tools. To stay with our chisel example, one cheap brand of chisels comes in a set of four: ½″, 1″, 1½″, and 2″ wide. Totally unnecessary. Two good chisels, ½″ and 1″ wide, will do everything.

And while it is true that no one can have too many tools, good boatkeeping does not need a hardware store full of equipment. Here is our idea of what should be a basic tool kit for maintenance and repair:

Power Tools

⅜″ variable speed drill w/sanding disc and polishing bonnet to fit twist drills, counter sinks, plug cutter.

Pad sander with both orbital and straight line action.

Variable speed saber saw with blades for wood and metal.

Bench grinder for sharpening tools.

Hand Tools

Standard carpenter's hammer.
Standard cross-cut saw.
Back saw.
Brace, with bits to 1″, screwdriver kit, and expansion bit.
'Yankee' screwdriver with regular and Phillips bits.
Plane.
'Surform' plane and rasp, flat and half-oval.
Rasp, half-oval.
Adjustable wrench.
Pliers; vise-grip, regular, battery, and diagonal-cutting.
Open end wrenches, from $\frac{7}{16}$″ to ¾″.
(If you're mechanically inclined, add socket wrenches, ignition tools, etc.)"

TOOLS FOR BOAT WORK

Following is a selection of tools and tool kits suitable for boatkeeper use, including some special-purpose tools made specially for marine application.

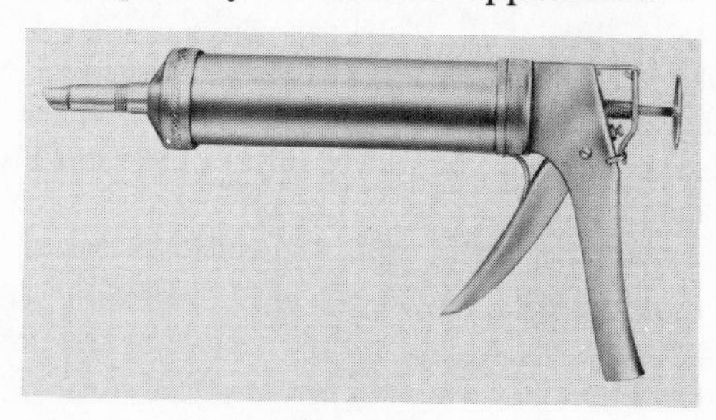

Fig. 1001

Caulking Guns

Heavy-duty caulking gun, *Fig. 1001*, is for use with bulk or cartridge sealants. Stroke of handle can be regulated to suit the individual hand, and a thumb-activated instant pressure release is featured. Capacity is $\frac{1}{10}$th gallon, bulk or cartridge. A similar gun, *Fig. 1002*, is available for use with cartridges only.

Albion Engineering Co., 1568–74 Adams Ave., Philadelphia, Pa. 19124.

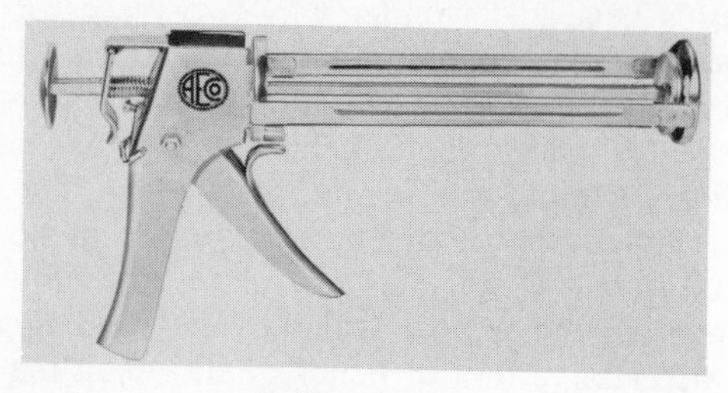

Fig. 1002

Bronze Safety Tools

Forged bronze safety tools are non-magnetic, spark resistant, rust-free, and they are said to be impervious to fresh and saltwater, bilge water, and even battery

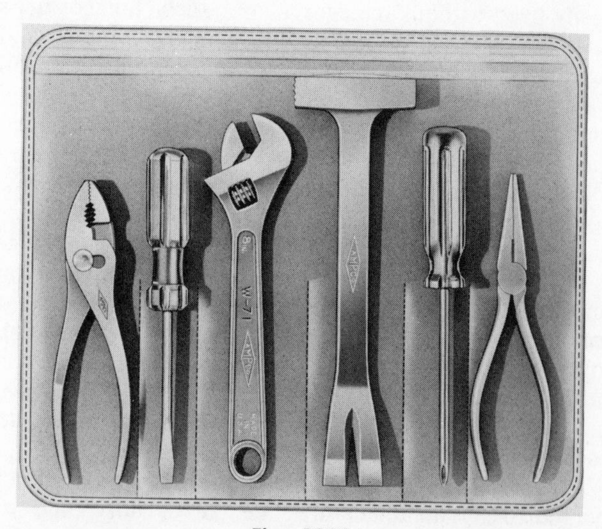

Fig. 1003

acid. "Tuna" tool kit, *Fig. 1003*, includes 6″ combination pliers, 3″ screwdriver, 8″ adjustable wrench, 10″ hammer and claw, 4¼″ Phillips screwdriver, and 6″ long nose pliers. Kits suitable for power boats include items such as box wrenches, pipe wrench, deck scraper, and putty knife.

Ampco Metal Division of Ampco-Pittsburgh Corp., P. O. Box 2004, Milwaukee, Wis. 53201.

Beryllium Copper Tools

Safety tools of Beryllium Copper are non-sparking, non-magnetic, and rust proof. Marine assortment shown in *Fig. 1004* includes 6″ slip joint pliers, 6″ adjustable wrench, 6½″ groove-joint pliers, 3¾″ screwdriver. Other tools available include hammers, wire brushes, scrapers, knives, pipe wrenches, and socket wrench sets.

Berylco Safety Tool Division, Kawecki Berylco Industries, Inc., P. O. Box 1462, Reading, Pa. 19603.

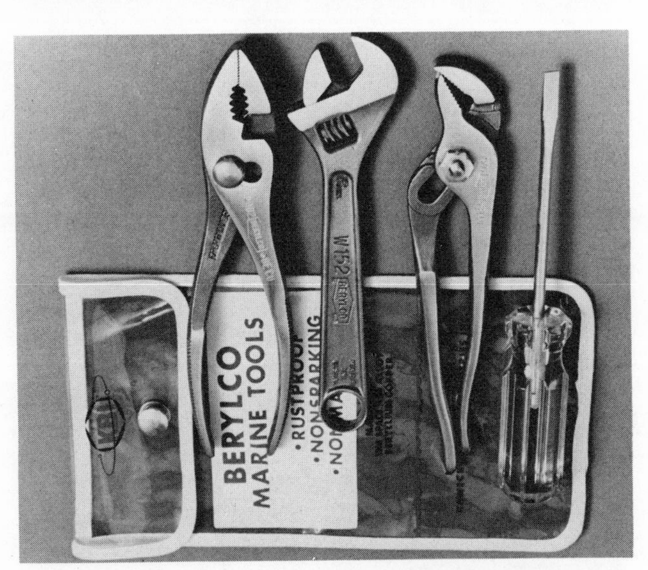

Fig. 1004

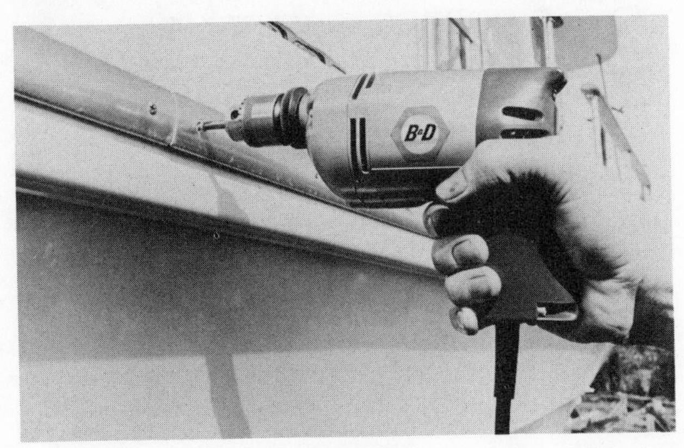

Fig. 1005

Commercial Duty 'Scru-Drill'

This ⅜″ power drill (*Fig. 1005*) is designed for fingertip conversion to screwdriver action. It will drive up to #10 wood screws or #12 self-tapping screws at full power, and a reversing switch permits quick removal of screws and nuts, according to the manufacturer. The positive clutch is said to allow maximum torque to be applied to the screw head in driving, and yet disengage when the screw is fully seated, to prevent damage to the screw head or stripping of the screw. Other power tools available include jig saws (saber saws), circular saws, sanders, and grinders, as well as a drill bit sharpener, and a cordless electric ¼″ drill.

The Black & Decker Manufacturing Co., Towson, Md., 21204.

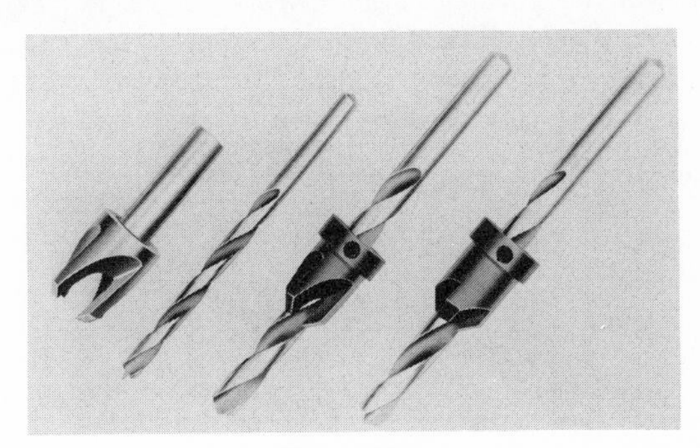

Fig. 1006

Counterbores, Plug Cutters

Any project involving screw-fastened wood joints should have screw heads set well below the surface of the wood, and covered with wood plugs for best appearance. Firm offers a complete line of drills, drill stops, countersinks, counterbores, and plug cutters *Fig. 1006*. The four-bladed plug cutters do not eject the plugs. The plugs remain in the board, where they can be broken out with a screw driver, or the board can be sawed to free the plug.

W. L. Fuller, Inc., P. O. Box 767, Warwick, R.I. 02888.

Variable Speed Jig Saw

Flush cut and miter sawing are possible with this variable speed jig saw (*Fig. 1007*), Its adjustable pivot-

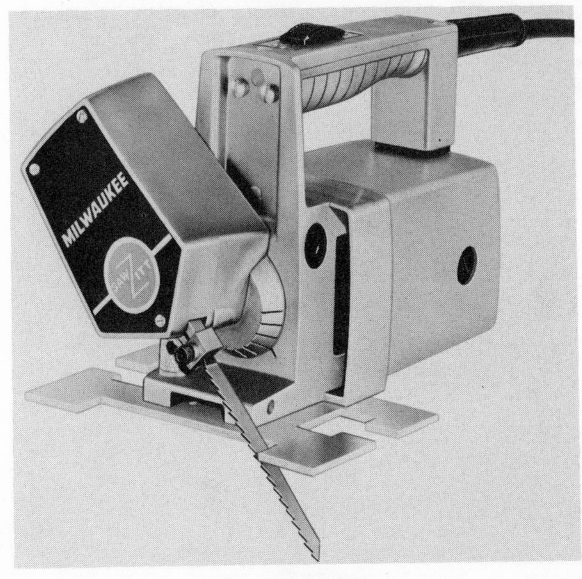

Fig. 1007

ing head is said to allow the tool to remain upright even on 45° cuts, and the turn-and-lock shoe assures correct blade clearance for straight, miter, and flush cuts. The ¼ hp motor operates on ball and roller bearings, and the speed control unit permits dialing to any speed between 1400 and 3500 strokes per minute. Complete line of power tools and accessories also includes a 12-volt electric drill that operates off a standard auto or marine battery, and is said to have the same power characteristics of a 110-volt drill.

Milwaukee Electric Tool Corp., 13135 W. Lisbon Rd., Brookfield, Wis. 53005.

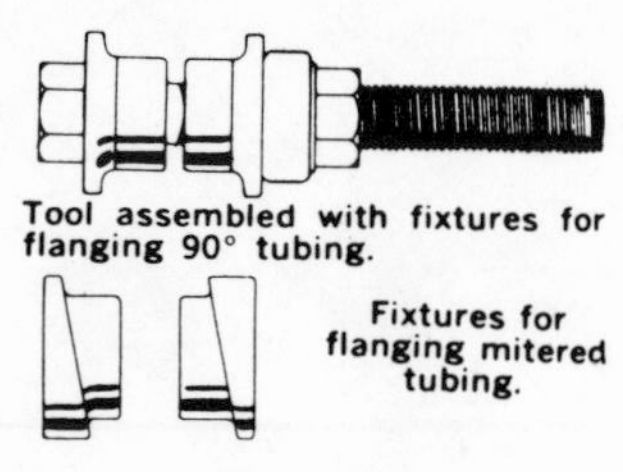

Fig. 1008

Flanging Tools

These are special-purpose tools designed for flanging brass or aluminum drain tubes installed in a transom. Nut and bolt of hardened steel with steel fixtures and thrust ball bearings (*Fig. 1008*) is said to flange tube in one easy operation. Tool is available in eight stock sizes; 1″ and 1¼″ diameters, and flange angles of 12°, 13°, 15°, and 90° in each diameter.

Moeller Manufacturing Co., Inc., Greenville, Miss. 38701; Niagara Falls, Ont., Canada.

Deluxe Hand Tool Kit

General purpose tool kit (*Fig. 1009*) includes a steel hammer, a 12′ Powerlock® tape, three screwdrivers with standard, Phillips, and cabinet tips, a three-way adjustable knife, a multi-purpose plier, a Surform® tool, and a utility hack saw. Firm also offers a complete line of standard hand tools including try squares, marking gauges, planes, spoke shaves, chisels, "Yankee" screwdrivers, drills, bit braces, and doweling jigs.

Dept. PID, The Stanley Works, New Britain, Conn. 06050.

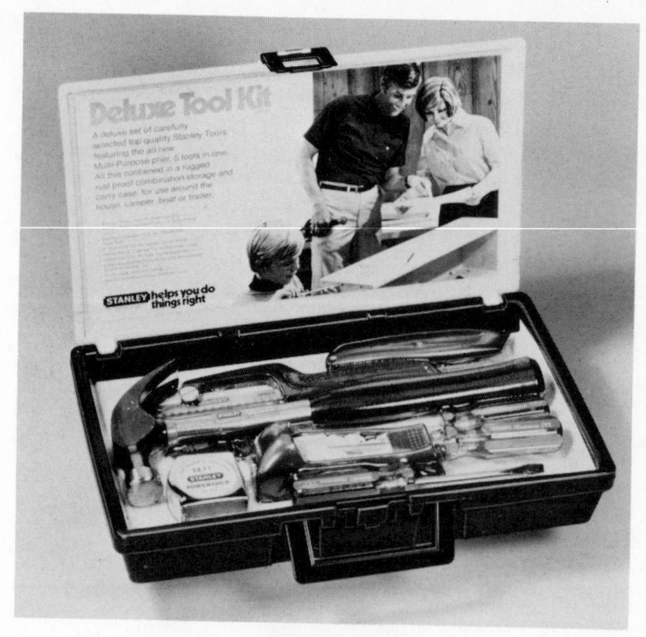

Fig. 1009

Mechanical Screw Starters

Screw starters for ferrous or non-ferrous screws (*Fig. 1010*) are said to eliminate fumbling with hard-to-start screws. They are available with duraluminum or shock resistant nylon handles, for both standard slotted and Phillips head screws, and the duraluminum starters have a magnet in one end for use in retrieving screws or nuts. Firm also offers inspection mirrors and a line of magnetic retrievers.

Ullman Devices Corp., P. O. Box 398, Ridgefield, Conn. 06877.

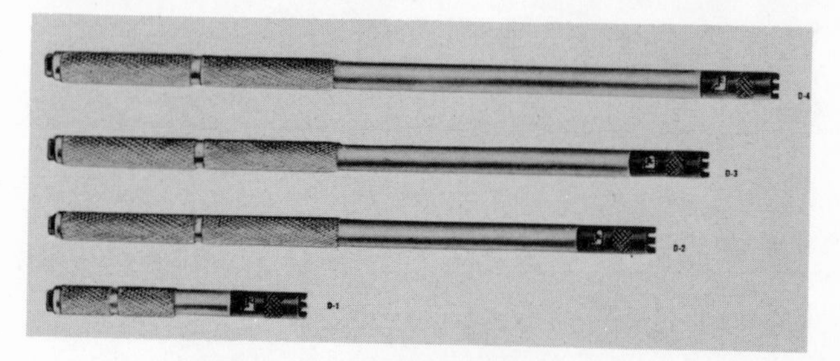

Fig. 1010

PROPER USE OF HAND TOOLS

Common hand tools are taken for granted all too often, and their mis-use accounts for many project failures and personal injuries. There's a right way to use every tool, as is shown in the illustrations (*Figs. 1011–1024*) excerpted from the *Stanley Tool Guide*. Available for 50¢ from The Stanley Works, New Britain, Conn. 06050, the *Stanley Tool Guide* is a 40-page booklet that's recommended reading for every serious boatkeeper. In addition to comprehensive information on tool use and care, it includes instructions for making common cuts in wood, and common wood joints.

HAMMER

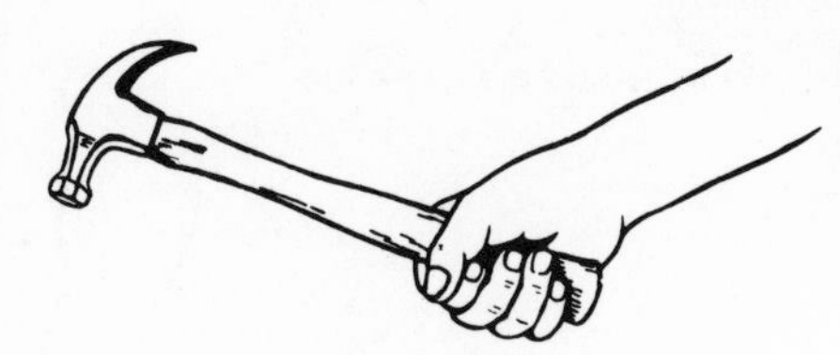

GRASP THE HAMMER FIRMLY NEAR THE END.

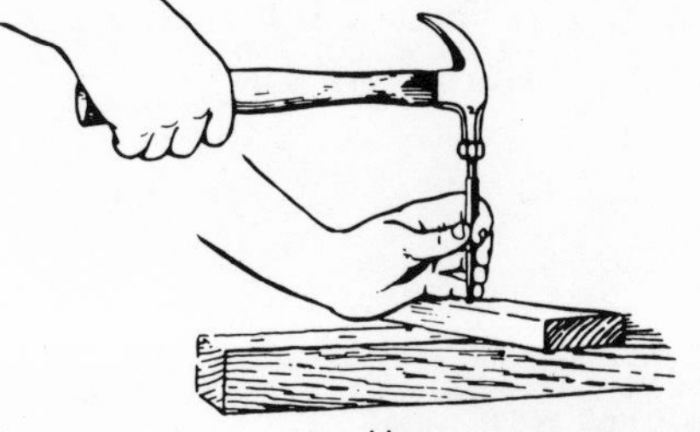

USE A NAIL SET TO DRIVE NAILS BELOW THE SURFACE OF ALL FINE WORK. TO PREVENT THE NAIL SET SLIPPING OFF THE HEAD OF THE NAIL, REST THE LITTLE FINGER ON THE WORK AND PRESS THE NAIL SET FIRMLY AGAINST IT. SET NAILS ABOUT 1/16" BELOW THE SURFACE OF THE WOOD.

THE BLOW IS DELIVERED THROUGH THE WRIST, THE ELBOW AND THE SHOULDER, ONE OR ALL BEING BROUGHT INTO PLAY, ACCORDING TO THE STRENGTH OF THE BLOW TO BE STRUCK. REST THE FACE OF THE HAMMER ON THE NAIL, DRAW THE HAMMER BACK AND GIVE A LIGHT TAP TO START THE NAIL AND TO DETERMINE THE AIM.

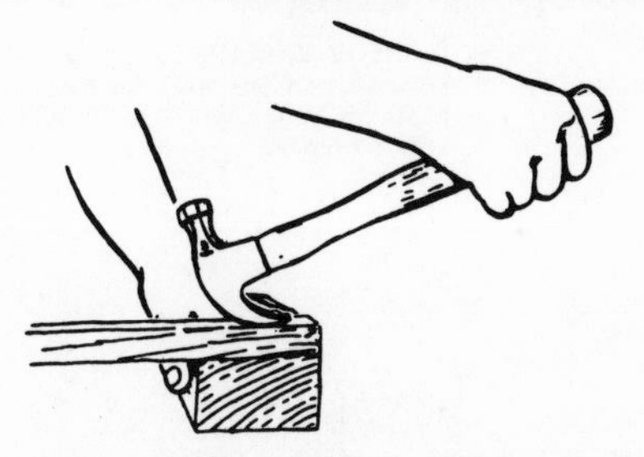

TO DRAW A NAIL: SLIP THE CLAW OF THE HAMMER UNDER THE NAIL HEAD; PULL UNTIL THE HANDLE IS NEARLY VERTICAL AND THE NAIL PARTLY DRAWN.

STRIKE THE NAIL SQUARELY TO AVOID MARRING THE WOOD AND BENDING THE NAIL. KEEP THE FACE OF THE HAMMER CLEAN TO AVOID SLIPPING OFF THE NAIL. IF A NAIL BENDS DRAW IT AND START A NEW ONE IN A NEW PLACE.

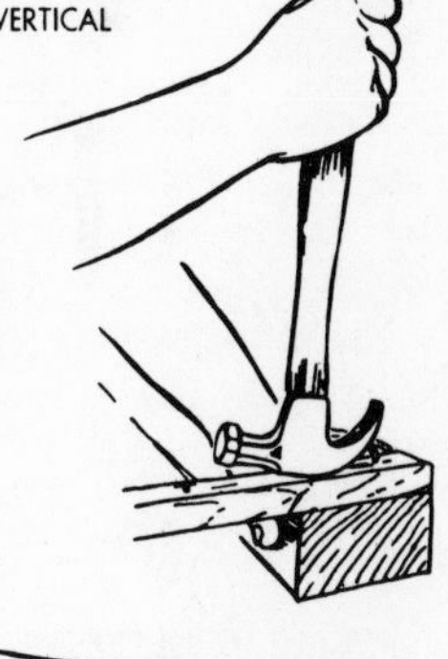

IF THE PULL IS CONTINUED, UNNECESSARY FORCE IS REQUIRED THAT WILL BEND THE NAIL, MAR THE WOOD AND PERHAPS BREAK THE HAMMER HANDLE.

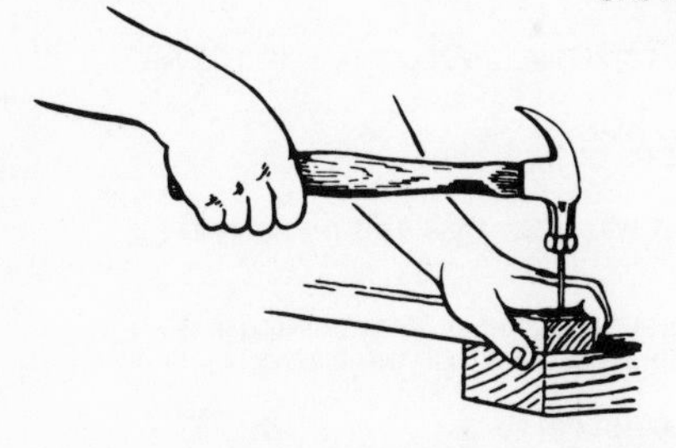

ALWAYS STRIKE WITH THE FACE OF THE HAMMER IT IS HARDENED FOR THAT PURPOSE. DO NOT DAMAGE THE FACE BY STRIKING STEEL HARDER THAN ITSELF. DO NOT STRIKE WITH THE CHEEK AS IT IS THE WEAKEST PART.

SLIP A PIECE OF WOOD UNDER THE HEAD OF THE HAMMER TO INCREASE THE LEVERAGE AND TO RELIEVE THE UNNECESSARY STRAIN ON THE HANDLE.

Fig. 1011

Courtesy The Stanley Works

SCREWDRIVER

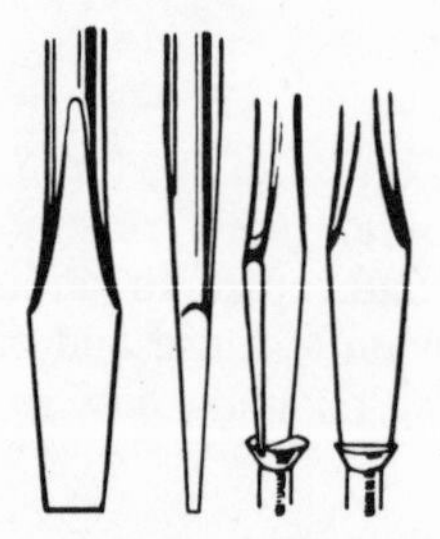

Select a screw driver of length and tip fitted to the work.
Screw drivers are specified by the length of the blade.
The tip should be straight and nearly parallel sided. It should also fit the screw slot and be not wider than the screw head.

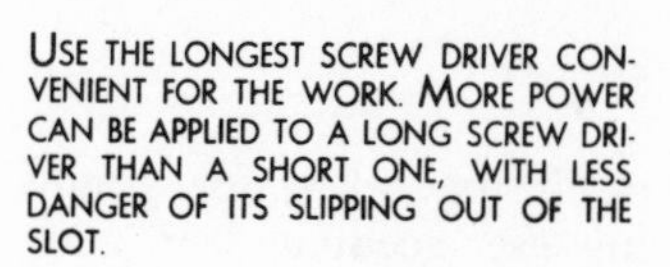

Use the longest screw driver convenient for the work. More power can be applied to a long screw driver than a short one, with less danger of its slipping out of the slot.

Hold the handle firmly in the palm of the right hand with the thumb and forefinger grasping the handle near the ferrule. With the left hand steady the tip and keep it pressed into the slot while renewing the grip on the handle for a new turn.

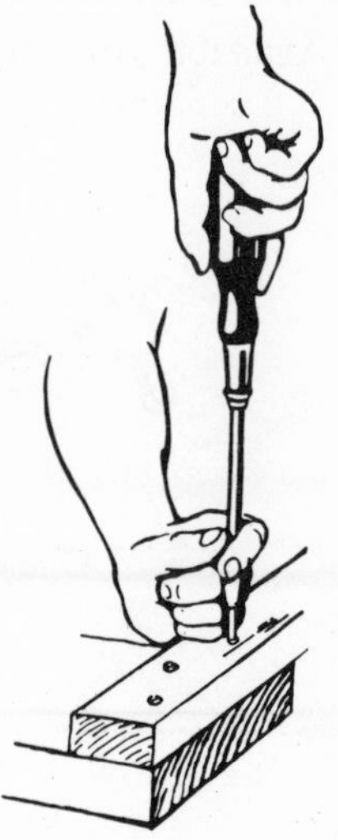

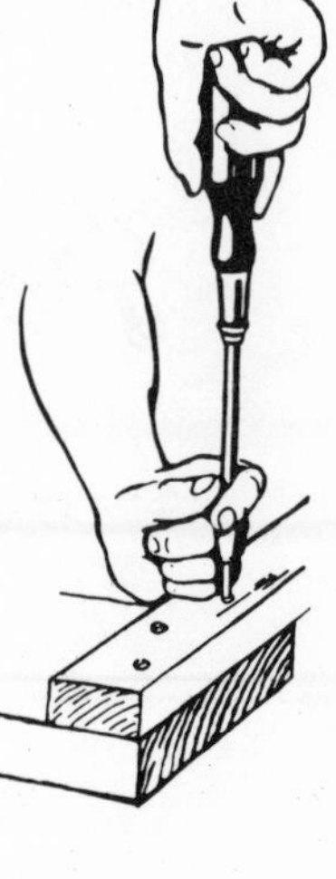

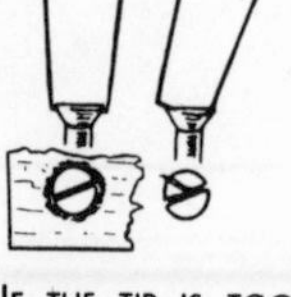

If the tip is too wide it will scar the wood around the screw head.
If the screw driver is not held in line with the screw it will slip out of the slot and mar both the screw and the work.

If no hole is bored for the threaded part of the screw the wood is often split or the screw is twisted off.
If a screw turns too hard, back it out and enlarge the hole.
A little soap on the threads of the screw makes it easier to drive.

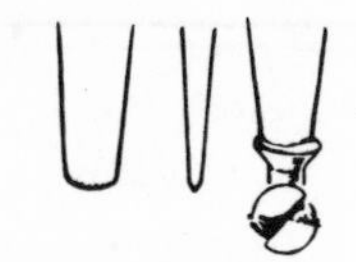

If the tip is rounded or beveled it will raise out of the slot spoiling the screw head. Regrind or file the tip to make it as shown above.

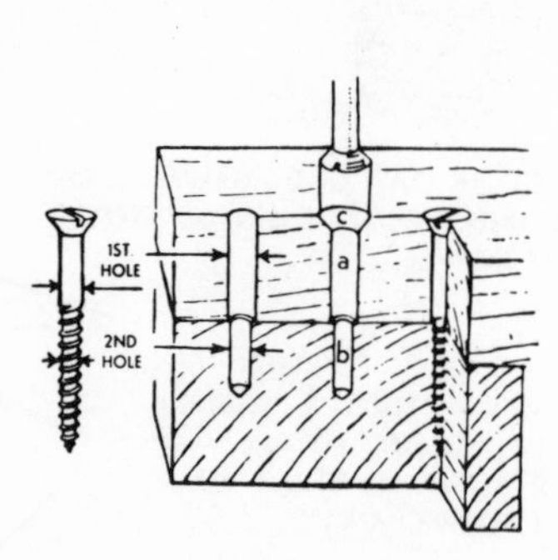

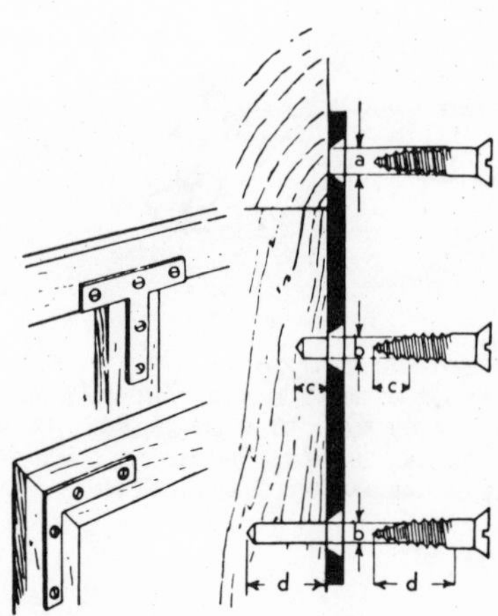

To fasten two pieces of wood together with screws:

1. Locate the positions of the screw holes.

2. Bore the first hole slightly smaller than the threaded part of the screw through both pieces of wood as at b. Bore only as deep as three quarters the length of the screw.

3. Bore the second hole in the first piece of wood slightly larger than the diameter of the screw shank, as at a.

4. Countersink the first holes to match the diameter of the heads of the screws, as at c.

5. Drive the screws tightly in place with the screw drivers.

To fasten hinges or other hardware in place with screws:

1. Locate the position of the piece of hardware on the work.

2. Recess the work to receive the hardware, if it is necessary.

3. Locate the positions of the screws.

4. Select screws that will easily pass thru the holes in the hardware, as at a.

5. Bore the pilot holes (second hole) slightly smaller than the diameter of the threaded part of the screws, as at b.

6. Drive the screws tightly in place.

If the wood is soft, bore as deep as half the length of the threaded part of the screw, as at c. If the wood is hard, (oak), the screw soft (brass), or if the screw is large, the hole must be nearly as deep as the screw, as at d. Holes for small screws are usually made with brad awls.

Fig. 1012

Courtesy The Stanley Works

HAND SAWS

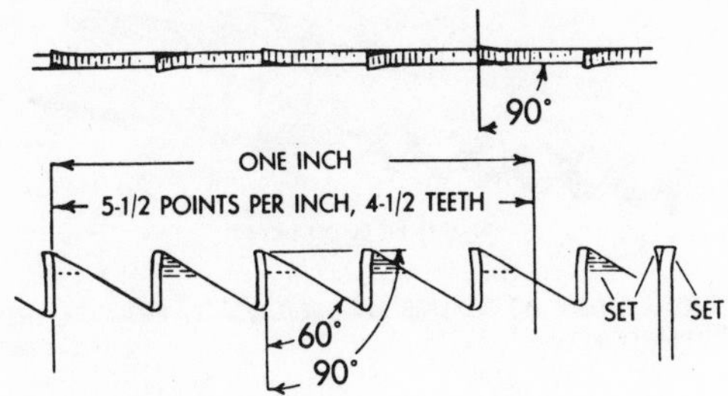

RIP SAW TEETH ARE SHAPED LIKE CHISELS. THEY CUT LIKE A GANG OF CHISELS IN A ROW.

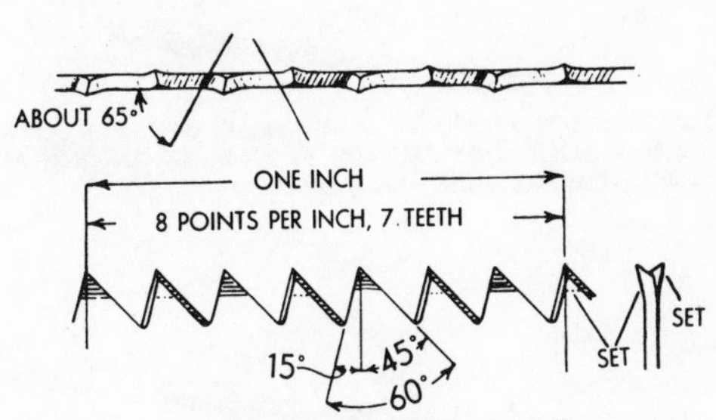

CROSS CUT SAW TEETH ARE LIKE KNIFE POINTS. THEY CUT LIKE TWO ROWS OF KNIFE POINTS AND CRUMBLE OUT THE WOOD BETWEEN THE CUTS.

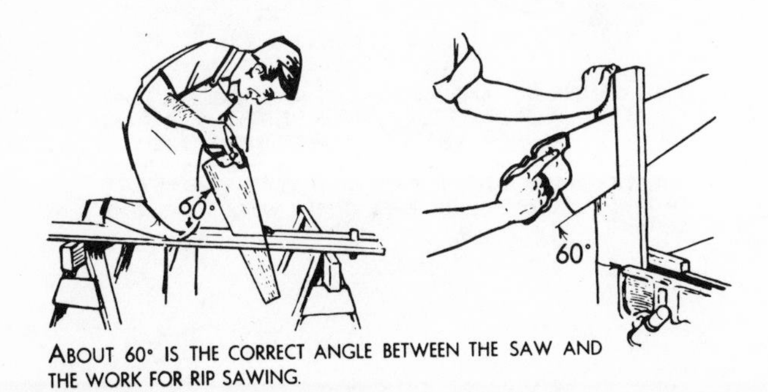

ABOUT 60° IS THE CORRECT ANGLE BETWEEN THE SAW AND THE WORK FOR RIP SAWING.

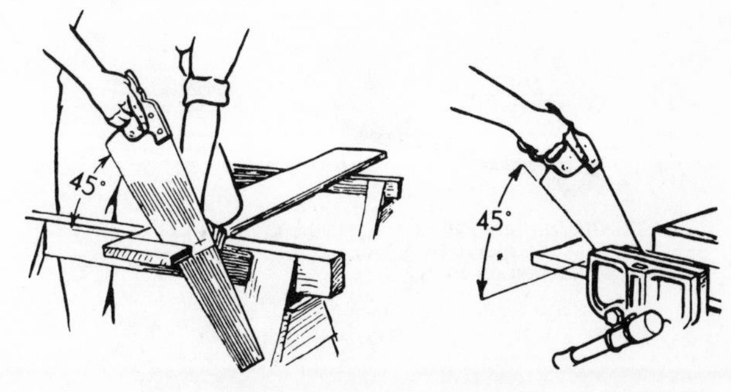

ABOUT 45° IS THE CORRECT ANGLE BETWEEN THE SAW AND THE WORK FOR CROSS CUT SAWING.

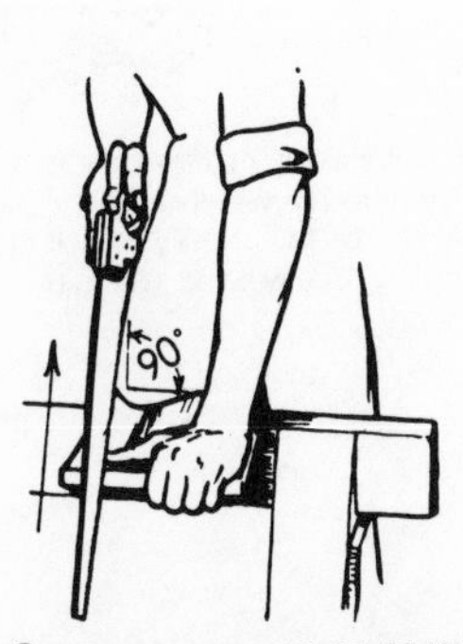

START THE SAW CUT BY DRAWING THE SAW BACKWARD. HOLD THE BLADE SQUARE TO THE STOCK. STEADY IT AT THE LINE WITH THE THUMB.

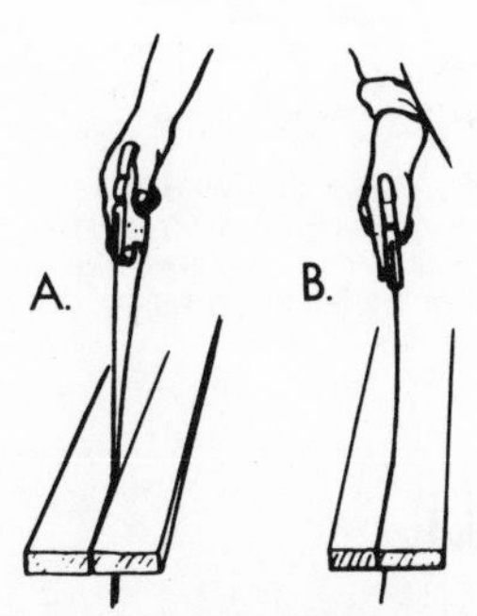

A. IF THE SAW LEAVES THE LINE TWIST THE HANDLE SLIGHTLY AND DRAW IT BACK TO THE LINE.
B. IF THE SAW IS NOT SQUARE TO THE STOCK, BEND IT A LITTLE AND GRADUALLY STRAIGHTEN IT. BE CAREFUL NOT TO PERMANENTLY BEND OR KINK THE BLADE.

THE BACK SAW IS A THIN CROSS CUT SAW WITH FINE TEETH, STIFFENED BY A THICK BACK. A POPULAR SIZE IS 12" WITH 14 PTS PER INCH. IT IS USED FOR FINE ACCURATE WORK.

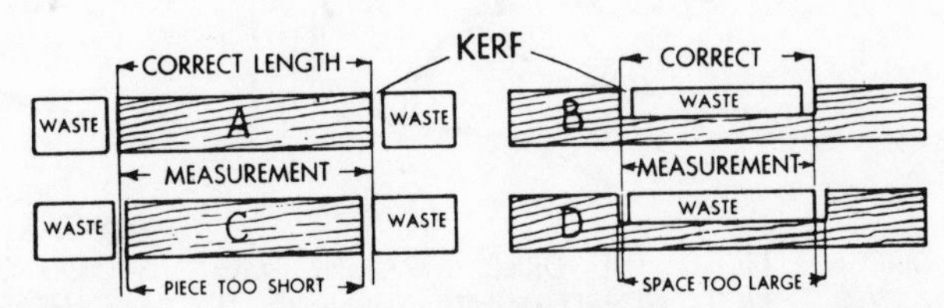

BE SURE TO SAW CAREFULLY ON THE WASTE SIDE OF THE LINE AS AT A AND B. SAWING ON THE LINE OR ON THE WRONG SIDE OF THE LINE MAKES THE STOCK TOO SHORT AS AT C OR THE OPENING TOO LARGE AS SHOWN AT D.

Fig. 1013

Courtesy The Stanley Works

Boring Tools

Twist Bits for Wood are used to make holes for screws, nails or bolts. They are sized by 32nds of an inch and range from No. 2=1/16" and larger.

Stanley Bit Gauge No.47

An Adjustable Bit Gauge may be used to regulate the depth of holes.

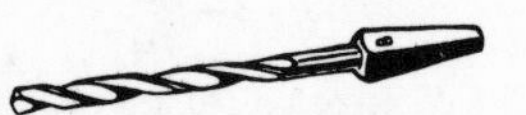

Bit Stock Drills are designed and tempered to make holes in metal, but may also be used in wood, especially in repair work where contact with nails or metal is possible. They are sized by 32nds of an inch and range from No. 2 = 1/16" and larger.

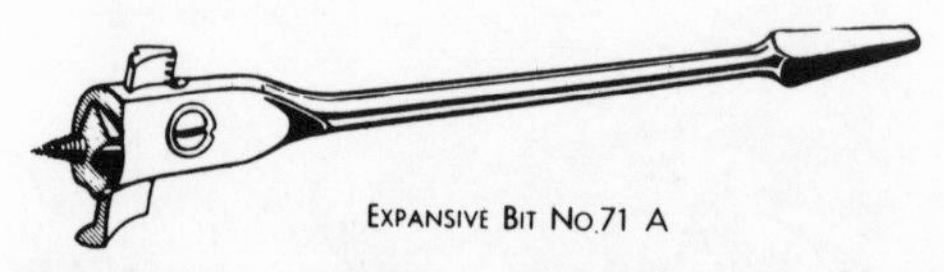

Expansive Bit No.71 A

The Expansive Bit takes the place of many large bits. The cutter may be adjusted for various sized holes. Moving the cutter adjusting screw one complete turn enlarges or reduces the hole 1/8". One half turn 1/16". Test the size on a piece of waste wood. For boring through, clamp a piece of waste wood on the back of the work to prevent splitting.

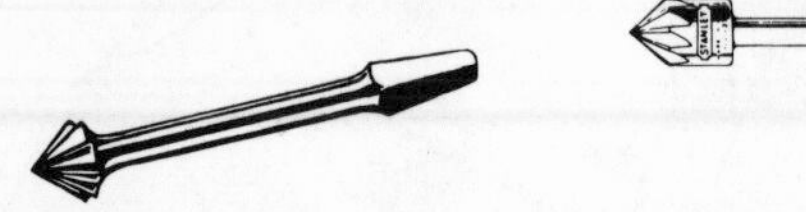

Countersink Bits are used to widen screw holes so that the heads of flat-head screws may be flush, or slightly below, the surface of the work.

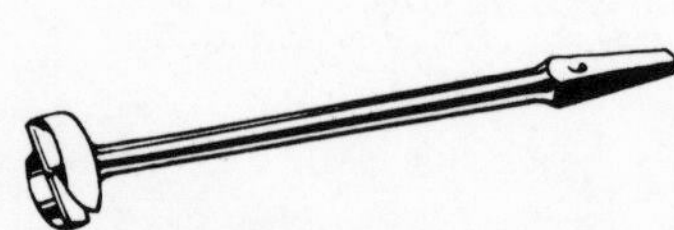

Forstner Bits are used to bore holes partway through where the auger bit screw or spur would go through the work, also on end grain, thin wood, or near an end where an auger bit would split the work. To center or start a Forstner bit, scribe a circle the size of the hole with dividers and press the rim of the Forstner bit into it. Forstner Bits are sized by 16ths of an inch from No. 4=1/4" and larger.

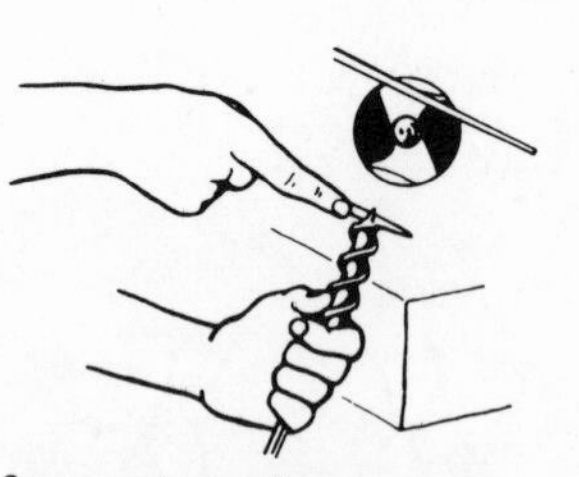

Sharpen Auger Bits with a bit file. For a keen edge, also whet with a slipstone. Sharpen the spurs on the inside to preserve the diameter.

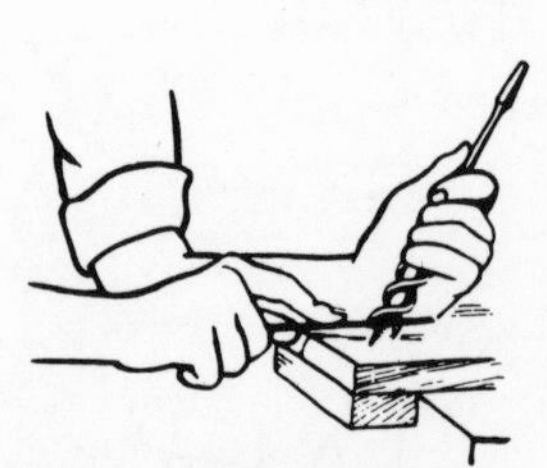

Sharpen the cutting edges on the top to maintain the clearance on the under side. The cutting edges must be kept even.

Fig. 1014

Hand Drill

Hold the drill steady in the direction desired and exert an even pressure. Turn the crank at a constant speed and not too fast.

Hold the drill straight. Do not wobble while turning, it makes the hole over-size and is likely to break the drill.

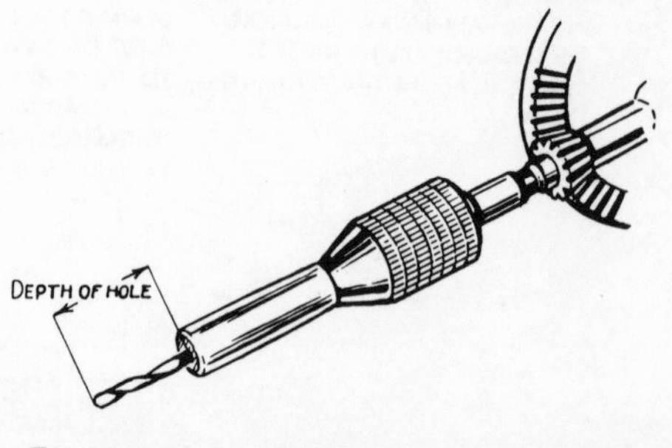

To drill holes of uniform depth, make a depth gauge. Cut a piece of wood or dowel the right length, so the drill will project the desired depth. When the piece of wood is drilled, slip it over the drill.

Fig. 1015

Courtesy The Stanley Works

BIT BRACE

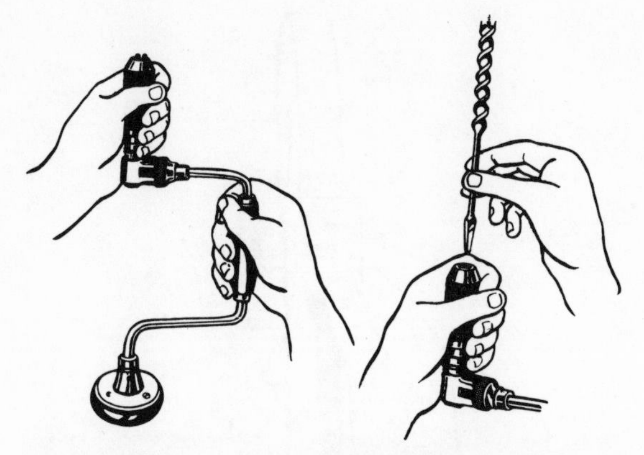

To place the bit in the chuck, grasp the chuck shell and turn the handle to the left until the jaws are wide open. Insert the bit shank in the square socket at the bottom of the chuck and turn the handle to the right until the bit is held firmly in the jaws.

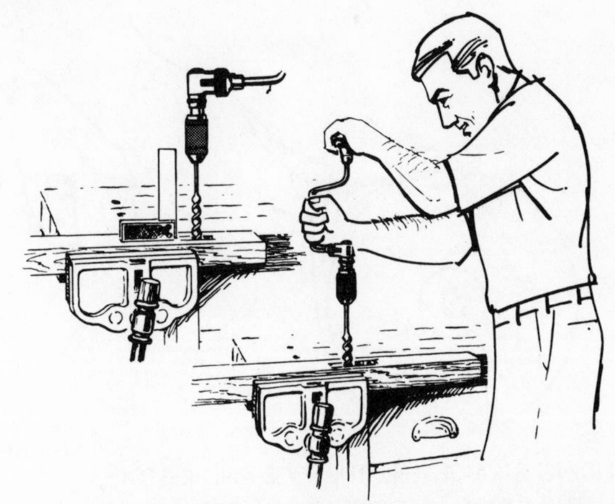

To bore a verticle hole, hold the brace and bit perpendicular to the surface of the work. Test by sight. Compare the direction of the bit to the nearest straight edge or to sides of the vise. A try square may be held near the bit.

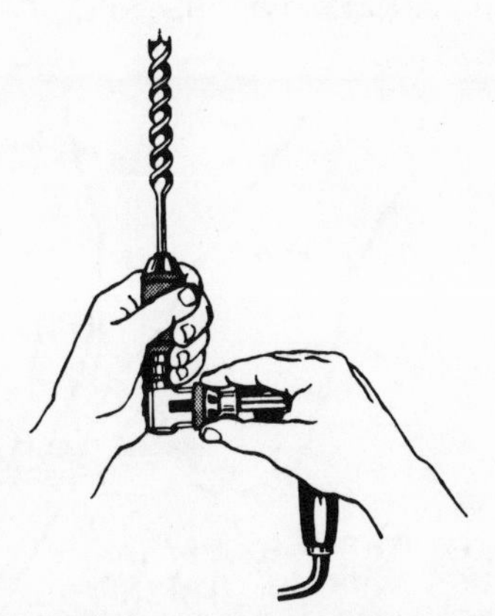

To operate the ratchet turn the cam ring. Turning the cam ring to the right will allow the bit to turn right and give ratchet action when the handle is turned left Turn the cam ring left to reverse the action
The Ratchet Brace is indispensable when boring a hole in a corner or where some object prevents making a full turn with the handle.

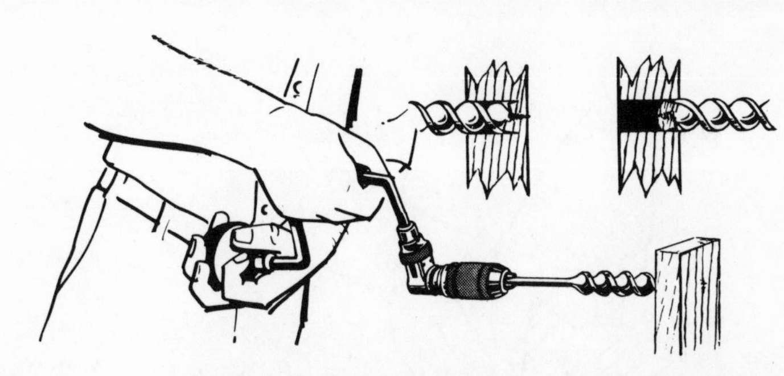

To bore a horizontal hole, hold the head of the brace cupped in the left hand against the stomach and with the thumb and forefinger around the quill. To bore thru without splintering the second face, stop when the screw point is thru and finish from the second face. When boring thru with an Expansive Bit it is best to clamp a piece of wood to the second face and bore straight thru.

Fig. 1016

BRAD AWL

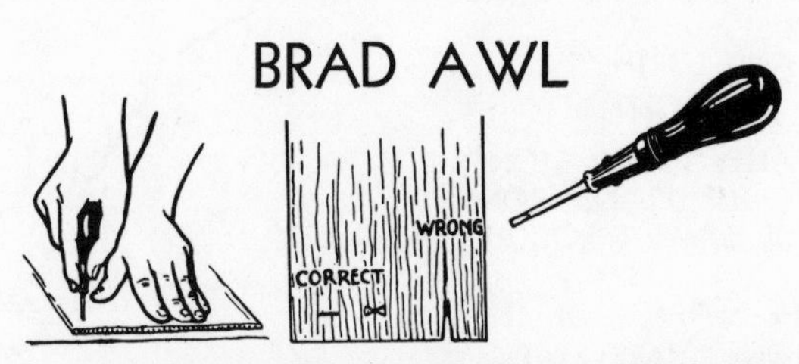

Brad Awls are used to make holes for small screws and nails. To avoid splitting the wood, start the awl with its edge across the grain, turning it back and forth slightly as you press down. Do not let the edge come parallel with the grain.

Fig. 1017

Courtesy The Stanley Works

HOW TO SHARPEN A PLANE IRON OR CHISEL

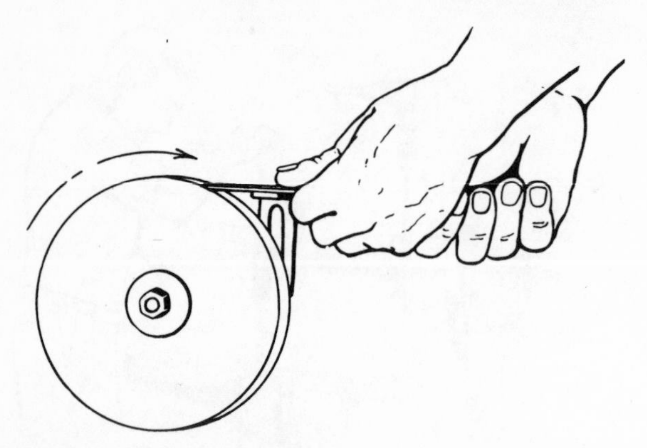

GRINDING STRAIGHTENS THE EDGE AND RESTORES THE BEVEL PREPARATORY TO SHARPENING BY WHETTING ON THE OIL STONE.
THE GRIND STONE SHOULD TURN TOWARD THE PLANE IRON.
USE THE GUIDE AS IT ASSURES A FLAT EVEN BEVEL.
KEEP THE PLANE IRON COOL TO PREVENT BURNING, OR SOFTENING THE STEEL, BY FREQUENT DIPPING IN WATER.

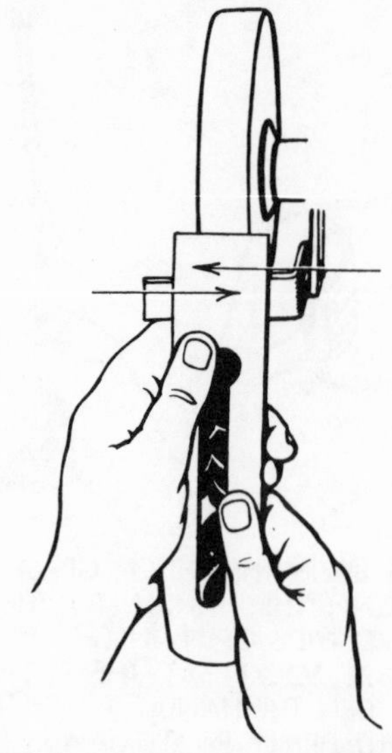

MOVE THE PLANE IRON FROM SIDE TO SIDE TO GRIND ALL PARTS OF THE BEVEL AND TO KEEP THE WHEEL TRUE.
THE EDGE SHOULD BE STRAIGHT AND ALMOST AT RIGHT ANGLES TO THE SIDES OF THE PLANE IRON.

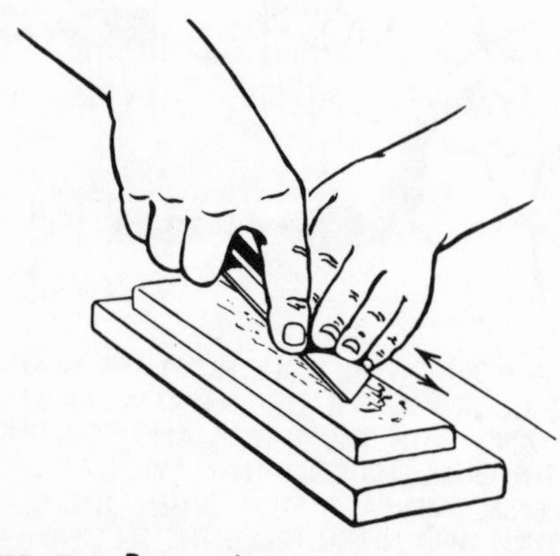

WHET THE PLANE IRON ON THE OIL STONE TO PRODUCE THE REAL SHARP CUTTING EDGE.
HOLD THE PLANE IRON IN THE RIGHT HAND WITH THE LEFT HAND HELPING.
PLACE THE BEVEL ON THE STONE WITH THE BACK EDGE SLIGHTLY RAISED.
MOVE THE PLANE IRON BACK AND FORTH.

TO KEEP THE BEVEL STRAIGHT

BE SURE THE HANDS MOVE PARALLEL TO THE STONE SO THAT THE ANGLE BETWEEN THE PLANE IRON AND THE STONE WILL STAY THE SAME THROUGHOUT THE STROKE.
USE ENOUGH OIL TO KEEP THE SURFACE OF THE STONE MOIST. IT KEEPS THE STONE SHARP BY PREVENTING PARTICLES OF STEEL FILLING THE PORES OF THE STONE.
TRY TO WEAR THE STONE EVENLY.

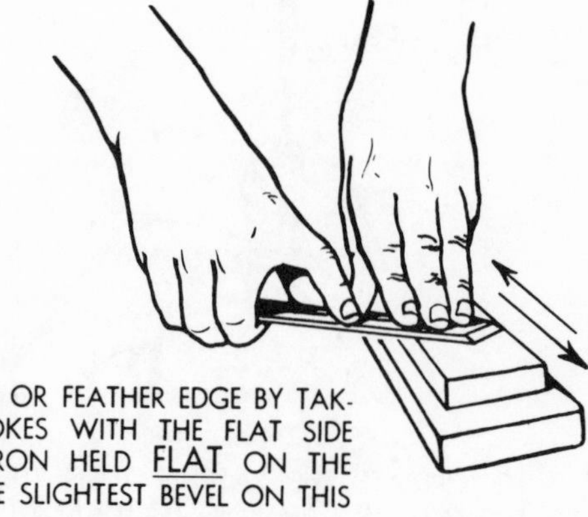

REMOVE THE WIRE OR FEATHER EDGE BY TAKING A FEW STROKES WITH THE FLAT SIDE OF THE PLANE IRON HELD FLAT ON THE STONE. AVOID THE SLIGHTEST BEVEL ON THIS SIDE.
IF A NICK OR A SHINY EDGE OF BLUNTNESS CAN BE SEEN, REPEAT BOTH PROCESSES OF WHETTING.

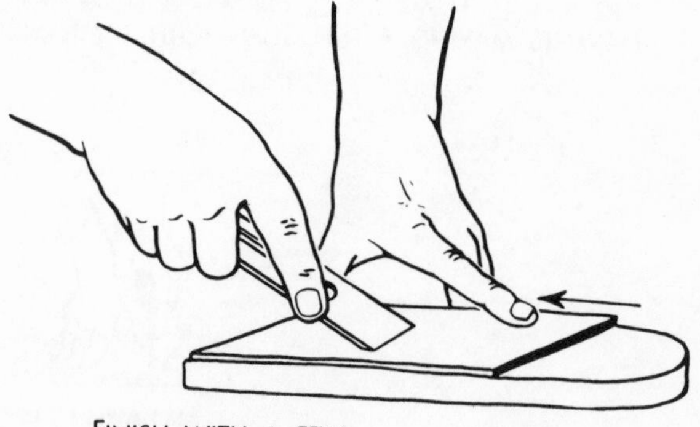

FINISH WITH A FEW STROKES ON A LEATHER STROP TO PRODUCE A KEENER EDGE.

Fig. 1018

Courtesy The Stanley Works

HOW TO ASSEMBLE THE DOUBLE PLANE IRON

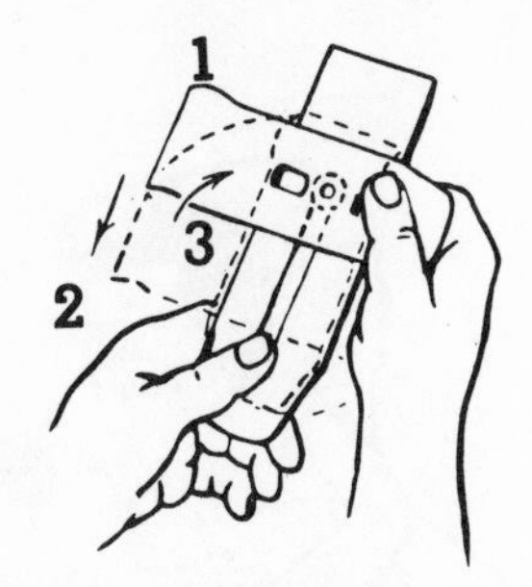

To put the Plane Iron and the Plane Iron Cap together. 1—Lay the Plane Iron Cap on the flat side of the Plane Iron, as shown, with the screw in the slot. 2—Draw the Plane Iron Cap back. 3—Turn it straight with the Plane Iron.

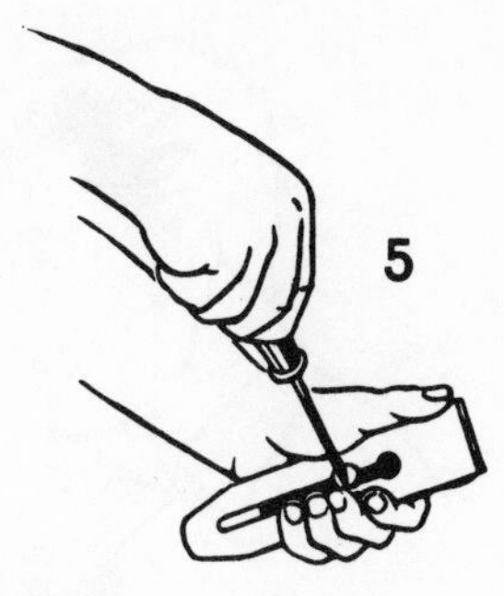

5—Hold the Plane Iron and the Plane Iron Cap firmly and tighten the screw to hold the two parts together.

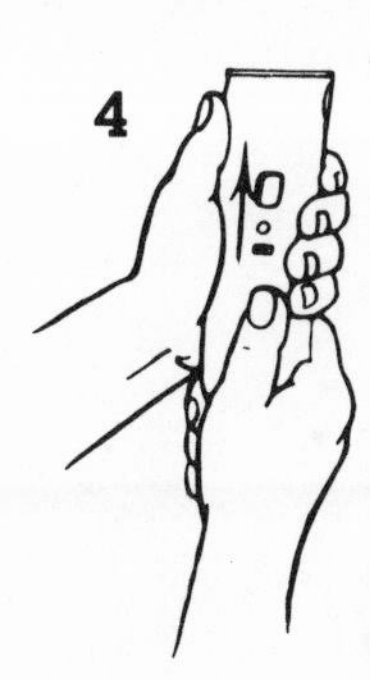

4—Advance the Plane Iron Cap until the edge is just back of the cutting edge of the Plane Iron. The Plane Iron Cap must not be dragged across the cutting edge.

The Plane Iron Cap should extend 1/16" back of the cutting edge for general work. On cross grained or curly wood it should be as near to the cutting edge as possible.

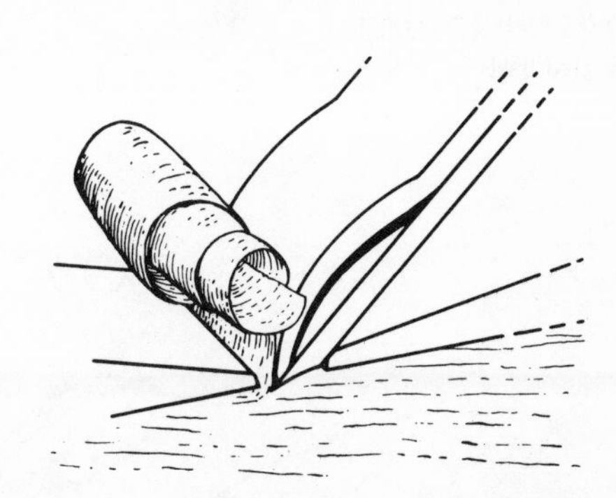

The Plane Iron Cap breaks and curls the shaving. Together with the toe of the Plane it prevents the wood splitting ahead of the cutting edge, producing a smooth surface. The Plane Iron Cap also serves to stiffen the Plane Iron.

Fig. 1019

HOW TO SET THE PLANE

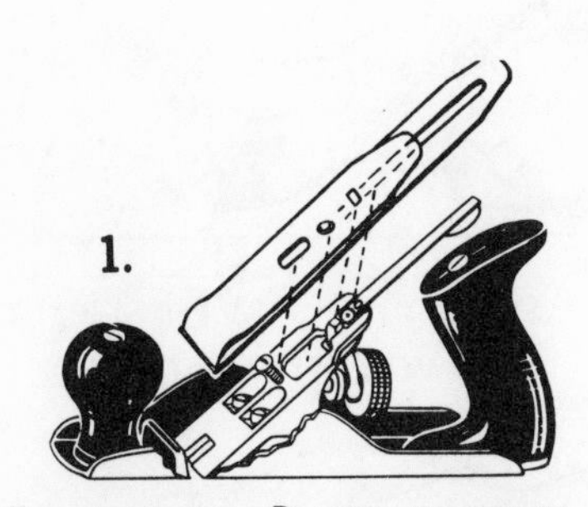

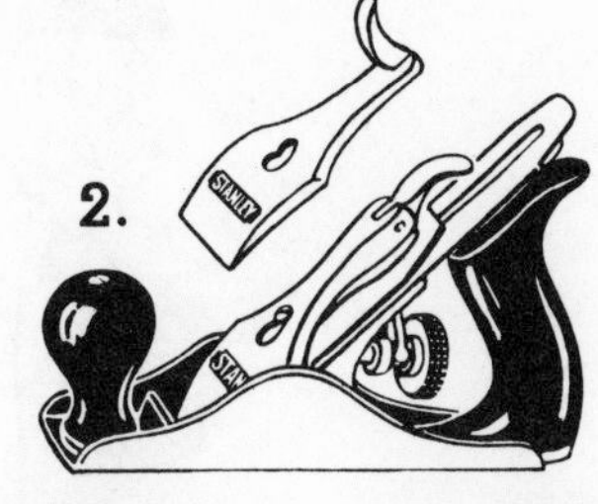

To put the Plane together lay the Plane Iron, bevel side down, on the Frog. Be sure the Roller on the Lateral Adjusting Lever, the end of the "Y" Adjusting Lever and the head of the Plane Iron Cap Screw are correctly seated.

Slip the Lever Cap under the Lever Cap Screw and press down the Cam. If the Plane Iron is in the correct position the Cam will easily snap in place. If the Cam will will not snap in place easily, slightly loosen the Lever Cap Screw.

If the Plane Iron, is not firmly held when the Cam is in place slightly tighten the Lever Cap Screw.

Fig. 1020

Courtesy The Stanley Works

To adjust for the thickness of the shaving sight along the bottom of the Plane and turn the Adjusting Nut until the cutting edge projects about the thickness of a hair.

The Plane Iron is pushed out when the Adjusting Nut moves out toward the handle.

The Plane Iron is drawn in when the Adjusting Nut moves in toward the Frog.

To adjust for the evenness of the shaving sight along the bottom of the Plane and move the Lateral Adjusting Lever toward the right or the left.

Fig. 1021

HOW TO USE THE PLANE

To cut a smooth straight edge the Plane is pushed with the grain, that is in the up hill direction of the fibres.
To keep the Plane straight press down on the knob at the beginning of the stroke and on the handle at the end of the stroke. Avoid dropping the Plane as shown by the broken lines. It rounds the corners.

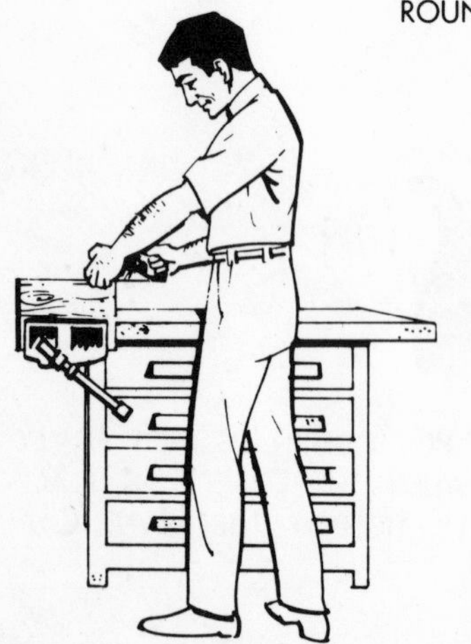

To start planing take an easy but firm position directly back of the work.

At the end of the stroke the weight of the body should be carried easily on the left foot.

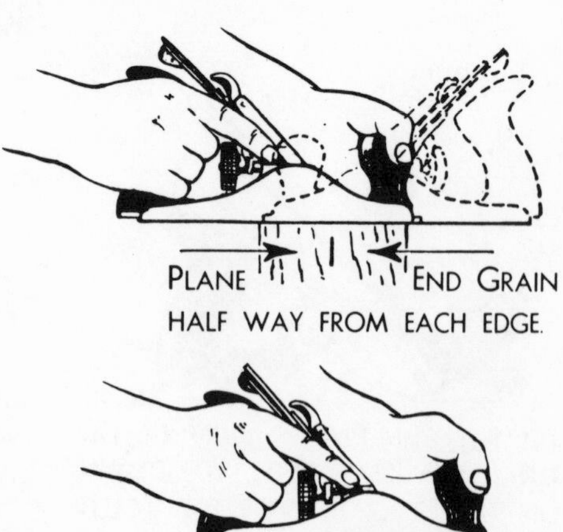

Plane End Grain half way from each edge.

If the Plane is pushed all the way the corners will break.

Fig. 1022

Courtesy The Stanley Works

HORIZONTAL CHISELING

TO CUT, HORIZONTALLY, WITH THE GRAIN: THE CHISEL IS HELD SLIGHTLY TURNED TO ONE SIDE AND THEN PUSHED FROM THE WORKER. IT IS HELD WITH THE BEVEL DOWN FOR A ROUGHING CUT AND WITH THE BEVEL UP FOR A PARING CUT.

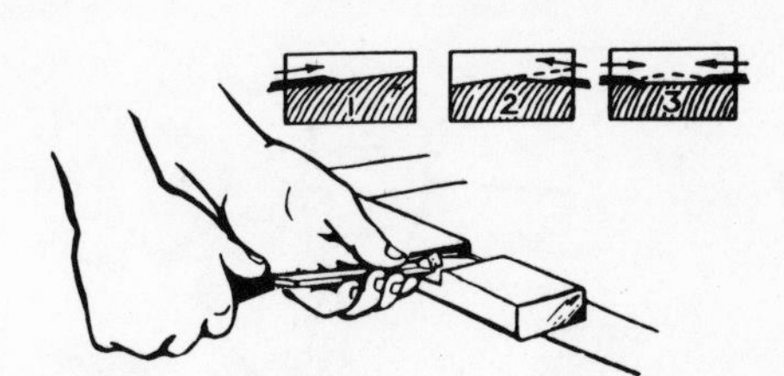

TO CUT, HORIZONTALLY, ACROSS THE GRAIN WITH THE WORK HELD IN THE VISE: PRESS THE FOREFINGER AND THUMB TOGETHER ON THE CHISEL TO ACT AS A BRAKE.
TO AVOID SPLINTERING THE CORNERS, CUT HALF WAY FROM EACH EDGE TOWARD THE CENTER. REMOVE THE CENTER STOCK LAST.

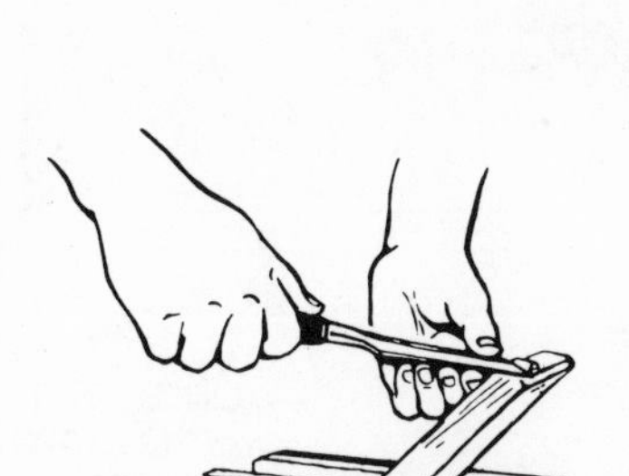

TO CUT A CHAMFER ON END GRAIN, THE CHISEL IS MOVED SIDEWAYS ACROSS THE CORNER OF THE WORK, HELD SO THAT THE CHISEL MAKES A SLIDING HORIZONTAL CUT.

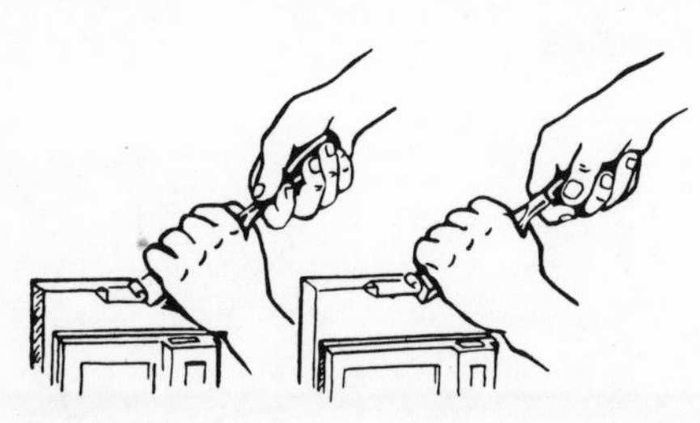

TO CUT A CHAMFER: HOLD THE CHISEL INCLINED TO ONE SIDE PARALLEL TO THE SLOPE OF THE CHAMFER AND CUT AS IN CHISELING HORIZONTALLY (WITH THE GRAIN.

TO CUT ACROSS THE GRAIN WITH THE WORK HELD AGAINST THE BENCH HOOK, THE HEEL OF THE LEFT HAND STEADIES THE WORK WHILE THE FINGERS PRESS THE CHISEL FIRMLY AGAINST THE WOOD.

TO CUT A ROUND CORNER, THE CHISEL IS MOVED SIDEWAYS ACROSS THE THE WORK MAKING A SERIES OF CUTS CLOSE TOGETHER EACH ONE TANGENT TO THE CURVE.

TO CUT A STRAIGHT, SLANTING, CORNER IS THE SAME AS HORIZONTAL CHISELING. THE WORK IS HELD IN THE VISE WITH THE GUIDE LINE HORIZONTAL.

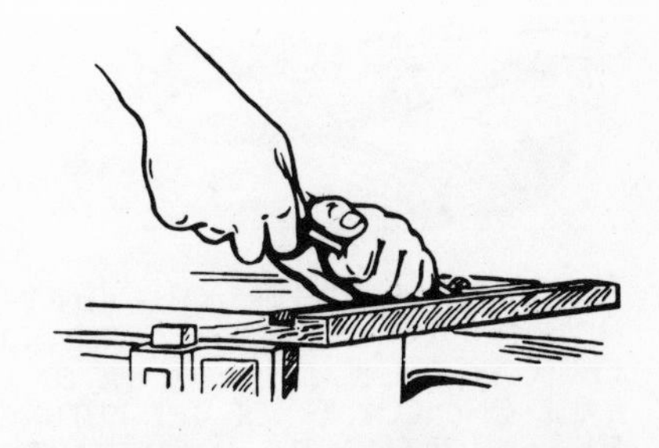

IF THE WORK IS WIDE THE CHISEL IS HELD BEVEL DOWN, SO THE HANDLE WILL CLEAR THE WORK AND THE BLADE WILL NOT DIG IN TOO DEEP, AS IT IS PUSHED FORWARD.

THE CHISEL IS CONTROLLED WITH THE LEFT HAND, PRESSING FIRMLY ON THE CHISEL AND THE WOOD. THE POWER IS APPLIED WITH THE RIGHT HAND. THE CHISEL IS HELD SLIGHTLY TURNED SO THE EDGE SLIDES ACROSS THE WORK OR THE CHISEL IS MOVED TO THE RIGHT AND LEFT AS IT IS ADVANCED, TO GIVE A SLIDING ACTION TO THE CUTTING EDGE. THIS IS EASIER THAN A STRAIGHT THRUST AND LEAVES A SMOOTHER SURFACE ON THE WORK.

AT ALL TIMES KEEP BOTH HANDS BACK OF THE CUTTING EDGE.

Fig. 1023

Courtesy The Stanley Works

VERTICAL CHISELING

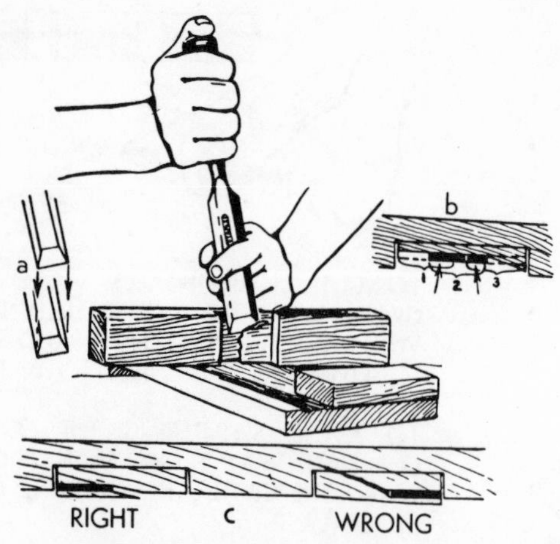

To cut, vertically, across the grain (a) the chisel should be slightly tilted to one side to give a sliding action to the cutting edge, or it may be held straight and moved to one side as it is advanced. (b) If the surface is wider than the chisel, part of the chisel pressed against the portion just cut, helps to guide and keep in line the part of the chisel cutting a new portion of the surface. (c) Cut with the grain, so the waste wood will split away from the guide line.

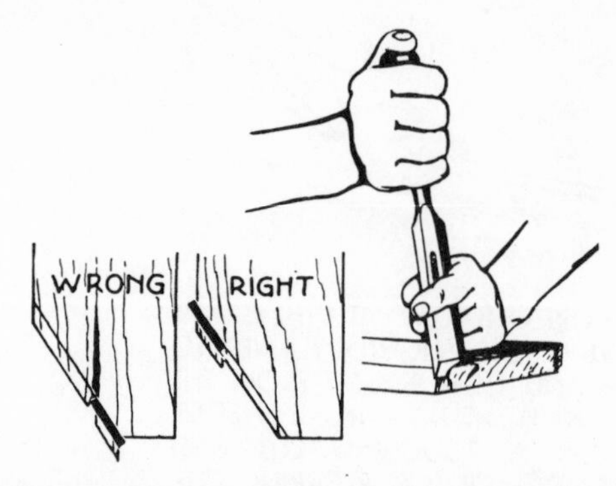

To cut, vertically, a slanting corner use the chisel in the same manner as in vertical cutting across the grain. Always work from the edge toward the end, so the wood will split away from the line. Working from the end toward the edge will split and ruin the work, as it is cutting against the grain.

To clean the corners of a tenon, notch, dado or rabbet: grasp the chisel by the blade, near the edge; raise one corner of the cutting edge by tilting the handle away and draw the chisel toward you. The work is held by the left hand while the chisel edge and one corner, guided by the right hand, act like a knife.

To cut a concave curved corner: hold the bevel side of the chisel against the work with the left hand; with the right hand press down and draw back at the same time, giving a sweeping curved direction to the cut.
Always work with the grain from the edge toward the end.

The mallet may be safely used on the chisel when the cutting edge is across the grain. When the edge is with the grain, the use of the mallet is very likely to split the wood. The mallet may be used on the chisel to beat out a mortise, to cut the ends of a mortise (when the bulk of the material has been bored out), when the wood is hard and in roughing out (when there is a large amount of material to be removed).

Fig. 1024

Courtesy The Stanley Works

11. MATERIALS & FASTENINGS

WOOD

TABLE 11-1 WEIGHT & STRENGTH OF TIMBER

Name.	Specific Gravity.	Lbs. in a Cub. Ft.	Tearing Force.	Crushing Force.	Breaking Force.	Modulus of Elasticity
			Lbs. on Sq. In.	Lbs. on Sq. In.	Lbs. on Sq. In.	Lbs. on Sq. In.
Acacia	.710	44.4	16,000	—	—	—
Alder	.555	34.6	14,186	6,895	9,540	1,087,000
Apple	.793	49.5	19,500	6,499	—	—
Ash	.753	47.0	17,000	9,000	12,200	1,645,000
Beech	.700	43.8	11,500	9,363	9,336	1,354,000
Birch	.750	46.9	15,000	6,402	11,671	1,645,000
Box	.1000	62.5	20,000	10,299	—	—
Cedar	.486	30.8	11,400	5,800	7,420	486,000
Chestnut	.535	33.4	13,300	—	10,656	1,137,000
Cypress	·655	41.0	6,000	—	—	—
Ebony	1.279	79.4	—	19,000	136,00	1,300,000
Elder	.695	43.4	10,230	8,467	—	—
Elm	.544	33.8	13,489	10,331	6,078	700,000
Fir, larch	.496	31.0	10,220	5,568	5,943	1,363,000
" pitch-pine	.660	41.2	7,818	—	9,792	1,226,000
" red pine	.577	36.1	14,300	5,375	8,844	1,458,000
" spruce	.512	32.0	10,100	6,500	12,346	1,804,000
" yellow pine	.461	28.8	—	5,445	—	1,600,000
Greenheart	1.001	62.5	—	—	16,654	2,656,000
Hawthorn	.910	56.8	10,500	—	—	—
Hazel	.860	53.7	18,000	4,600	—	—
Hornbeam	.760	47.4	20,240	7,289	—	—
Laburnum	.920	57.4	10,500	—	—	—
Lancewood	.675	42.1	—	6,614	17,354	812,000
Lignum-vitae	1.333	83.2	11,800	9,921	11,400	558,000
Lime	.760	47.4	23,500	—	11,202	1,152,000
Mahogany, Australian	.952	59.4	—	9,921	20,238	1,157,000
" Honduras	.560	35.0	—	—	11,475	1,593,000
" Spanish	.853	53.2	21,800	8,198	7,560	1,255,000
Oak, British	.934	58.3	10,000	10,055	10,032	1,451,000
" Dantzic	.756	47.2	12,780	7,723	8,742	1,191,000
" red	.872	64.4	10,253	5,987	10,596	2,149,000
" Riga	.688	43.0	—	—	12,888	1,610,000
Poplar	.511	31.9	7,200	5,124	10,260	1,134,000
Sycamore	.590	36.8	13,000	—	9,630	1,036,000
Teak, African	.983	61.3	21,000	9,320	14,976	2,305,000
" Indian	.880	55.0	15,000	—	14,600	2,800,000
Walnut	.671	41.8	8,130	6,645	8,000	—
Willow	.405	25.3	—	—	6,570	—
Yew	.807	50.3	8,000	—	—	—

TABLE 11-2 STANDARD SIZES OF LUMBER

TYPE OF LUMBER	NOMINAL SIZE (in inches) Thickness	Width	ACTUAL SIZE S4S AT COMM. DRY SHP. WT. (in inches) Thickness	Width
Dimension	2	4	1⅝	3⅝
	2	6	1⅝	5⅝
	2	8	1⅝	7½
	2	10	1⅝	9½
	2	12	1⅝	11½
Timbers	4	6	3⅝	5½
	4	8	3⅝	7½
	4	10	3⅝	9½
	6	6	5½	5½
	6	8	5½	7½
	6	10	5½	9½
	8	8	7½	7½
	8	10	7½	9½
Common Boards	1	4	25/32	3⅝
	1	6	25/32	5⅝
	1	8	25/32	7½
	1	10	25/32	9½
	1	12	25/32	11½
Shiplap Boards	1	4	25/32	* 3⅛
	1	6	25/32	* 5⅛
	1	8	25/32	* 7⅛
	1	10	25/32	* 9⅛
	1	12	25/32	*11⅛
Tongued and Grooved Boards	1	4	25/32	* 3¼
	1	6	25/32	* 5¼
	1	8	25/32	* 7¼
	1	10	25/32	* 9¼
	1	12	25/32	*11¼

*—Width at face

Courtesy Weyerhaeuser Sales Co.

TABLE 11-3 WOODWORKER'S GLUING CHART

TYPE OF WORK	GLUE FOR LOW-COST WATER-RESISTANT JOINT (In order of preference)
All general gluing of hard and softwoods	Plastic resin glue Casein glue Polyvinyl glue
Particle and chip boards to wood	Plastic resin glue Casein glue Contact cement Polyvinyl glue
Plywood to decorative plastic laminates	Casein glue Contact cement Plastic resin glue
Laminating heavy framing members	Casein glue
Veneering, inlays, cabinet work	Plastic resin glue (extended) Polyvinyl glue
Bonding oily woods (teak, pitch pine, osage, yew)	Casein glue (sponge surface with dilute caustic soda solution 1 hour before gluing)
End-wood joints, mitered joints, scarf joints	Polyvinyl glue Casein glue (heavy mix)
Loose-fitting joints, relatively rough surfaces	Polyvinyl glue Casein glue (heavy mix)
Doweling	Plastic resin glue Polyvinyl glue
Hardboard to plywood, wood or itself	Plastic resin glue Casein glue Polyvinyl glue Contact cement
Porous materials, such as linoleum and canvas to wood	Plastic resin glue Casein glue Contact cement
Plastics, metal and foil to wood	Epoxy glue

TABLE 11-4 WEIGHT & STRENGTH OF METALS

METAL	Specific Gravity	Lb. in a Cu. Ft.	Tearing Force	Crushing Force	Modulus of Elasticity
			Lb. on Sq. in.	Lb. on Sq. in.	Lb. on Sq. in.
Aluminum, cast	2.560	160.0	—	—	—
Aluminum, sheet	2.670	166.9	—	—	—
Brass, cast	8.396	524.8	18,000	10,300	9,170,000
Brass, sheet	8.525	532.8	31,360	—	—
Brass, wire	8.544	533.0	49,000	—	14,230,000
Bronze	8.222	513.4	—	—	—
Copper, bolts	8.850	531.3	36,000	—	—
Copper, cast	8.607	537.9	19,000	—	—
Copper, sheet	8.785	549.1	30,000	—	—
Copper, wire	8.878	548.6	60,000	—	—
Iron, cast, average	7.125	445.3	16,500	112,000	17,000,000
Iron, wrought, average	7.680	480.0	60,000	36,000	28,000,000
Lead, cast	11.352	709.5	1,792	6,900	—
Lead, sheet	11.400	712.8	3,328	—	720,000
Nickel, cast	7.807	487.9	—	—	
Steel, hard	7.818	488.6	103,000	—	42,000,000
Steel, soft	7.834	489.6	121,700	—	29,000,000
Zinc, cast	7.028	439.3	8,500	—	13,500,000
Zinc, sheet	7.291	455.7	7,111	—	12,650,000

TABLE 11-5 STAINLESS STEEL, MONEL, & COPPER NICKEL IN MARINE USE

Material	Application	Yield Strength	Tensile Strength	Elongation % in 2"
302 S.S.)	rails, trim, cable, hardware,	40 KSI	90 KSI	50
304 S.S.)	galley equipment	42 KSI	84 KSI	55
305 S.S.	bolts, nuts, screws, fasteners	35 KSI	85 KSI	50
316 S.S.	general use, preferred choice in salt spray	42 KSI	84 KSI	50
316L S.S.	preferred choice for welding	34 KSI	81 KSI	50
17-4 PH S.S.	propeller shafts	175 KSI	205 KSI	15
Monel Alloy 400	pump parts, water boxes, valves, tubing, fasteners	35 KSI	80 KSI	45
Money Alloy K-500	valves, pump shafts, high strength applications	130 KSI	160 KSI	22
70/30 Copper-Nickel	pipe, tubing, water boxes, etc.	25 KSI	60 KSI	45
90/10 Copper-Nickel	pipe, tubing, water boxes, etc.	16 KSI	44 KSI	42

TUBING, PIPE & FITTINGS

TABLE 11-6

DIMENSIONS OF K, L AND M-TYPES COPPER TUBING FROM 3/8" TO 2"

Nominal Size	Outside Diameter	Inside Diameter			Wall Thickness		
	Types K-L-M	Type K	Type L	Type M	Type K	Type L	Type M
3/8	.500	.402	.430		.049	.035	
1/2	.625	.527	.545		.049	.040	
5/8	.750	.652	.666		.049	.042	
3/4	.875	.745	.785		.065	.045	
1	1.125	.995	1.025		.065	.050	
1 1/4	1.375	1245	1265	1291	.065	.055	.042
1 1/2	1.625	1481	1505	1527	.072	.060	.049
2	2.125	1959	1985	2009	.083	.070	.058

(All Dimensions in Inches)

Copper tubing is available in three wall thicknesses, K, L and M

TABLE 11-7

STANDARD STEEL PIPE
(All Dimensions in Inches)

Nominal Size	Outside Diameter	Inside Diameter
1/8	0.405	0.269
1/4	0.540	0.364
3/8	0.675	0.493
1/2	0.840	0.622
3/4	1.050	0.824
1	1.315	1.049
1 1/4	1.660	1.380
1 1/2	1.900	1.610
2	2.375	2.067
2 1/2	2.875	2.469

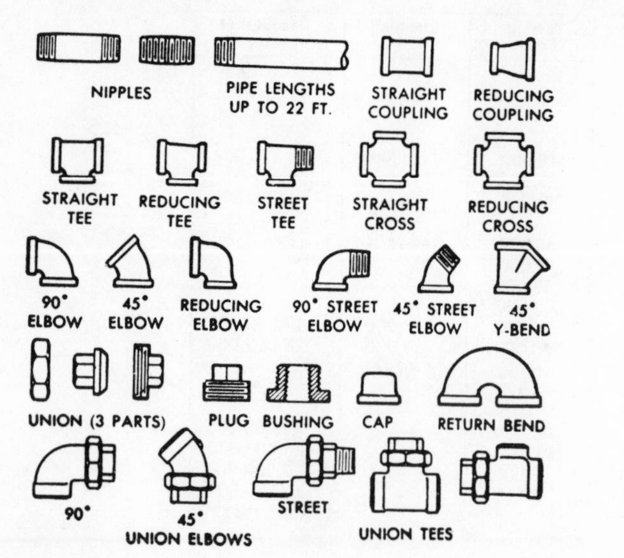

Fig. 1101. Here are the common steel pipe fittings. Nipples are simply short lengths of pipe threaded on both ends. Reducing fittings join two different sizes of pipe.

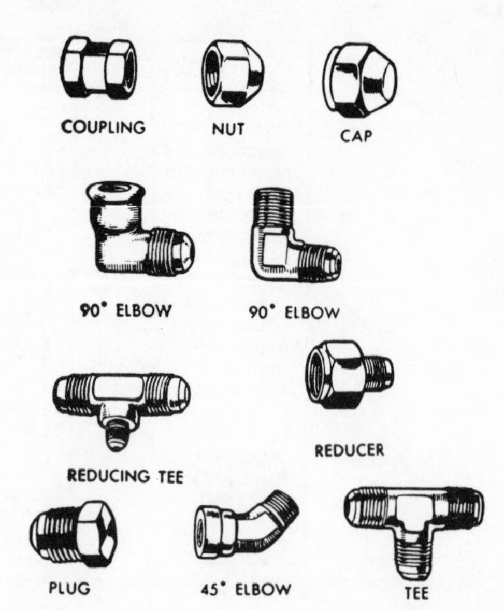

Fig. 1102. Compression fittings of the flared-tube type are the easiest for the novice to handle when working with copper tubing.

FASTENINGS

Use Figs. 1103-1106 to determine exact sizes, types, and designations when ordering nails, screws, and bolts.

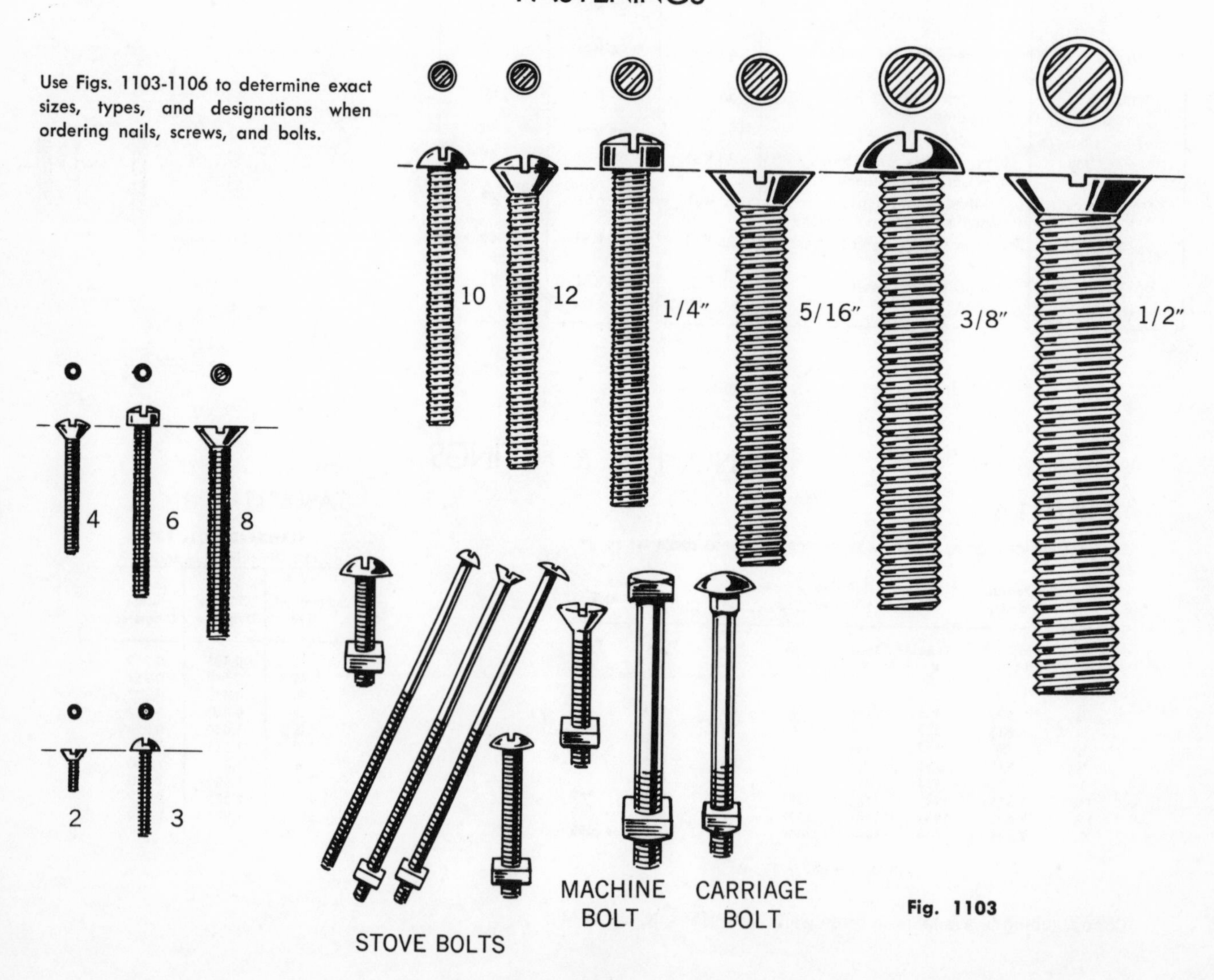

Fig. 1103

NAILS

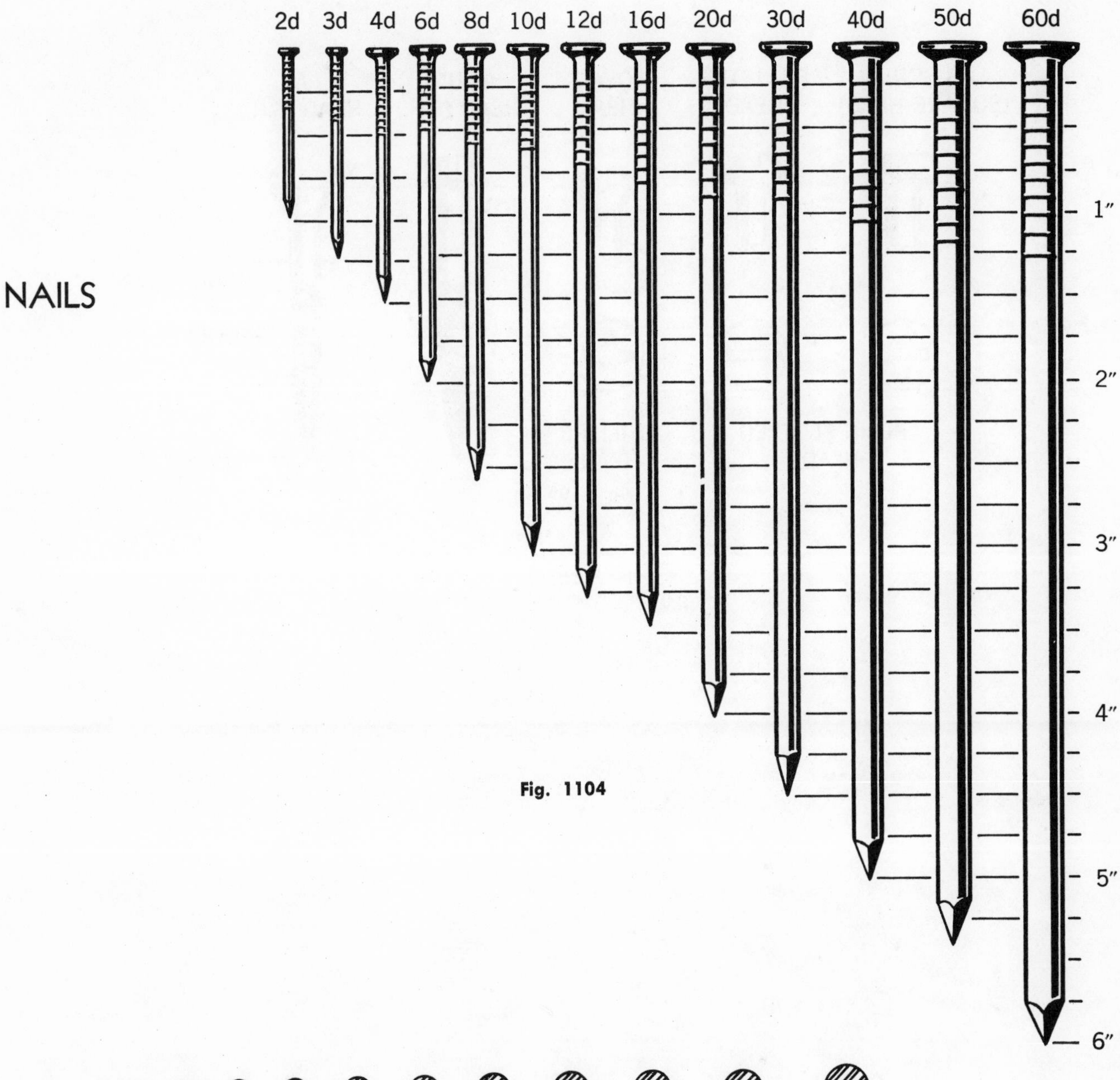

Fig. 1104

SCREWS

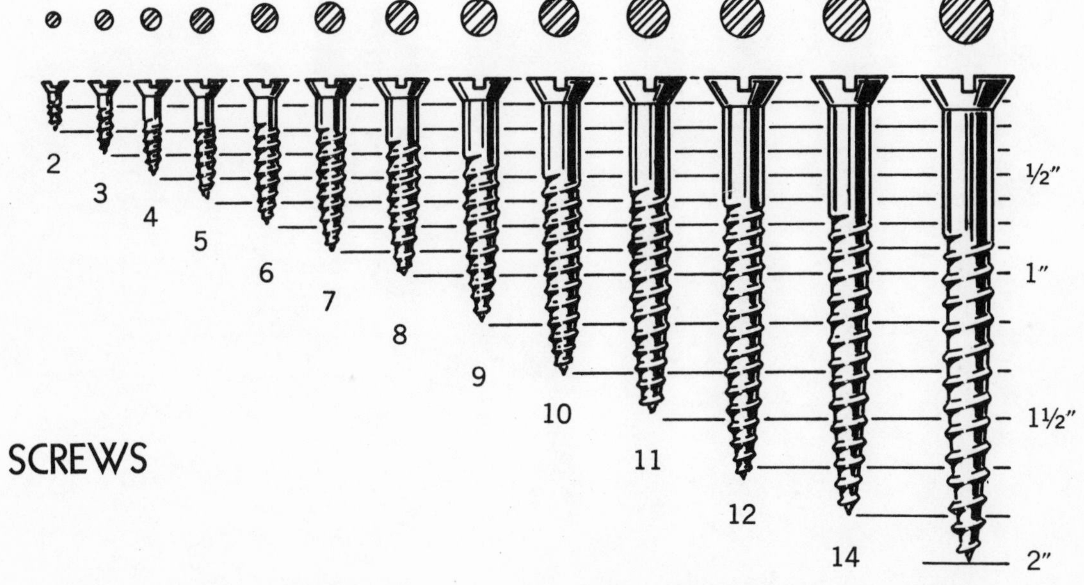

Fig. 1105

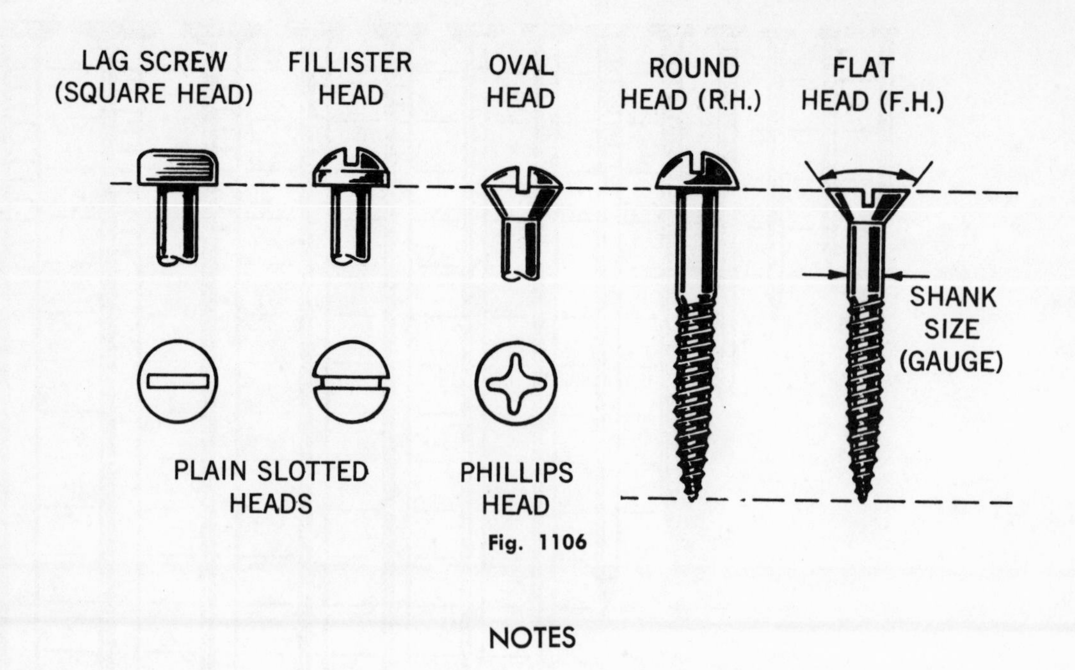

Fig. 1106

NOTES